Agricultural Policy Monitoring and Evaluation 2014

OECD COUNTRIES

OECD

BETTER POLICIES FOR BETTER LIVES

This work is published under the responsibility of the Secretary-General of the OECD. The opinions expressed and arguments employed herein do not necessarily reflect the official views of OECD member countries.

This document (and any map included herein) is without prejudice to the status of or sovereignty over any territory, to the delimitation of international frontiers and boundaries and to the name of any territory, city or area.

Please cite this publication as:
OECD (2014), *Agricultural Policy Monitoring and Evaluation 2014: OECD Countries*, OECD Publishing.
http://dx.doi.org/10.1787/agr_pol-2014-en

ISBN 978-92-64-21090-5 (print)
ISBN 978-92-64-21507-8 (PDF)

Series/Periodical: Agricultural Policy Monitoring and Evaluation 2014
ISSN 2221-7363 (print)
ISSN 2221-7371 (online)

The statistical data for Israel are supplied by and under the responsibility of the relevant Israeli authorities. The use of such data by the OECD is without prejudice to the status of the Golan Heights, East Jerusalem and Israeli settlements in the West Bank under the terms of international law.

Photo credits: Cover © Andrzej Kwieciński.

Corrigenda to OECD publications may be found on line at: *www.oecd.org/about/publishing/corrigenda.htm*.

Foreword

This report Agricultural Policies: Monitoring and Evaluation 2014 – OECD Countries monitors agricultural policy developments in OECD member countries. The OECD uses a comprehensive system for measuring and classifying support to agriculture – the Producer and Consumer Support Estimates and General Services Support Estimates (PSEs, CSEs and GSSEs) and related indicators. They provide insight into the increasingly complex nature of agricultural policy and serve as a basis for OECD's agricultural policy monitoring and evaluation.

The Executive Summary synthesises the key findings of the report. Part I provides a description and an overall assessment of agricultural policy developments and support in the OECD area. Part II summarises the developments in agricultural policies in each individual OECD country (with the European Union considered as a whole). The Statistical annex contains detailed background tables with indicators of agricultural support covering OECD countries.

The Executive summary and Part I are published on the responsibility of OECD Committee for Agriculture. The remainder of the report is published on the responsibility of the Secretary-General of the OECD.

Acknowledgements

This report was prepared by the Trade and Agriculture Directorate of the OECD with the active participation of member countries. The following people from the OECD Secretariat contributed to drafting this report: Morvarid Bagherzadeh (co-ordinator), Jesús Antón, Ken Ash, Jonathan Brooks, Carmel Cahill, Dalila Cervantes-Godoy, Dimitris Diakosavvas, Mitsuhiro Inamura, Hyunchul Jeong, Shingo Kimura, Andrzej Kwieciński, Martin von Lampe, Jussi Lankoski, Alexandra de Matos Nunes, Olga Melyukhina, Catherine Moreddu, Véronique de Saint-Martin, Frank van Tongeren and Václav Vojtech. Statistical and technical assistance was provided by Christine Arriola (co-ordinator), Florence Bossard, Eric Espinasse, Frano Ilicic, Joanna Ilicic-Komorowska, Alexandra de Matos Nunes and Christine Le Thi. Alexandra de Matos Nunes co-ordinated the preparation of the tables and graphs for publication. Administrative and editing services were provided by Martina Abderrahmane, Marina Giacalone-Belkadi and Michèle Patterson.

Table of contents

List of acronyms and abbreviations 9

Executive summary 13

Part I

Agricultural policies: Monitoring and evaluation 2014, OECD countries

Chapter 1. Developments in agricultural policy and support 17
    Key economic and market developments 18
    Main changes in agricultural policies 20
    Developments in agricultural support 27
    Assessing support and reforms 44
    References 48
    Annex 1.A1. Definition of OECD indicators of agricultural support 49
    Annex 1.A2. Revised General Services Support Estimate: Overview of main changes . 55

Part II

Developments in agricultural support by country

Chapter 2. Developments in agricultural support in the OECD area 67

Chapter 3. Developments in agricultural policies and support in Australia 73

Chapter 4. Developments in agricultural policies and support in Canada 81

Chapter 5. Developments in agricultural policies and support in Chile 89

Chapter 6. Developments in agricultural policies and support in the European Union . . 97

Chapter 7. Developments in agricultural policies and support in Iceland 111

Chapter 8. Developments in agricultural policies and support in Israel 119

Chapter 9. Developments in agricultural policies and support in Japan 127

Chapter 10. Developments in agricultural policies and support in Korea 137

Chapter 11. Developments in agricultural policies and support in Mexico 145

Chapter 12. Developments in agricultural policies and support in New Zealand 153

Chapter 13. Developments in agricultural policies and support in Norway 163

Chapter 14. Developments in agricultural policies and support in Switzerland 171

Chapter 15. Developments in agricultural policies and support in Turkey   179

Chapter 16. Developments in agricultural policies and support in the United States .   187

Annex II.A1. Sources and definitions of contextual indicators.   199

Statistical annex

Summary tables of estimation of support   201

Tables

Part I

1.1. Key economic indicators.   18
1.A2.1. GSSE categories   56
1.A2.2. Estimate of support to agriculture for 2011 published in the 2013
            and the 2014 reports   60

Part II

2.1. OECD: Estimates of support to agriculture (USD)   71
2.2. OECD: Estimates of support to agriculture (EUR).   72
3.1. Australia: Contextual indicators, 1995, 2012   75
3.2. Australia: Estimates of support to agriculture.   77
4.1. Canada: Contextual indicators, 1995, 2012.   83
4.2. Canada: Estimates of support to agriculture   85
5.1. Chile: Contextual indicators, 1995, 2012.   91
5.2. Chile: Estimates of support to agriculture   93
6.1. European Union: Contextual indicators, 1995, 2012   99
6.2. European Union: Estimates of support to agriculture   101
7.1. Iceland: Contextual indicators, 1995, 2012.   113
7.2. Iceland: Estimates of support to agriculture   115
8.1. Israel: Contextual indicators, 1995, 2012   121
8.2. Israel: Estimates of support to agriculture.   123
9.1. Japan: Contextual indicators, 1995, 2012   129
9.2. Japan: Estimates of support to agriculture.   131
10.1. Korea: Contextual indicators, 1995, 2012   139
10.2. Korea: Estimates of support to agriculture.   141
11.1. Mexico: Contextual indicators, 1995, 2012   147
11.2. Mexico: Estimates of support to agriculture   149
12.1. New Zealand: Contextual indicators, 1995, 2012.   155
12.2. New Zealand: Estimates of support to agriculture   157
13.1. Norway: Contextual indicators, 1995, 2012   165
13.2. Norway: Estimates of support to agriculture.   167
14.1. Switzerland: Contextual indicators, 1995, 2012.   173
14.2. Switzerland: Estimates of support to agriculture   175
14.3. Switzerland: Outlays for direct payments   177
15.1. Turkey: Contextual indicators, 1995, 2012   181
15.2. Turkey: Estimates of support to agriculture.   183
16.1. United States: Contextual indicators, 1995, 2012   189
16.2. United States: Estimates of support to agriculture.   191

16.3. Comparison of the 2011 estimate of support to agriculture for the United States
as published in the 2013 report and in the current report   192

Figures

Part I

1.1. Commodity prices index, 2006 to 2013   19
1.2. Evolution of OECD support indicators, 1986-2013   28
1.3. Producer Support Estimates by country, 2012 and 2013   29
1.4. Contribution of various factors to the change
in the Producer Support Estimate in 2013   30
1.5. Producer Support Estimate by country, 1995-97 and 2011-13   31
1.6. Composition of Producer Support Estimate by country, 2011-13   32
1.7. Producer Nominal Protection Coefficient (NPC) by country,
1995-97 and 2011-13   33
1.8. Use and composition of support based on area, animal numbers,
receipts and income by country, 1995-97 and 2011-13   34
1.9. OECD: Support conditional on the adoption of specific production practices,
1995-97 and 2011-13   35
1.10. OECD: Single Commodity Transfers, 1995-97 and 2011-13   36
1.11. Composition of General Services Support Estimate, 2011-13   39
1.12. Consumer Support Estimate by country, 1995-97 and 2011-13   40
1.13. Total Support Estimate by country, 1995-97 and 2011-13   41
1.14. Emerging Economies: Producer Support Estimate by country,
1995-97 and 2010-12   43
1.15. Total Support Estimate by country, 1995-97 and 2010-12   44
1.16. OECD: Changes in level and composition of producer support   45

Part II

2.1. OECD: Level and composition of Producer Support Estimate, 1986-2013   68
3.1. Australia: PSE level and composition by support categories, 1986-2013   74
3.2. Australia: Main macroeconomic indicators, 1995-2013   75
3.3. Australia: Agro-food trade, 1995-2012   75
4.1. Canada: PSE level and composition by support categories, 1986-2013   82
4.2. Canada: Main macroeconomic indicators, 1995-2013   83
4.3. Canada: Agro-food trade, 1995-2012   83
5.1. Chile: PSE level and composition by support categories, 1995-2013   90
5.2. Chile: Main macroeconomic indicators, 1995-2013   91
5.3. Chile: Agro-food trade, 1995-2012   91
6.1. European Union: PSE level and composition
by support categories, 1986-2013   98
6.2. European Union: Main macroeconomic indicators, 1995-2013   99
6.3. European Union: Agro-food trade, 1995-2012   99
7.1. Iceland: PSE level and composition by support categories, 1986-2013   112
7.2. Iceland: Main macroeconomic indicators, 1995-2013   113
7.3. Iceland: Agro-food trade, 1995-2012   113
8.1. Israel: PSE level and composition by support categories, 1995-2013   120
8.2. Israel: Main macroeconomic indicators, 1995-2013   121
8.3. Israel: Agro-food trade, 1995-2012   121

9.1. Japan: PSE level and composition by support categories, 1986-2013 128
9.2. Japan: Main macroeconomic indicators, 1995-2013 129
9.3. Japan: Agro-food trade, 1995-2012 129
10.1. Korea: PSE level and composition by support categories, 1986-2013 138
10.2. Korea: Main macroeconomic indicators, 1995-2013 139
10.3. Korea: Agro-food trade, 1995-2012 139
11.1. Mexico: PSE level and composition by support categories, 1991-2013 146
11.2. Mexico: Main macroeconomic indicators, 1995-2013 147
11.3. Mexico: Agro-food trade, 1995-2012 147
12.1. New Zealand: PSE level and composition by support categories, 1986-2013 ... 154
12.2. New Zealand: Main macroeconomic indicators, 1995-2013 155
12.3. New Zealand: Agro-food trade, 1995-2012 155
13.1. Norway: PSE level and composition by support categories, 1986-2013 164
13.2. Norway: Main macroeconomic indicators, 1995-2013 165
13.3. Norway: Agro-food trade, 1995-2012 165
14.1. Switzerland: PSE level and composition by support categories, 1986-2013.... 172
14.2. Switzerland: Main macroeconomic indicators, 1995-2013 173
14.3. Switzerland: Agro-food trade, 1995-2012 173
15.1. Turkey: PSE level and composition by support categories, 1986-2013 180
15.2. Turkey: Main macroeconomic indicators, 1995-2013 181
15.3. Turkey: Agro-food trade, 1995-2012 181
16.1. United States: PSE level and composition by support categories, 1986-2013 .. 188
16.2. United States: Main macroeconomic indicators, 1995-2013 189
16.3. United States: Agro-food trade, 1995-2012 189

List of acronyms and abbreviations

AANZFTA	Asean Australia-New Zealand Free Trade Agreement
ACHIPIA	Chilean agency for food safety and quality (*Agencia Chilena para la Calidad e Inocuidad Alimentaria*)
ACRE	Average Crop Revenue Election (United States)
AMS	Aggregate Measurement of Support
APTA	Asia-Pacific Trade Agreement
ARC	Agriculture Risk Coverage (United States)
ASEAN	Association of South East Asian Nations
ATRA	The American Taxpayer Relief Act of 2012 (or "fiscal cliff" bill, United States)
BPS	Basic Payment Scheme (European Union)
BRM	Business Risk Management (Canada)
CAP	Common Agricultural Policy (European Union)
CCP	Counter-Cyclical Payments
CETA	Comprehensive Economic and Trade Agreement (Canada – European Union)
CFIA	Canadian Food Inspection Agency
CNDP	Complementary National Direct Payments (European Union)
COOL	Country of Origin Labelling (United States)
CRP	Conservation Reserve Program (United States)
CWB	Canadian Wheat Board
DCFTA	Deep and Comprehensive Free Trade Area (European Union)
EAFRD	European Agricultural Fund for Rural Development
EAGF	European Agricultural Guarantee Fund
EEA	European Economic Area
EFTA	European Free Trade Association
EQIP	Environmental Quality Incentives Program (United States)
EPA	Economic partnership agreement
ETS	Emissions trading scheme (New Zealand)
EU	European Union
FAO	Food and Agriculture Organization of the United Nations
FDA	United States Food and Drugs Administration
FPT	Federal, Provincial and Territorial Agreements (Canada)
FTA	Free Trade Agreement
FY	Financial (fiscal) year
GDP	Gross Domestic Product
GF2	Growing Forward 2 (Canada – multilateral FPT agricultural policy framework)
GSP	Generalised System of Preferences
IAF	Irrigation Acceleration Fund (New Zealand)

INDAP	National Institute for Agricultural Development (*Instituto Nacional de Desarrollo Agropecuario*; Chile)
IPARD	Instrument for Pre-Accession Assistance for Rural Development (Turkey)
LDC	Least Developed Countries
LEADER	Links Between Actions for the Development of the Rural Economy (European Union)
LFA	Less Favoured Areas (European Union)
MERCOSUR	Southern Common Market
MFN	Most Favoured Nation
NAFTA	North American Free Trade Agreement
NAIT	National Animal Identification and Tracing (New Zealand)
OECD	Organisation for Economic Co-operation and Development
ODEPA	Office of Agricultural Policies, Trade and Information (Chile)
OIE	World Organisation for Animal Health
PLC	Price loss coverage (United States)
PPP	Purchasing Power Parity
PROAGRO	Programme providing direct payments (Mexico)
PROCAMPO	Programme providing payments based on historical areas (Mexico)
PROGAN	Programme providing payments based on historical livestock numbers (Mexico)
R&D	Research and Development
RDCs	Rural Research and Development Corporations (Australia)
RMA	Resource Management Act 1991 (New Zealand)
SAFTA	South Asian Free Trade Area
SAG	Agriculture and Livestock Service (*Servicio Agrícola Ganadero*; Chile)
SAPS	Single Area Payment Scheme (European Union)
SFF	Sustainable Farming Fund (New Zealand)
SMP	Skimmed milk powder
SNAP	Supplemental Nutrition Assistance Program
SPS	Single Payment Scheme (European Union)
STAX	Stacked Income Protection Plan (United States)
TBT	Technical Barriers to Trade
TNA	Transitional National Aid (European Union)
TPP	Trans-Pacific Partnership Agreement
TRQ	Tariff Rate Quota
TTIP	Transatlantic Trade and Investment Partnership (EU, US)
URAA	Uruguay Round Agreement on Agriculture
WTO	World Trade Organization

OECD indicators of support

ACT	All Commodity Transfers
CSE	Consumer Support Estimate
GCT	Group Commodity Transfers
GSSE	General Services Support Estimate
MPS	Market Price Support
NAC	Nominal Assistance Coefficient

NPC	Nominal Protection Coefficient
OTP	Other Transfers to Producers
PEM	Policy Evaluation Model
PSE	Producer Support Estimate
SCT	Single Commodity Transfers
TSE	Total Support Estimate

Currencies

AUD	Australian dollar
CAD	Canadian dollar
CHF	Swiss frank
CLP	Chilean peso
EUR	Euro
ILS	Israeli shekel
ISK	Icelandic krona
JPY	Japanese yen
KRW	Korean wong
MXN	Mexican peso
NOK	Norwegian krone
NZD	New Zealand dollar
TRY	New Turkish lira
USD	United States dollar

Executive summary

Support to farmers in OECD countries remains at more than one-sixth of farm receipts

In 2013, support to producers across the OECD area amounted to USD 258 billion or EUR 194 billion as measured by the Producer Support Estimate (PSE). This is equivalent to 18% of gross farm receipts in OECD countries, down slightly from about 19% in 2012. This is about half the level observed since OECD first began measuring support in the mid-1980s, when the PSE as a percentage of gross farm receipts was 37%.

The potentially most distorting support still represents around half of the total…

As a result of relatively high commodity prices, market price support has declined in recent years, but still represented almost half of the PSE in 2013. The share of potentially most production and trade distorting support, defined as transfers based on output and variable inputs use (without input constraints), was as high as 86% in 1986-88 and has come down to 51% in 2011-13.

… although there is a general move away from support directly linked to production

OECD countries are moving at different speeds away from supporting farmers through policies that raise domestic prices. Other mechanisms to channel support are progressively being introduced, such as payments based on fixed area, fixed livestock numbers, and farm income or receipts, which do not directly affect current production decisions. The less that support is directly coupled to production decisions, the less production and market distorting it is.

Improving environmental performance is an important challenge

Ensuring the sustainable use of natural resources, notably land, water and biodiversity, remains an important challenge for the agricultural sector in OECD countries. Countries' policy approaches to natural resource management vary widely, but well targeted agri-environmental policies continue to represent only a small share of the overall policy setting.

Large variations in support levels across OECD countries remain

Differences in support levels across countries remain large. The lowest levels of support are observed in New Zealand, Australia and Chile, where less than 3% of gross farm receipts were due to policy transfers in the 2011-13 period. On the other hand, in Norway, Switzerland, Japan, Korea and Iceland between one half and two-thirds of gross farm receipts originate from policy transfers.

Total support to agriculture relative to national income continues to fall

The estimated total support to agriculture as a percentage of GDP declined from 3% on average in 1986-88 to less than 1% in 2011-13. This declining trend is observed in all OECD countries, reflecting in part the shrinking importance of the agricultural sector in the overall economy.

Some OECD countries have introduced new agriculture policy frameworks

New frameworks for agriculture policies will become operational in 2014 in some OECD countries. Growing Forward 2 in Canada puts more emphasis on longer term investments to improve productivity and sustainability, but maintains its supply-management schemes. Redistribution of direct payments within and between member states of the European Union, more flexibility at the national level to implement policies as well as more policy efforts to improve the environmental performance of farming are key elements of the new Common Agricultural Policy 2014-20. Japan has announced policy changes that include phasing out production quotas in the highly protected rice sector and restricting some direct payments to "core" farmers. Mexico has announced a shift in policy direction with plans to re-orient its major support program to re-couple payments to farm purchases of inputs. Switzerland has fine-tuned its direct payment scheme to better target specific agricultural practices and to make it more decoupled from livestock production, while maintaining high levels of overall protection. The Agricultural Act of 2014 in the United States removes untargeted income support and increases spending on revenue and income risks schemes.

Multilateral negotiations at the WTO have advanced

At the 9th WTO Ministerial Meeting in Bali in December 2013 an agreement was reached on a package comprising three main elements; trade facilitation, agriculture and food security, and development issues. This package, while covering a much smaller range of issues than the original Doha Development Agenda, has given renewed impetus to negotiations and could have a major bearing on the multilateral rules that govern agricultural trade.

Agriculture policy performance could be greatly improved by targeting current policy objectives

There is clear, but unequal, progress across the OECD area in moving towards agriculture support that is less market distorting and more efficient in transferring income to farm households. At the same time, there is much less progress in moving towards a better alignment of policy effort and stated policy priorities – including increased productivity, sustainability and profitability.

Further policy reforms could usefully focus on addressing these and other policy priorities expressed by Ministers of Agriculture during their meeting at OECD in 2010.

An increased focus on innovation will be necessary to improve agriculture productivity and sustainability in the long run, and strengthen the ability of the sector to adapt to changes in markets, natural resources availability, and economic opportunities. Improving the capacity of the agriculture sector to contribute to economic growth and jobs reinforces the need to improve the wider policy environment in which the sector operates so as to attract financial and human resources and facilitate innovative business development. A comprehensive approach to improve coherence with macroeconomic, trade, structural, social and environmental policies and to reduce impediments to structural adjustment can in most countries significantly improve policy performance, both domestically and internationally.

PART I

Agricultural policies: Monitoring and evaluation 2014, OECD countries

PART I

Chapter 1

Developments in agricultural policy and support

This chapter provides a description and an overall assessment of agricultural policy developments and support across the OECD area.

The statistical data for Israel are supplied by and under the responsibility of the relevant Israeli authorities. The use of such data by the OECD is without prejudice to the status of the Golan Heights, East Jerusalem and Israeli settlements in the West Bank under the terms of international law.

Key economic and market developments

The recovery of the world economy remained slow and uneven in 2013 and growth stayed below potential (Table 1.1). An important development was the deterioration of financial conditions in major emerging market economies outside China. The expectation of tighter monetary policies in the United States prompted capital outflows and large currency depreciations in emerging economies with large external financing needs: Brazil, India, Indonesia, South Africa and Turkey (OECD, 2013a). This has slowed down global growth and raised concerns about the interactions between United States monetary policies and financial vulnerabilities in some emerging market economies.

Table 1.1. **Key economic indicators (OECD area, unless indicated otherwise)**

	Average 2001-10	2011	2012	2013
	Per cent			
Real GDP growth[1]				
World[2]	3.4	3.7	3.1	2.7
OECD[2]	1.7	1.9	1.6	1.2
United States	1.6	1.8	2.8	1.7
Euro area	1.1	1.6	-0.6	-0.4
Japan	0.8	-0.6	1.9	1.8
Non-OECD[2]	6.8	6.3	5.1	4.8
China	10.5	9.3	7.7	7.7
Output gap[3]	0.3	-1.9	-2.0	-2.6
Unemployment rate[4]	6.8	8.0	8.0	8.0
Inflation[5]	2.2	2.5	2.1	1.5
Fiscal balance[6]	-3.9	-6.6	-5.9	-4.8
Memorandum Items				
World real trade growth	4.9	6.3	3.0	3.0

1. Year-on-year increase; last three columns show the increase over a year earlier.
2. Moving nominal GDP weights, using purchasing power parities.
3. Per cent of potential GDP.
4. Per cent of labour force.
5. Private consumption deflator. Year-on-year increase; last 3 columns show the increase over a year earlier.
6. Per cent of GDP.
Source: OECD (2013a), OECD Economic Outlook, Vol. 2013/2, OECD Publishing, Paris, http://dx.doi.org/10.1787/eco_outlook-v2013-2-en, Paris, last updated 15 November 2013.

Consumption growth continued to be weak in most of the euro area reflecting weak income growth, high unemployment and declines in property values. In the United States and Japan, household demand was more resilient, as labour market outcomes improved and asset values rose.

Employment remains a key challenge in many economies, with unemployment reaching 8% on average across the OECD area. Unemployment is most severe in those parts of the euro area which continued to see contractions of economic activity. It was as high as 26% in Spain and 28% in Greece. Unemployment rates increased in 2013, as well in some other member countries of the European Union: Belgium, Finland France, Italy, Luxembourg and the Netherlands all saw the portion of unemployed amongst the active labour force rising. While the unemployment rate in the United States has fallen to around 6%, it is still high by historical standards. Long-term unemployment remains very high and the young are the most severely hit by subdued economic growth in many parts of the world. Reduced employment opportunities in industry and services will tend to slow down structural change in agriculture.

World trade grew at a pace comparable with global GDP. Export growth from OECD economies was held back by declining demand growth from emerging economies, which itself slowed down in recent years by weak import demand from OECD economies, especially in the euro area.

Energy prices have not shown much movement in the aggregate (Figure 1.1). While prices of natural gas and coal have fallen, oil spot prices remained above USD 105 per barrel (Brent). West Texas Intermediate (WTI) continued to be priced substantially below Brent prices as the surge in energy production from unconventional sources continued in the United States. Since 2009, US natural gas prices have been declining and appear to be decoupled from US oil prices, but elsewhere oil and gas prices continue to move together (IMF, 2013). The different developments in gas prices are potentially important for prices of nitrogen fertilizers, an important input into agricultural production.

Figure 1.1. **Commodity prices index, 2006 to 2013**

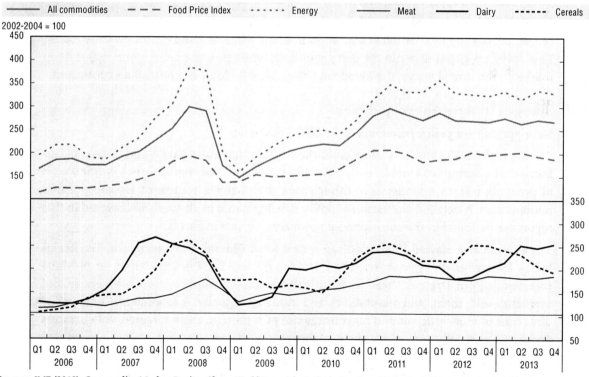

Sources: IMF (2013), Commodity Market Review (from World Economic Outlook, October 2013), Washington: The International Monetary Fund for All Commodities, Food and Energy Indices; FAO (2014), FAO Food Price Index dataset, Rome: for meat, dairy and cereal indices. Base year is 2002-04. www.fao.org/worldfoodsituation/foodpricesindex/en/.

StatLink ⧉ http://dx.doi.org/10.1787/888933109099

Slowing growth in emerging economies is having an impact on commodity (raw materials) prices. In particular metals prices have declined in 2013, as a consequence of stalled growth in demand from China while supply has continued to rise in the wake of large investments in mining capacity in recent years.

While the global food price index showed no big movements between 2012 and 2013 (Figure 1.1), the market developments in major crops and livestock products followed quite different paths.

Grain prices, and to a lesser extent oilseed prices, declined during 2013 (OECD, 2013d). Maize markets saw an accelerated decline of price levels during the second half of the year in anticipation of good harvests in 2014. Those price declines followed a strong positive supply response to high prices in the previous year, and wheat and maize production reached record highs in 2013 due to good harvests in major producing countries. Rice prices also declined throughout the year, following a growing production and allowing for a further replenishment of stocks.

Sugar markets experienced a large over supply in 2013, which resulted in downward pressure on prices, and accumulation of global stocks.

Lower sugar, and coarse grain, prices also boosted global ethanol production. Biodiesel production, on the other hand, stagnated as biodiesel demand in the European Union declined.

In contrast to prices of major crops, meat prices were rising in 2013. Relatively low supplies of beef were the result of slow recovery of livestock herds after several years of decline, especially in the United States. World poultry prices moved up as well, being strongly influenced by higher prices for Brazilian poultry. The upward movement of pork prices followed supply contraction in the European Union.

Dairy prices showed a significant rise in 2013. The main driving factor behind this movement is a supply shortfall of almost 6% in China while demand continued to be robust. This drove up global demand for dairy products, while production in some major dairy markets – the United States, the European Union, New Zealand and Australia – contracted.

Main changes in agricultural policies

New agriculture policy frameworks in OECD countries

Several OECD countries have embarked on implementing new agriculture policy frameworks during 2013 and in early 2014. In some cases, the changes are a continuation of previous reform directions, in other cases the changes represent a more pointed reorientation. A detailed discussion of policy developments in all countries covered in this report can be found in the corresponding country chapters in Part II.

Canada has started implementing a new joint Federal, Provincial, and Territorial policy framework on agriculture, called *Growing Forward 2* (GF2). This builds on previous frameworks, but stresses three broad priority areas: innovation, competitiveness and market development, and adaptability and industry capacity. It emphasises new policy directions of more efficient and responsible use of resources; more targeted, collaborative and result-oriented approaches, and enabling market-based solutions.

GF2 introduces three new federal programmes to support innovation, marketing and competitiveness. The federal government complements these programmes through support to biophysical research and other activities. The policy framework continues to allow flexibility for provinces and territories to design and deliver non-risk management programmes. Most farm-level environmental programmes are designed and administered by provincial governments. Major support policies continue to be delivered under the heading of business risk management. Those measures provide support in case of income declines, co-finance savings, support production insurance and provide assistance in case of natural disasters.

The focus on forward looking measures to improve productivity and sustainability of the agricultural sector are important steps in the right direction. This is in stark contrast to continuation of market intervention in the dairy and poultry sectors which constrain structural adjustment, productivity growth, and increased competitiveness.

The **European Union** has continued to define the details of implementation of the Common Agricultural Policy 2014-20 and the legislative process was concluded in December 2013. The implementation of the CAP 2014-20 started in January 2014 with full entry into force planned in January 2015. A transitional regulation applies in 2014 to bridge the gap between the existing legal framework and the elements of the new CAP that will be implemented only from 2015. The CAP continues to be composed of two pillars. Pillar I, which is entirely funded through the EU budget, provides direct support to farmers and finances market measures, and Pillar II, which is co-funded by EU member states, covers rural development support as well as agri-environmental measures and payments to areas with natural constraints. It will be possible for member states to transfer funds both ways between the two pillars within specific limits and conditions. The overall budget for the CAP is lower than the previous envelope and amounts to EUR 363 billion (USD 505 billion) over six years in 2011 prices.

The new CAP contains important elements of redistribution of direct payments, both within and between member states. By introducing so called internal convergence of direct payments under the Basic Payment Scheme there is a progression towards flat rates per hectare at national or regional level. So called external convergence of payments applies the same principle to progressing towards flatter payment rates between member states. Further fine-tuning of the basic Payment Scheme includes a reduction of amounts paid per recipient above a certain threshold, the option to grant higher payments to the first hectares per recipient, a compulsory top-up of payments to young farmers and simplified procedures for small farmers who receive only small amounts of direct support.

A focus on improving the environmental performance of agriculture is introduced by making 30% of the direct payment entitlement contingent on certain farming practices, including crop diversification, maintenance of permanent pastures and the establishment of ecological focus areas. The precise definition of the latter was still in progress as of April 2014. Alternatively, member states have flexibility to implement national certification schemes instead. In addition, existing cross-compliance conditions are redefined and continue to apply for the direct payments.

While the direct payment system has become "flatter" under the CAP 2014-20, member states are granted more flexibility to define the specific implementation, in particular of measures under Pillar II. This flexibility includes the possibility to use an increased share of up to 13% of the national budget envelope for commodity-specific payments and in addition 2% can be allocated to protein crops.

The milk quota regime will end by 31 March 2015 and sugar quotas will be eliminated in September 2017. The Common Organisation of Markets for 2014-20 maintains existing instruments for market intervention, including public intervention and aid for private storage. Third-country trade remains subject to import and export licences and import duties and tariff quota management in specific commodities. Although export refunds are set to zero, provisions are made that allow their future use. In the CAP 2014-20, the rules on recognition of Producer organisations and interbranch organisations are expanded beyond fruits and vegetables.

Under Horizon 2020, the over-arching framework for funding innovation and research in the European Union, EUR 3.8 billion have been budgeted for "Food security, sustainable agriculture, marine and maritime research and the bioeconomy" over the period 2014-20. As a result, funding for research and innovation in agriculture, food and the bioeconomy is expected to double.

The European Union has over the years made substantial progress in reducing the level of trade distorting support. However, the CAP 2014-20 offers more flexibility to member states to re-introduce commodity-specific and output-linked measures. A better alternative would be for member states to focus support on measures to improve the long-term productivity, profitability, sustainability and competitiveness of the sector.

Japan has announced, in December 2013, the first major agricultural policy change since the introduction of income support payments in 2011. The "Plan to Create Vitality for Agricultural, Forestry and Fishery Industries and Local Communities" aims at revitalising the agricultural sector in view of significant drops in output and farming incomes over the past two decades. The plan continues to focus support on core (potentially viable) farmers.

The Plan foresees major changes to rice policies. The allocation of the rice production quota, which limits production and keeps the price above the market equilibrium level, will be phased out by March 2018. A number of changes have been planned for the payments for rice and upland crops. Starting in 2014, the direct payment for rice production will be reduced by half and will be abolished in 2018. The price-contingent payment for rice will be eliminated in 2014. At the same time, incentives to diversify crops (e.g. rice for feed) will be reinforced by increasing the amount of payments as well as introducing a quantity based payment to support rice farmers who want to shift from table rice production into other crops. Other changes are foreseen to the direct payments for upland crops (wheat, barley, soybean, sugar beet, starch potato, buckwheat and rapeseed) and to the system of income-based payments (which is available to producers of rice, wheat, barley, soybean, sugar beet and starch potato). A new payment to community organisations engaging in preserving rural resources including rural infrastructure such as irrigation and drainage facilities will be introduced in 2014.

In line with the reform plan the Basic Plan on Food, Agriculture and Rural Areas, which is the national framework for implementing policies on food, agriculture and rural areas, will be revised.

The abolition of income support payments to rice farmers and the phasing out of rice production quota are important first steps in the direction of more market orientation. However, the policy package is also likely to stimulate the production of diversion crops such as rice for feed and manufacturing, wheat and soybean and will tend to keep the price of rice high. Further efforts are also warranted to encourage farm land consolidation.

In **Mexico**, a new policy framework for the food and agriculture sector was approved in December 2013. The plan, which extends over a six-year period, contains a large set of diverse objectives: productivity, competitiveness, sustainability, equity and guaranteeing food security.

The most important change is the replacement of the long-standing PROCAMPO by a new programme called "Productive PROAGRO" in 2014. While payments are grandfathered to existing recipients of PROCAMPO, the new payment system requires farmers to produce and the new payments are linked to specific actions to enhance output. This policy change marks a re-linking of support to production and inputs and reduces the transfer efficiency of payments by increasing leakages to upstream sectors. Agricultural support should instead focus on strategic investments in the long term productivity, sustainability and profitability of the sector. This includes steps towards removing limits to private ownership of land.

Switzerland has adopted a new policy framework for 2014-17 (*Politique Agricole 2014-17*). The main policy objectives have not changed and emphasise food security, an efficient and sustainable use of natural resources, maintenance of cultural landscapes and assuring the role of agriculture in rural areas.

The policy reform re-arranges and fine-tunes the direct payment scheme, intends to improve the efficiency and effectiveness of the measures, and to set up a system of direct payments better targeted to the various objectives. The main change is the suppression of general area payments and a reallocation of payments to support certain agricultural practices. Another important shift is the replacement of general headage payments to ruminants by an area payment to pastures with milk and beef production. The reform of the system of direct payments will also result in some redistribution of subsidies from livestock and dairy production to the arable sector, resulting in some redistribution from mountain and hilly regions to lowlands. The environmental cross-compliance conditions are maintained in the new system of payments. The overall budgeted annual amount of these payments remains stable for the whole period.

The impact of the new policy framework is expected to be most prominent in the livestock sector. The shift of direct payment from animal numbers to land area will induce producers to use land more extensively. This can be expected to reduce stocking density, in particular in mountain regions. In the plain regions, the major change in the direct payment system is a shift to current area payment for crop production, which could lead to shifting some of the pasture land use to crop production.

The new policy framework does not change the existing high levels of border protection that shield Swiss agriculture from foreign competition and elevate prices for consumers and the processing industry.

In the **United States**, a new farm law, the Agricultural Act of 2014 (2014 Farm Act), was enacted on 7 February 2014. The 2014 Farm Act makes major changes in commodity programmes: it ends fixed annual payments based on historical production; it ends Countercyclical Payments and the Average Crop Revenue Election programme and removes upland cotton from coverage under Title I programmes. At the same time, it adds new crop insurance options. Two new programmes, Price Loss Coverage and Agriculture Risk Coverage, introduce instruments to manage risks stemming from crop market developments. The 2014 Farm Act also ends the dairy price support programme and introduces a new margin protection programme for dairy producers.

Conservation programmes are streamlined, and programmes are expanded for specialty crops, organic farmers, bioenergy, rural development, and beginning farmers and ranchers. The 2014 Farm Act modifies some provisions of the Supplemental Nutrition Assistance Program (SNAP, formerly known as food stamps). The legislation also renews the Supplemental Disaster Assistance programmes for livestock and for orchard and nursery trees, vines, and bushes.

While ending farm support regardless of farm prices or income is a positive development, the ultimate economic impacts of the new programmes remain to be seen. In particular, the increasing emphasis on financially supporting insurance against revenue and income risks warrants a rigorous evaluation of the cost-effectiveness of such measures. These policies tend to offer modest benefits at high cost and can lead to even higher expenditures when prices come down from their historically high levels.

Multilateral negotiations at the World Trade Organisation address agricultural policies

At the multilateral level, the ministerial meeting of members of the World Trade Organisation in December 2013 in Bali resulted in several decisions and declarations that have a bearing on the multilateral rules that govern agricultural trade and domestic support to the sector (Box 1.1). The Bali package covers a much smaller range of issues than the original Doha agenda, but has given renewed impetus to the negotiations. A temporary "peace clause" was agreed on the issue of exemptions sought by some countries from existing provisions in the Uruguay Agreement on Agriculture to allow more flexibility for the acquisition of stocks of foodstuffs for food security purposes. Stronger notification and transparency requirements are part of this "peace clause" agreement on public stockholding and are also incorporated in other elements of the Bali package, in particular in the understanding on Tariff Rate Quota administration and the declaration on export competition. Those requirements, if fully respected, would constitute a significant improvement towards enhanced transparency.

Box 1.1. Outcome of the Bali WTO ministerial

The 9th WTO Ministerial Meeting took place in Bali from 3-7 December 2013. Agreement was reached on a Bali package comprising three main elements; trade facilitation, agriculture and food security, and development issues. This package, while covering a much smaller range of issues than the original Doha agenda, has given renewed impetus to negotiations on the remaining Doha issues, among them Non-Agricultural Market Access (NAMA), agriculture and services. In addition, Ministers have instructed the Trade Negotiations Committee "to prepare within the next 12 months, a clearly defined work programme on the remaining Doha Agenda issues."

The Bali Package contains four separate decisions or declarations specific to agriculture, in addition to which there is a decision on cotton. Other decisions, notably on trade facilitation could impact significantly on trade in food and agricultural products.

Agriculture and Food Security – Main Provisions of the Agreements
General Services

This decision makes explicit that a range of programmes related to land reform, drought and flood management and rural employment programmes can be considered as falling within the range of general services permitted in Annex 2, paragraph 2 of the Uruguay Round Agreement on Agriculture (URAA). This decision, part of the original proposal put forward by the G33 group of countries, attracted wide support from developed and developing countries.

Public Stockholding for Food Security Purposes

This draft decision also responds to a proposal from the G33 to exempt from discipline the acquisition of stocks of foodstuffs by developing countries with the objective of

---

Box 1.1. **Outcome of the Bali WTO ministerial** (*cont.*)

supporting low-income or resource poor producers (or as proposed in another part of the proposed text [...] at subsidised prices [...] with the objective of reducing hunger and poverty [...]). This issue proved to be one of the most intractable with countries across the full spectrum of development struggling to define modalities which would allow the policy space sought by some countries while ensuring that the pre-existing provisions of Annex 2 of the URAA would not be diluted in a way that would render them totally ineffective, or otherwise distort trade or impinge negatively on the food security of other countries.

The compromise ultimately arrived at provides an "interim solution" in the form of a peace clause exempting public stockholding for food security purposes from challenge under the terms of Annex 2 of the URAA, provided certain other quite onerous conditions are met. These include a general safeguard requirement that the programmes do not distort trade and do not adversely affect the food security of other Members. The programme in respect of which exemption is claimed must already exist, that is, no new programme can benefit from this exemption (although there is nothing to prevent new programmes being established as long as they are in conformity with the original provisions). The country claiming exemption has to declare that is has breached or is in danger of breaching its Aggregate Measurement of Support (AMS) commitments. There are also quite demanding notification and transparency requirements, which, if fully respected, would constitute a significant improvement – both because additional information is asked for and because in the past many countries did not notify their AMS levels at all, or notified so late as to render the information less useful. Finally, there will be an obligation to consult if required by other Members.

Together, these provisions of the interim solution go some way towards limiting the risk of dilution of the URAA disciplines on domestic support generally, while also providing some incentive to work towards a "permanent solution".

Understanding on Tariff Rate Quota Administration

In addition to strengthened provisions concerning publication, notifications and processing of applications, the most significant elements of this understanding relate to measures to be taken when there is systematic under fill of Tariff-Rate Quotas (TRQs) that cannot be explained by normal commercial conditions. The trigger definition of systematic under fill is less than 65% for two consecutive years. The intent is to ensure an effective re-allocation of quota in these cases. A process of tracking and consultation, involving a three year cycle, will be put in place. If the issue is not resolved at the end of the period the importing country should provide unencumbered access, either on the basis of first come first served, or using unconditional licensing on demand. A small number of countries, the United States and a number of small Caribbean and Central American states choose to opt out of the automatic prolongation of this provision beyond the 12th Ministerial Conference (2019) which is otherwise provided for in the understanding.

Export Competition Declaration

This declaration re-affirms Ministerial commitment to elimination of all forms of export subsidies and disciplines on all export measures with equivalent effect and re-asserts the continuing validity of the 2008 modalities text. Ministers also committed to enhanced transparency and improved monitoring in relation to all forms of export subsidies and all export measures with equivalent effect. This will take the form of dedicated, annual consultations in the WTO Committee on Agriculture on the basis of timely notifications, complemented by additional information which will be gathered by the WTO Secretariat using a questionnaire. It was agreed that the next MC in 2015 would revert to this question.

Box 1.1. **Outcome of the Bali WTO ministerial** (*cont.*)

Cotton Decision

Ministers re-affirmed earlier commitments (2004, 2005 and 2011) to address issues around cotton ambitiously, expeditiously and specifically. They undertook to enhance transparency and monitoring in relation to the trade-related aspects of cotton and to that end to hold a dedicated discussion on a biannual basis in the context of the Committee on Agriculture in Special Session to examine relevant trade-related developments across the three pillars of Market Access, Domestic Support and Export Competition. They reiterated the importance of development assistance in relation to cotton, including the Consultative Framework Mechanism on Cotton. They requested periodic reports on the development assistance related aspects and that the issue be on the agenda at each Ministerial meeting.

"Non-Agriculture Specific" Elements of the Bali Package of relevance to Agriculture

The agreement on Trade Facilitation incorporating reforms of border procedures to reduce costs, remove bottlenecks and speed up transit times will apply to all goods, including food and agriculture products. The agreement is a mix of binding commitments and "best endeavours" language. On the positive side, the agreement reaffirms and reinforces provisions of transparency and uniform application, including practical provisions for enhanced accessibility of information, and against arbitrary decisions. A number of provisions have strong potential to reduce corruption, including provisions on advance rulings, fees and charges, uniform documentation and procedures throughout the territory and the promotion of electronic payments. Positive also are provisions which call for choosing the least trade restrictive among various policy options. Less positive is the use of best endeavours language, some narrowing of scope and the resort to commitments on principle in some cases rather than specific modalities and the dilution of the provision on the mandatory use of Customs brokers by grandfathering existing provisions.

There is recognition of the special efforts needed for facilitating trade for small and medium enterprises, and of the particular vulnerability of perishable products. Priority should be granted to perishable products and other measures taken to smooth their passage across borders.

Actual outcomes on trade facilitation and the time frame in which they will occur will depend on the schedules of commitments adopted by developing countries, including emerging economies. The three tiered approach to commitments of developing countries (*a.* to be implemented immediately; *b.* calling for extra time; and *c.* requiring technical assistance) allows for considerable flexibility. But clearly there is significant potential for developing and least-developed (LDC) countries to benefit from increased trade in food and agricultural products.

Similarly, although not specific to agriculture some elements of the package of "development and LDC" issues, could impact agricultural and food trade in a significant way, notable duty-free, quota-free access for LDCs and to a lesser extent, preferential rules of origin for LDCs.

Source: World Trade Organisation (2013), Bali Ministerial Declaration and decisions, Geneva. *http://wto.org/ english/thewto_e/minist_e/mc9_e/balipackage_e.htm.*

Trade in food and agriculture products is also subject to the agreement on Trade Facilitation, which addresses reforms of border procedures to reduce costs, remove bottlenecks and speed up transit times. The agreement is a mix of binding commitments and "best endeavours" language, and reaffirms and reinforces provisions of transparency and uniform application. While there is significant potential for developing and least-developed (LDC) countries to benefit from increased trade in food and agricultural products, actual outcomes on trade facilitation and the time frame in which they will occur will depend on the schedules of commitments adopted.

Developments in agricultural support

This section provides a quantitative assessment of policy support to agriculture, based on a set of OECD indicators. These indicators express the diversity of support measures applied in different countries and are comparable across countries and time, with different indicators focusing on different dimensions of support policies. While the Producer Support Estimate as a percentage of gross farm receipts (%PSE) is the OECD's key indicator to measure policy efforts to support agricultural producers, a range of other indicators allows looking at other dimensions of support. Annex 1.A1 provides definitions of the indicators used in the report, including the revised methodology for estimating general services transfers applied for the first time.

The evaluation begins with the presentation of the changes in agricultural support levels in 2013 and the main drivers behind these changes. Next, longer term trends in the level and the structure of support are shown, highlighting how countries' efforts to reform agricultural policies contributed to reductions of policy distortions in agriculture over time. Finally, implications of agricultural support for consumers and its overall cost to OECD economies are examined.

Producer support in the OECD area in 2013 fell back to the 2011 historical low

About one-sixth of farm gross receipts in OECD countries is due to public policies that support farmers. This is indicated by the percentage Producer Support Estimate (%PSE) which, on average for the OECD area, fluctuated between 18% and 19% over the 2011-13 period (Figure 1.2). In value terms, the PSE in 2013 totalled USD 258 billion or EUR 194 billion.

The OECD average %PSE for the 2011-13 period of 18% compares to about 30% for 1995-97 and 37% for the 1986-88 period (Table A.1). Most of the decline took place since the mid-1990s.

A similar long-term downward trend in producer support is reflected in other indicators that complement the %PSE (Figure 1.2). The Nominal Assistance Coefficient (NAC) of 1.23 indicates that total gross farm receipts in the OECD area were on average 23% higher in 2011-13 than if they were generated at world market prices and with no budgetary support – a differential that has narrowed significantly since 1986-88, when it was 59%.

Similarly, the Nominal Protection Coefficient (NPC) of 1.10 suggests that farmers in OECD countries, overall, received prices that were 10% above international market levels in 2011-13, compared to almost 50% above during the 1986-88 period.

In recent years, the declining support trends are also driven by relatively firm world market commodity prices. With higher world prices, policies to support domestic prices in OECD countries generated smaller transfers, resulting in the overall reduction in support to producers.

Figure 1.2. **Evolution of OECD support indicators, 1986-2013**

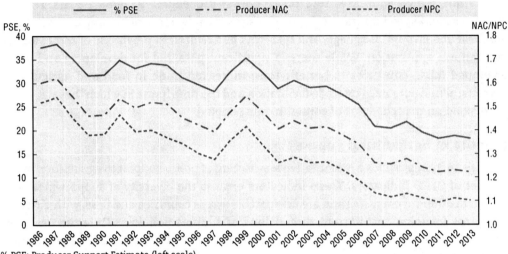

% PSE: Producer Support Estimate (left scale).
NAC: Nominal Assistance Coefficient (right scale); NPC: Nominal Protection Coefficient (right scale).
The OECD total includes Chile and Israel from 1995. The OECD total does not include the non-OECD EU member states. Austria, Finland and Sweden are included in the OECD total for all years and in the EU from 1995. The Czech Republic, Estonia, Hungary, Poland, the Slovak Republic and Slovenia are included in the OECD total for all years and in the EU from 2004.
Source: OECD (2014), "Producer and Consumer Support Estimates", *OECD Agriculture Statistics Database, http:// dx.doi.org/10.1787/agr-pcse-data-en.*

StatLink ⎙ *http://dx.doi.org/10.1787/888933109118*

Changes in producer support between 2012 and 2013 are uneven, with significant declines in some countries and little change or even increases in others

Changes in support to producers show much variation across individual OECD countries. Support to producers fell significantly in **Israel** and **Canada**, where the decline reached about 2 and 3 percentage points respectively, and in **Iceland**, **Norway** and **Switzerland**, where the decline was above 6 percentage points. Compared to the previous year, support in 2013 increased significantly in **Korea**. In all other countries or regions, changes in producer support as a percentage of gross farm receipts are relatively minor (Figure 1.3).

As discussed in Box 1.2, these results were generally driven by price developments on international markets, except in **Canada** where budgetary spending contributed significantly to the decrease in the value of support provided in 2013.

The decline in market price support in most countries was due to higher border prices for milk products and beef, and to a lesser extent other livestock products and some fruits.

In the long run, support is declining in all countries but differences in levels remain large

Compared to the levels in the second half of the 1990s, support to producers fell in all OECD countries. However, these levels continue to vary widely (Figure 1.5). **New Zealand**, **Australia**, and **Chile** are at one end of the range, where less than 3% of producer gross receipts was due to agricultural policy transfers in 2011-13. At the other end are **Norway**, **Japan**, **Switzerland**, and **Korea** where support policies generated over half of gross farm receipts, and **Iceland**, where support to producers averaged 44% over the 2011-13 period. Between these two ends of the spectrum are all other OECD countries, but within this range support levels are also widely spread – from 19% in the **European Union** and **Turkey** to 8% in the **United States** in 2011-13. With support levels at around 12-14%, **Mexico** and

Figure 1.3. **Producer Support Estimates by country, 2012 and 2013**

Per cent of gross farm receipts

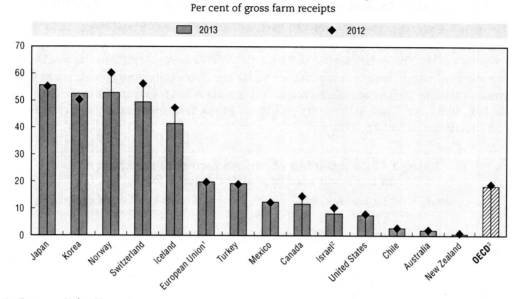

1. European Union 27.
2. The statistical data for Israel are supplied by and under the responsibility of the relevant Israeli authorities. The use of such data by the OECD is without prejudice to the status of the Golan Heights, East Jerusalem and Israeli settlements in the West Bank under the terms of international law.
3. The OECD total does not include the non-OECD EU member states.
Source: OECD (2014), "Producer and Consumer Support Estimates", *OECD Agriculture Statistics Database, http://dx.doi.org/10.1787/agr-pcse-data-en.*

StatLink ⟨⟩ *http://dx.doi.org/10.1787/888933109137*

Canada are within this range. In the **European Union**, which accounts for almost half of support in monetary terms, and close to 40% of the value of OECD agricultural production, producer support at 19% is close to the OECD average.

These large variations in support levels across the OECD area reflect differences in economic, social and political choices that result in policies which induce larger or smaller transfers to the agricultural sector from consumers and taxpayers.

Countries differ significantly in the ways they provide support

The composition of support is arguably even more important than the level. Assistance may be provided by supporting market prices, or by giving a subsidy to reduce the cost of inputs; support may take the form of a payment per hectare, per animal, or as a top-up to farmers' income. Support may be given under the condition that farmers are actually engaged in production, or without such a condition. Payments can be conditional on the respect of specific production practices. These distinctions are important as support delivered in these various ways has different impacts on agricultural production, trade and incomes. Also, some forms of support are more suitable for targeting to specific objectives and beneficiaries. For example, support based on farming area, animals kept, or farm income can be targeted to specific farms or locations, and the amount of outlay can be tailored to the problem at hand. In contrast, blanket price support cannot discriminate between beneficiaries.

The composition of the PSE shows that OECD countries differ significantly by the degree to which they use various support measures (Figure 1.6 and Table A.5). Some countries continue to rely mostly on output-based support, which is potentially the most production

Box 1.2. **What drove changes in the monetary value of support in 2013?**

Figure 1.4 presents contributions of various factors to the annual changes in the monetary value of support. Panel A maps the contributions of market price support (vertical axis) and budgetary payments (horizontal axis) to the total PSE. Two diagonal lines are the locus where these contributions are equal. The closer the country points are to the vertical axis, the higher the contribution of changes in market price support to the change in PSE, while the closer the country points are to the horizontal axis, the higher the contribution of budgetary payments.

Figure 1.4. **Contribution of various factors to the change in the Producer Support Estimate in 2013**

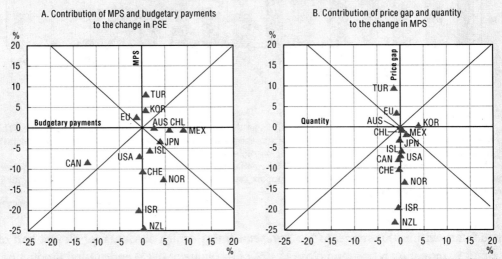

Source: OECD (2014), Producer and Consumer Support Estimates, *OECD Agriculture Statistics Database*, http://dx.doi.org/10.1787/agr-pcse-data-en.

StatLink ᔍᖤ http://dx.doi.org/10.1787/888933109156

It can be seen that the prevailing factor driving the changes in monetary support across OECD countries were changes in market price support, as the majority of country points are located along the vertical MPS axis of Figure 1.4, Panel A. This played a particularly strong role in the decrease in support to producers in Israel, New Zealand,* Norway and Switzerland. The more modest changes in support to producers in Korea, Turkey and the European Union (increase) and in Iceland and the United States (decrease), are also mainly due to changes in market price support. In Canada, lower producer support can be attributed to the decrease in both market price support and budgetary payments. Canada is the only country where budgetary payments decreased significantly, as disbursements under risk-related programmes were lower. In Japan, the decrease in market price support is offset by increases in budgetary payments. In Australia, Chile and Mexico, higher payments explain the rise in support to producers, which remain very low in the first two countries.

Panel B further disaggregates changes in the market price support by its two components – the gap between domestic and border prices (vertical axis) and quantities of production which receive this support (horizontal axis). The majority of country points are aligned closely to or are almost on the vertical axis, indicating that the variations in market price support were predominantly driven by the changes in the price gaps. However, in **Korea** and to a lesser extent in **Mexico** and **Norway**, higher quantity produced also concur to the increase, or the lower decrease, in support to producers.

Box 1.2. What drove changes in the monetary value of support in 2013? *(cont.)*

Some insight into the factors that shifted the relative levels of domestic and border prices in 2013 can be obtained by looking at what changed border prices expressed in national currencies. The lower price differential in most countries was largely explained by higher border prices measured in national currency and USD in 2013 (Table A.54). Only in *Japan* was higher border price due to a depreciation of the JPY, although the reduction in the price gap can also be attributed to lower domestic prices for rice producers. The higher price differential in *Chile and Korea* results mainly from lower border prices, which were not accompanied by equivalent decreases in domestic producer prices.

* In New Zealand, price support is measured only for poultry and eggs and is due to non-tariff protection applied on SPS grounds.

Figure 1.5. **Producer Support Estimate by country, 1995-97 and 2011-13**

Per cent of gross farm receipts

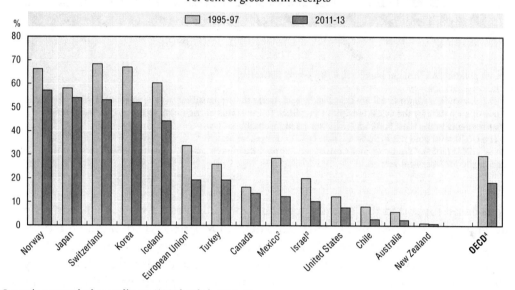

Countries are ranked according to %PSE levels in 2011-13.
1. EU15 for 1995-97 and EU27 for 2011-13.
2. For Mexico, 1995-97 is replaced by 1991-93.
3. The statistical data for Israel are supplied by and under the responsibility of the relevant Israeli authorities. The use of such data by the OECD is without prejudice to the status of the Golan Heights, East Jerusalem and Israeli settlements in the West Bank under the terms of international law.
4. The OECD total does not include the non-OECD EU member states. The Czech Republic, Estonia, Hungary, Poland, the Slovak Republic and Slovenia are included in the OECD total for both periods and in the EU for 2011-13.
Source: OECD (2014), "Producer and Consumer Support Estimates", *OECD Agriculture Statistics Database,* http://dx.doi.org/10.1787/agr-pcse-data-en.

StatLink ᴍᴤᴩ http://dx.doi.org/10.1787/888933109175

and trade distorting. The majority of this support is generated through border protection and domestic price regulation, and to a lesser extent through subsidies paid per tonne of output. Such measures constitute over 90% of the total PSE in *Korea* in 2011-13, around 80% in *Turkey, Japan* and *Israel*, over 70% in *Iceland*, and over 60% in *Canada*. Countries that provide in similar ways 40% to 50% of producer support include *Norway* and *Switzerland*.

Few OECD countries use predominantly support based on inputs. While support provided to farmers in *Chile* amounts to just 3% of gross farm receipts, almost all of it is delivered as subsidies to farm inputs. Support to investments constitutes the major type of

Figure 1.6. **Composition of Producer Support Estimate by country, 2011-13**

Per cent of gross farm receipts

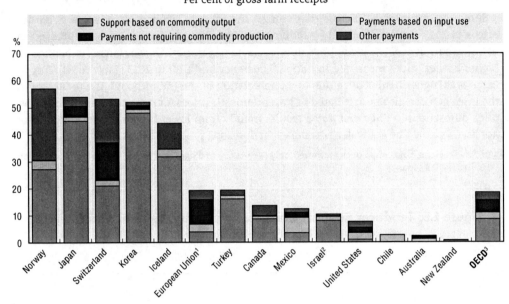

A (Area planted), An (Animal numbers), R (Receipts), I (Income).

1. EU27 in 2011-13.
2. The statistical data for Israel are supplied by and under the responsibility of the relevant Israeli authorities. The use of such data by the OECD is without prejudice to the status of the Golan Heights, East Jerusalem and Israeli settlements in the West Bank under the terms of international law.
3. The OECD total does not include the non-OECD EU member states.

Source: OECD (2014), "Producer and Consumer Support Estimates", *OECD Agriculture Statistics Database, http://dx.doi.org/10.1787/agr-pcse-data-en.*

StatLink ⟲ *http://dx.doi.org/10.1787/888933109194*

input-based support in this country, together with subsidies for various on-farm services; this support is destined mainly to smallholders. In **Mexico**, support based on farm input use accounted for 45% of the PSE, while market price support was the second largest component with over one quarter of producer support. Input subsidies in this country are directed predominantly at the lowering of energy, insurance and price hedging costs for farmers, as well as for investments. Amongst these, energy subsidies are the most distorting support, although they are provided within an overall support level which is around 12% of gross farm receipts.

Other OECD countries support producers predominantly through payments based on area, livestock numbers, farm income or receipts (discussed in more detail below).

Most countries moved towards less distortive support by reducing agricultural protection...

Most distortive measures are reflected in the output price received by the farmer and measured by the producer Nominal Protection Coefficient (NPC). Agricultural protection levels have declined in almost all OECD countries (Figure 1.7, Table A.1 and Table A.2). Those with historically high price support have seen considerable falls in domestic market protection. Domestic prices were more than twice the level of border prices in the mid-1990s in five countries, including **Korea** and **Switzerland** where they were almost three times higher. In **Korea** and **Japan**, domestic prices remain almost twice the level of border prices, but **Norway**, **Iceland** and **Switzerland** saw important reductions, with domestic

Figure 1.7. **Producer Nominal Protection Coefficient (NPC) by country, 1995-97 and 2011-13**

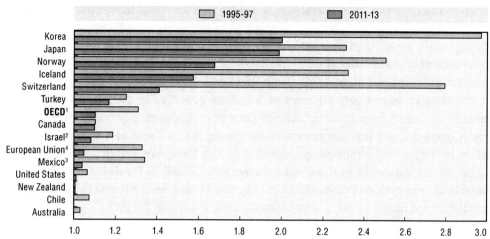

Countries are ranked according to NPC levels in 2011-13.

1. The OECD total does not include the non-OECD EU member states. The Czech Republic, Estonia, Hungary, Poland, the Slovak Republic and Slovenia are included in the OECD total for both periods and in the EU for 2011-13.
2. The statistical data for Israel are supplied by and under the responsibility of the relevant Israeli authorities. The use of such data by the OECD is without prejudice to the status of the Golan Heights, East Jerusalem and Israeli settlements in the West Bank under the terms of international law.
3. For Mexico, 1995-97 is replaced by 1991-93.
4. EU15 for 1995-97; EU27 for 2011-13.

Source: OECD (2014), "Producer and Consumer Support Estimates", *OECD Agriculture Statistics Database, http://dx.doi.org/10.1787/agr-pcse-data-en.*

StatLink ᵐˢᵖ *http://dx.doi.org/10.1787/888933109213*

prices exceeding border prices by respectively 68%, 57% and 41% on average in 2011-13 (NPCs of 1.68, 1.57 and 1.41). This apparent progress notwithstanding, domestic price distortions continue to be considerable in all these countries. Reform of market regimes for key agricultural commodities moved domestic prices in the **European Union** close to the border price levels, with the price differential between internal EU prices and world prices falling from 33% in 1995-97 to 5% in 2011-13. The reduction in the price difference is also significant and gradual in **Israel**, where the price differential fell from 19% to 8% between the two periods. More importantly, producers in **Australia, Chile, Mexico, New Zealand**, and the **United States** receive at present prices which on average are either fully or closely aligned with international levels.

... increasing the use of payments that are more decoupled from current production...

As OECD countries move away from price support, they have introduced other ways to channel support to the farm sector, mainly through payments. There is a great deal of variation in the design of such measures in the choice of the payment base, which may be area, livestock numbers, farm income or receipts, as well as to whether these parameters correspond to current or base (historic) levels. In addition there are different conditions attached to the granting of payments. Farmers may or may not be obliged to actually produce agricultural commodities in order to become recipients of payments. Both implementation criteria and amount of payment determine the size and composition of production impacts (OECD, 2008). Payments based on non-current area, animal numbers, receipts, or income that are provided with no obligation to produce are more prominent today in almost all OECD countries.

The share of support in the form of payments based on area, animals, receipts, and income for the OECD area as a whole increased from 9% of the OECD PSE in 1986-88, to 19% in 1995-97 and to 39% in 2011-13 (Table A.5). Figure 1.8 shows that these changes took place in almost all OECD countries, with significant re-orientation in the **European Union**, where such payments constituted over 60% of the total PSE in 2011-13. This re-orientation was also considerable in **Australia, Norway, Switzerland** and the **United States** with such support constituting around half of total support in these countries. **Korea** and **Japan**, the countries that continue to rely largely on support based on commodity output, also introduced payments de-linked from commodities. In **Canada** and **Mexico**, payments based on area, animals, receipts, and income account respectively for 28% and 26% of total support to producers. Some important programmes (e.g. the **European Union**'s Single Payment Scheme, Direct Payments in the **United States**, PROCAMPO in **Mexico**, area payments in **Switzerland**, exceptional circumstance payments and environmental payments in **Australia**) do not oblige farmers to produce in order to receive support.

Figure 1.8. **Use and composition of support based on area, animal numbers, receipts and income by country, 1995-97 and 2011-13**

Per cent of total support to producers

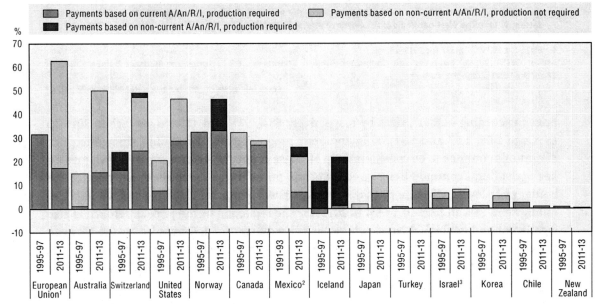

The countries are ranked according to the 2011-13 levels.
1. EU15 for 1995-97; EU27 for 2011-13.
2. For Mexico, 1995-97 is replaced by 1991-93.
3. The statistical data for Israel are supplied by and under the responsibility of the relevant Israeli authorities. The use of such data by the OECD is without prejudice to the status of the Golan Heights, East Jerusalem and Israeli settlements in the West Bank under the terms of international law.
Source: OECD (2014), "Producer and Consumer Support Estimates", *OECD Agriculture Statistics Database, http://dx.doi.org/10.1787/agr-pcse-data-en.*
StatLink 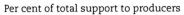 *http://dx.doi.org/10.1787/888933109232*

... and making them conditional on the adoption of specific production practices...

If producers want to receive support, they are increasingly obliged to contribute to improvements in environmental performance, rural amenities, or better treatment of animals. In 2011-13, over one-third of support to OECD farmers had such conditions, whereas in 1995-97 this share was only 10% (Figure 1.9, Table A.6). For the most part, the conditions are additional requirements attached to broad-based payments. In order to receive the full payment granted

Figure 1.9. **OECD: Support conditional on the adoption of specific production practices, 1995-97 and 2011-13**

Per cent of total support to producers

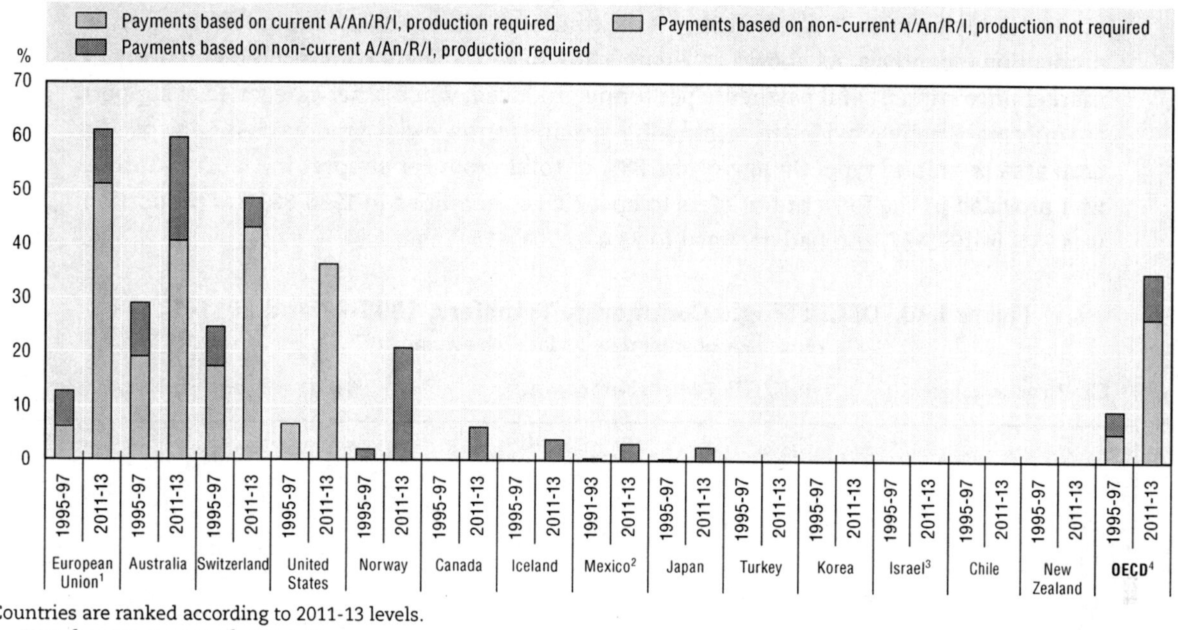

Countries are ranked according to 2011-13 levels.

1. EU15 for 1995-97; EU27 for 2011-13.
2. For Mexico, 1995-97 is replaced by 1991-93.
3. The statistical data for Israel are supplied by and under the responsibility of the relevant Israeli authorities. The use of such data by the OECD is without prejudice to the status of the Golan Heights, East Jerusalem and Israeli settlements in the West Bank under the terms of international law.
4. The OECD total does not include the non-OECD EU member states. The Czech Republic, Estonia, Hungary, Poland, the Slovak Republic and Slovenia are included in the OECD total for both periods and in the EU for 2011-13.

Source: OECD (2014), "Producer and Consumer Support Estimates", OECD Agriculture Statistics Database, http://dx.doi.org/10.1787/agr-pcse-data-en.
StatLink ⫍⫍⫍⫍ http://dx.doi.org/10.1787/888933109251

on the basis of criteria such as number of hectare or animal, or level of income, farmers need to comply with these so-called "cross-compliance" conditions. These are used in the **European Union** and **Switzerland** for close to two-thirds of payments; in the **United States** for about half of payments, and in **Chile** for over one-third of payments. A larger number of countries offer to producers, on a voluntary basis, payments requiring the adoption of specific farm practices. Most of the conditions are linked to agri-environmental practices. While the share of these agri-environmental payments has significantly increased in many countries, their share in total support remains below 10% except in **Australia**, the **United States** and the **European Union**, and some countries do not offer this type of incentive.

... and providing less support tied to specific commodities

The shift away from market price support and the introduction of payments decoupled to different degrees from commodity output increase the flexibility of producers in their choices of product mixes. For example, a payment tied to a specific commodity means that in order to receive payment a farmer must produce that commodity. Alternatively, payment may be provided to any commodity in a designated group (for example, any crop within a cereal group), or simply to any commodity without distinction. This progressively adds freedom to farmers who receive support in defining their production mix, thus strengthening the role of market signals in guiding their decisions.

The link between support and incentives to produce specific commodities has considerably weakened, and this happened mostly due to the fall in the market price support observed since the late 1980s. The Single Commodity Transfers (SCT) indicator measures support that is directed at specific commodities and creates commodity-specific production incentives. As shown in Figure 1.10, these transfers consist predominantly of market price support and payments per tonne produced, while other categories of support are only marginally provided in commodity-specific forms, e.g. payments based on specific crop area or animal type. On aggregate, 88% of total producer support in OECD countries was provided in the form of transfers to specific commodities in 1986-88, this proportion was 75% in 1995-97, and had declined to 53% by 2011-13 (Table A.8).

Figure 1.10. **OECD: Single Commodity Transfers, 1995-97 and 2011-13**
Percentage of gross receipts for each commodity

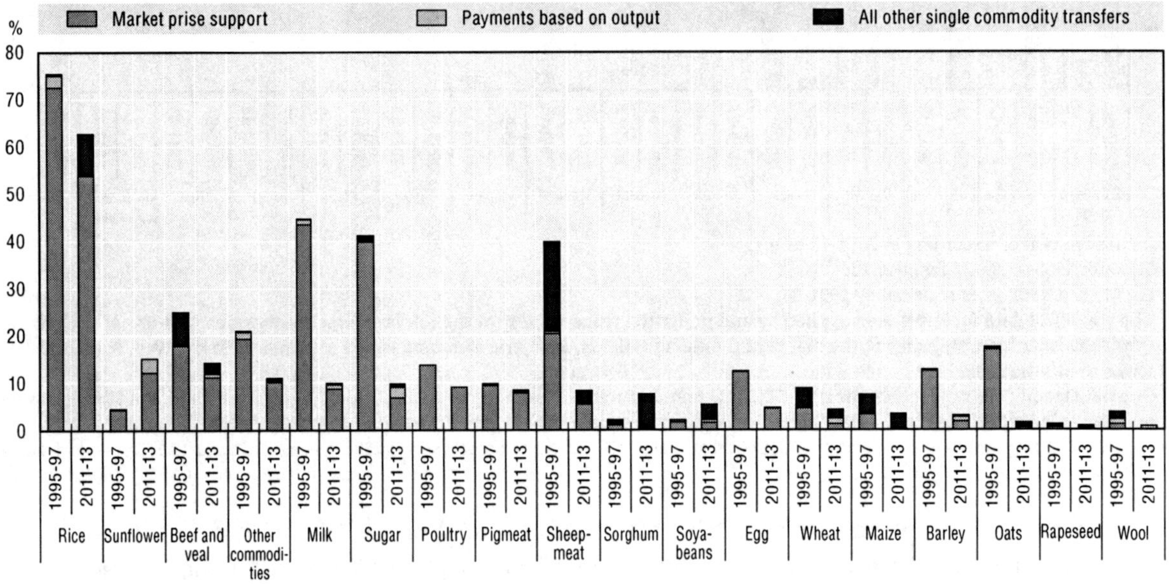

Commodities are ranked according to % SCT levels in 2011-13.
Source: OECD (2014), "Producer and Consumer Support Estimates", *OECD Agriculture Statistics Database, http://dx.doi.org/10.1787/agr-pcse-data-en.*
StatLink *http://dx.doi.org/10.1787/888933109270*

Rice was the only product in 2011-13 for which commodity-specific support accounted for a large part – almost two-thirds – of gross receipts. For other commodities, SCTs are below 15% of commodity receipts (and in some cases far below those levels). For milk and sugar, which in the past strongly depended on commodity specific support, SCTs decreased to around 10% of commodity receipts, compared to 40-45% in the mid-1990s, and 50-60% in the late 1980s.

However, reduced policy distortions in recent years are mostly due to high world prices

In assessing the changes in producer support in most recent years, it should be noted again that the level and composition mainly reflect the market conditions in which the policies operate. As emphasised throughout this report, the period since the late 2000s has been marked by historically high agricultural prices. The declining level of support, in particular market price support, as a result is not only the consequence of changes in the policy settings, but also of rising world prices. Price support programmes in many cases work countercyclical to markets and become inactive during high price periods. Should prices decrease from their current high levels, measures to support domestic prices and border protection could be activated once again and support would rise, although this effect would be less pronounced in countries which rely to a larger extent on support not linked to current market prices.

Support to general services for the sector have declined in real terms since the mid-1990s

In addition to support provided to producers individually (the PSE), the agricultural sector is assisted through public financing of services such as agricultural research and development, training, inspection, marketing and promotion and public stockholding. The General Services Support Estimate (GSSE) measures the associated monetary transfers. The methodology used to measure the GSSE has been revised to clarify the definition of the indicator and its components, as outlined in Box 1.3. A consequence of this revision is a more narrow definition of the GSSE which now excludes support to up-and downstream industries. The various implications by country of the more restricted definition and data improvements on the level and composition of the GSSE are summarised in Box 1.3 and with greater details in Annex 1.A2.

Box 1.3. **Main characteristics of the revised GSSE methodology**

In this report, the General Services Support Estimate (GSSE) indicator has been calculated using a revised methodology. As the GSSE is a component of the Total Support Estimate (TSE), both GSSE and TSE data series have been revised over the whole 1986-2013 period, and differ from those published last year (OECD, 2013b).

The revised methodology clarifies the boundaries of the GSSE indicator and its components:

- The boundaries of the GSSEs have been re-defined to cover policies where primary agriculture is the main beneficiary. This definition is narrower than the one applied previously because it now excludes support to services for which primary agriculture is not the main beneficiary. It should be noted, however, that governments fund rural services, which benefit primary agriculture, even if farmers are not the main beneficiaries, and provide support to upstream and downstream industries, which indirectly benefits the primary sector, but are no longer covered by OECD indicators of support to agriculture.

- The definitions of GSSE categories have been clarified and sub-categories added in order to better reflect recent changes in policy priorities. The new categories and sub-categories are defined in Box 1.A1.2.

The main changes include:

- The removal of expenditures that do not correspond to the narrower definition of the GSSE. This includes expenditures for rural infrastructure, which do not benefit farmers primarily; the US Supplemental Nutrition Assistance Programme (SNAP, formerly known as "food stamp") expenditure as far as it relates to the expenditure share that does not directly benefit primary agriculture level (i.e. the share that ends up in processing, retail, and other services involved in delivering the programme); investment subsidies in food processing, and others.

- The transfer of some GSSE expenditures from one GSSE category to the other, or to the CSE (e.g. support to individual first stage processors).

- The addition of some new expenditure categories such as the financing of knowledge dissemination or agriculture input control.

Box 1.3. **Main characteristics of the revised GSSE methodology** *(cont.)*

The revised definition of the GSSE and its components helps improve the consistency and comparability of the estimates and clarifies the policy coverage. When implementing the revised methodology, efforts were made to improve the coverage and consistency of estimates across countries. Changes in the GSSE (PSE, CSE and TSE) series reflect these improvements as well as changes in definition. It should be noted, however, that while significant improvements were achieved during this first year of implementation, efforts to improve coverage and consistency will continue in the future.

Annex 1.A1 includes revised definitions of the GSSE and its components as applied in this report. Annex 1.A2 outlines main changes in definition, classification and results by country. Mostly as a result of changes in coverage, the 2011 GSSE for the OECD area published in this report is 60% lower than it was in the 2013 edition, moving from USD 109 billion to USD 44 billion. The OECD TSE, which is the sum of PSE, GSSE and transfers from taxpayers to consumers, drops by 17%, from USD 409 billion in the 2013 report to USD 342 billion in this report. Most changes occur in the US estimates, which are reduced by 91% for the GSSE and 48% for the TSE, while in other OECD countries, variations in estimates between the two reports range between -12% and +5% for the GSSE, and -5% to +6% for the TSE (Table 1.A2.2). The most frequent changes in GSSE are found in expenditure on agricultural knowledge transfer and reflect the fact that expenditure on agricultural education are now fully included in the measure of policy effort, while in the previous methodology, expenditure on students, which did not remain in the agri-food sector, was excluded. While a new expenditure item was added in the inspection and control category (for farm input), numbers change only marginally in most countries. This might indicate that information is not yet available. Expenditure on infrastructure development and maintenance and on marketing and promotion is generally lower due to the narrower definition, focusing on primary agriculture. In the US estimate, this leads to the removal of major programmes, which results in a striking reduction of expenditures for marketing and promotion. The revision of the GSSE definition also results in support to individual first-stage processors being moved from the GSSE, which includes only support to collective schemes under the category marketing and promotion, to the CSE, which captures support to processors being considered as first-stage consumers. The detailed review of GSSE measures also resulted in some being reclassified as PSE measures in some countries.

Expenditures on general services in the OECD area have nearly doubled in USD in 2011-13 compared to 1986-88, most of the increase having taken place before the mid-1990s. The share of GSSE in total support to agriculture (see below) rose from 9% in 1986-88 to 13.5% in 1995-97 and then fell to 12.7% in 2011-13 (Table A.3). It should be kept in mind that a rising share of GSSE in the total support to agriculture before the mid-1990s partly reflects a falling PSE. However, lower government expenditure on general services in proportion of total support in 2011-13 compared to the mid-1990s reflects the decline in expenditure in real terms. This decline may compromise improvements in the sector's productivity and competitiveness, which are more likely to be achieved through investments in these areas than with production subsidies. In some countries, however, these services are increasingly provided by the private sector, including as part of public-private partnerships.

Support for general services accounts for the largest part of total transfers to the agricultural sector in **New Zealand,** reaching 73% in 2011-13, and it is substantial in **Australia** and **Chile,** in both countries around 50%, and in **Canada** where it amounted to 26%. In all other OECD counties, the share of GSSE in total support, although generally rising since the 1980s, constituted only between 5% and 18% in 2011-13. General services for agriculture accounted for relatively minor share of GDP in 2011-13, ranging between 0.5% and 0.15% in most countries, except New Zealand (0.21%), Korea (0.24%), and Iceland (0.2%).

OECD countries have different priorities in supporting general services (Figure 1.11 and Table A.7). The agricultural knowledge and innovation system was the most heavily supported general service in **Australia, Mexico** and **Norway**, the **European Union** and **Israel** in 2011-13. For **Japan, Korea** and **Chile,** infrastructure carries the largest weight, consisting mainly of expenditures for irrigation systems. In **Canada** and **New Zealand**, knowledge and innovation systems and inspection services share the main part (around 40% each) of support to general services. Most of general services spending in **Iceland** was allocated to inspection services (42%) and stockholding (43%) in 2011-13. Inspection also receives a significant share of funding for general services (around or above 20%) in **Chile** and **Norway**. Around 60% of total GSSE in **Turkey** for 2011-13 related to the operation of state market agencies, including the coverage of losses incurred in market intervention procedures, duty losses, and equity injections to these agencies classified under marketing and promotion. A significant share of government effort on general services supports collective schemes for processing and marketing, including the development of producer groups or value-chains, and promotion campaigns in the **European Union** (20%), the **United States** (15%) and **Switzerland** (12%). Finally, expenditures in the **United States** are distributed relatively evenly across various types of services.

Figure 1.11. **Composition of General Services Support Estimate, 2011-13**
Percentage share in GSSE

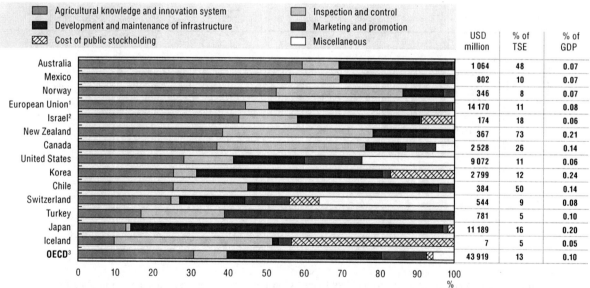

Countries are ranked according to the percentage shares of Agricultural knowledge and innovation system 2011-13.
A revised GSSE definition with new categories was introduced in 2014. When possible, the revision was implemented for the whole time series. The GSSE series and the resulting TSE are not comparable with the series published previously (for more details, see Annex 1.A2).
1. European Union 27.
2. The statistical data for Israel are supplied by and under the responsibility of the relevant Israeli authorities. The use of such data by the OECD is without prejudice to the status of the Golan Heights, East Jerusalem and Israeli settlements in the West Bank under the terms of international law.
3. The OECD total does not include the non-OECD EU member states.
Source: OECD (2014), "Producer and Consumer Support Estimates", OECD *Agriculture Statistics Database*, *http://dx.doi.org/10.1787/agr-pcse-data-en.*

StatLink ᵐˢᵖ *http://dx.doi.org/10.1787/888933109289*

Consumers of agricultural commodities have benefited from the reductions in price support...

Consumers contribute to producer support as they buy agricultural commodities on domestic markets at prices which are supported above the international levels. The Consumer Support Estimate (%CSE) expresses the monetary value of consumer costs to support agricultural prices as a per cent of consumption expenditures (measured at the farm gate). When the %CSE is negative, it indicates an implicit tax imposed by policies that support agricultural prices. Consumers may be partly compensated, e.g. through direct budgetary subsidies to processors, various forms of food aid programmes, etc.

All OECD countries, on aggregate, tax their consumers, except the **United States** where this tax is offset by direct subsidies to consumers through domestic food aid programmes. This offsetting effect was even stronger in the most recent period, with the result that %CSE in the **United States** increased from 3% in 1995-97 to 12% in 2011-13. Other countries also provide various consumer subsidies, e.g. payments to processors and food assistance programmes in the **European Union** and **Mexico**, a milk consumption subsidy in **Korea**, consumer aid for wool in **Iceland**, and flour and cereal foods subsidies in **Norway**; but this assistance offsets the overall price taxation of consumers only to a small degree.

As the market price support for agricultural products decreased over the past decades, the consumer contribution to agricultural support also fell, with the %CSEs becoming less negative (Figure 1.12). The largest reductions in the %CSEs since the mid-1990s have occurred in **Switzerland**, **Korea**, **Norway**, **Iceland**, the **European Union**, and **Israel**, countries where the

Figure 1.12. **Consumer Support Estimate by country, 1995-97 and 2011-13**

Per cent of consumption expenditure at farm gate

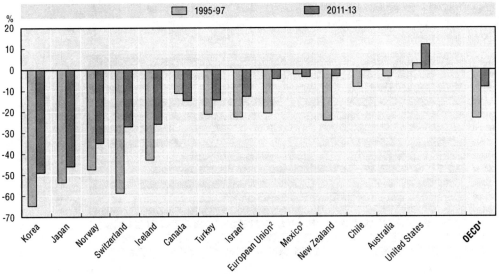

Countries are ranked according to 2011-13 CSE levels. A negative percentage CSE indicates an implicit tax on consumption.

1. The statistical data for Israel are supplied by and under the responsibility of the relevant Israeli authorities. The use of such data by the OECD is without prejudice to the status of the Golan Heights, East Jerusalem and Israeli settlements in the West Bank under the terms of international law.
2. EU15 for 1995-97; EU27 for 2011-13.
3. For Mexico, 1995-97 is replaced by 1991-93.
4. The OECD total does not include the non-OECD EU member states. The Czech Republic, Estonia, Hungary, Poland, the Slovak Republic and Slovenia are included in the OECD total for both periods and in the EU for 2011-13.

Source: OECD (2014), "Producer and Consumer Support Estimates", *OECD Agriculture Statistics Database*, http://dx.doi.org/10.1787/agr-pcse-data-en.

StatLink 🔗 http://dx.doi.org/10.1787/888933109308

difference is over 10 percentage points. This was due to the fact that many of these countries made consistent reform efforts to shift away from policies intervening in market prices. **Canada**, where the %CSE increased from minus 11% in 1995-97 to minus 15%, driven by policies that have further raised poultry prices beyond world reference levels, represents the exception to this general trend of decreasing consumer burden of agricultural support.

Despite a general reduction in market price support, consumers in countries which largely rely on price interventions to support agriculture continue to bear the high costs of agricultural support. As measured by the %CSE, additional costs incurred by consumers amounted to almost one-half of total expenditures on agricultural commodities (measured at farm gate prices) in **Korea** and **Japan**, slightly above one-third in **Norway**, and around one-quarter in **Iceland** and **Switzerland** in 2011-13.

... while support relative to national income falls

The Total Support Estimate (TSE) is the broadest indicator of support, representing the sum of transfers to agricultural producers individually (the PSE) and collectively (the GSSE), as well as budgetary subsidies to consumers. The trend in the TSE can be more clearly evaluated on the basis of the %TSE, i.e. the TSE value expressed as a percentage of GDP (Figure 1.13 and Table A.4). The %TSE equalled 0.8% for the OECD as a whole in 2013, meaning that the total transfers arising from agricultural support policies accounted for 0.8% of OECD countries aggregate GDP.

Figure 1.13. **Total Support Estimate by country, 1995-97 and 2011-13**

Per cent of GDP

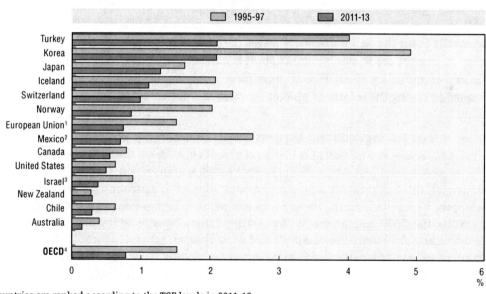

Countries are ranked according to the TSE levels in 2011-13.

A revised GSSE definition with new categories was introduced in 2014. When possible, the revision was implemented for the whole time series. The GSSE series and the resulting TSE are not comparable with the series published previously (for more details, see the Annex 1.A1).

1. EU15 for 1995-2003; EU27 for 2011-13.
2. For Mexico, 1995-97 is replaced by 1991-93.
3. The statistical data for Israel are supplied by and under the responsibility of the relevant Israeli authorities. The use of such data by the OECD is without prejudice to the status of the Golan Heights, East Jerusalem and Israeli settlements in the West Bank under the terms of international law.
4. The OECD total does not include the non-OECD EU member states. The Czech Republic, Estonia, Hungary, Poland, the Slovak Republic and Slovenia are included in the OECD total for both periods and in the EU for 2011-13.

Source: OECD (2014), "Producer and Consumer Support Estimates", *OECD Agriculture Statistics Database*, http://dx.doi.org/10.1787/agr-pcse-data-en.

StatLink ◼◼◼ http://dx.doi.org/10.1787/888933109327

In the long-term, the relative scale of total support to agriculture is consistently falling in the OECD area, with the %TSE declining from 2.8% on average in 1986-88 to 1.5% in 1995-97 and 0.8% in 2011-13. This declining trend is observed in all OECD countries, reflecting the shrinking importance of the agricultural sector in the overall economy. **Turkey** and **Korea** stand apart with the weight of agricultural support, at 2.1% in 2011-13, more than double the OECD average despite the fact that these shares have substantially decreased since the 1995-97 period. For **Turkey**, this mostly reflects the share that agriculture occupies in the overall economy, which was 9% of GDP in 2012. Thus, even a relatively lower level of agricultural support places a higher burden on the **Turkish** economy than a much higher support in countries where agriculture represents a far smaller share, e.g. **Norway**, **Switzerland**, **Korea** or **Japan**.

The trajectories of support in the emerging economies differ from those in OECD countries

Agriculture policies in the key emerging economies monitored by OECD (Brazil, China, Indonesia, Kazakhstan, Russia, South Africa and Ukraine) demonstrate trends that differ from those observed in the OECD area. Following profound economic reforms in the 1980s and 1990s, previous agricultural regulation systems were dismantled or largely liberalised in these countries. In some, relative agricultural prices declined far below the international levels in the early post-reform period, with the result that agriculture faced considerable price taxation (or negative market price support). However, more recently, agricultural support levels in most of the emerging economies considered in Box 1.4 have tended to rise, in particular in China and Indonesia. This reflects increasing availability of budgetary resources, policy priorities turning more towards agricultural and rural development, and recently, a strengthened emphasis on food security concerns which these countries tend to view mostly from the self-sufficiency angle (Box 1.4). Exceptions to the rising trend of support to farmers are Russia, where support is currently at the same level as in the mid-1990s and accounts for about 15% of gross farm receipts, and South Africa where it has decreased following the reform of market intervention in the sector.

Box 1.4. **Agricultural support trends in emerging economies**

Emerging economies are included in the OECD *Agricultural Policy Monitoring and Evaluation* reports every second year. While the current 2014 edition of the report does not cover these economies, this box provides a brief overview of support to agriculture in Brazil, China, Indonesia, Kazakhstan, Russia, South Africa and Ukraine, as presented in the 2013 edition. Currently, the OECD is in a process of preparing comprehensive agricultural reviews for Colombia and Viet Nam. After completion of those reviews, scheduled for 2015, these two countries will also be included into the subsequent editions of the monitoring report.

Among emerging economies covered by the 2013 report, three groups of countries can be distinguished, each sharing similar characteristics (Figure 1.14):

● In China and Indonesia, dominated by small-scale farming and driven by a food security objective based on high level of self-sufficiency in grain production, the level of support tends to grow and currently is close to the OECD average. In these countries, grain prices (rice and wheat in China and rice in Indonesia), are regulated and largely isolated from changes on international markets. As a result, depending on the relative levels of grain prices on domestic *vis-à-vis* international markets, grain producers are implicitly supported or taxed, driving the aggregate level of support up or down. In addition, grain

---

Box 1.4. **Agricultural support trends in emerging economies** (*cont.*)

producers benefit from various types of budgetary support such direct payments per unit of land (in China) and input subsidies (both in China and Indonesia). Livestock producers are supported in both countries mostly through border protection keeping domestic prices above international levels, in particular for poultry and beef in Indonesia and for milk, beef, pigmeat and sheepmeat in China.

Figure 1.14. **Emerging economies: Producer Support Estimate by country, 1995-97 and 2010-12**

Per cent of gross farm receipts

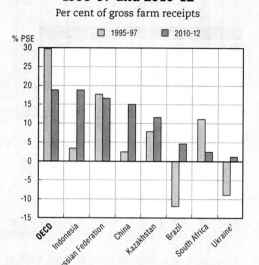

1. For Ukraine, 1995-97 is replaced by 1996-97.
Source: OECD (2013c, 2014), Producer and Consumer Support Estimates, *OECD Agriculture Statistics Database,* *http://dx.doi.org/10.1787/agr-pcse-data-en.*

StatLink ⬛⬛⬛ *http://dx.doi.org/10.1787/888933109346*

● In Kazakhstan, Russia and Ukraine, abundant in land resources and with most of the land operated by large-scale farms, the level of support fluctuates strongly, driven by changes in the macroeconomic framework and by related changes in agricultural policies. In these countries, while price policies tax some commodities, in particular grains, through e.g. export restrictions, other commodities, in particular livestock, benefit from various forms of border protection and from low prices of feed. Overall, while the level of support in Russia is close to the OECD average, in Ukraine the relatively high level of support provided to selected livestock commodities and sugar is offset by heavy implicit tax on grain producers. As a result, on aggregate, support in Ukraine is low and fluctuates at levels close to zero. In Kazakhstan, the level of support increased in recent years compared to that in the mid-1990s, but remains moderate.

● In Brazil and South Africa, the level of support is low, but the vast majority of support is provided through the most distortive forms, such as market price support and input subsidies. In Brazil, a wide range of commodities is covered by minimum guaranteed prices, but price levels do not diverge much from international market levels with the exception for rice, milk and cotton. Brazilian farmers benefit also from interest rate subsidies. In South Africa, market price support is provided through import tariffs, but resulting price distortions are very small. Only for sugar and milk domestic prices are higher than on international markets. A key component of budgetary support to South

Box 1.4. **Agricultural support trends in emerging economies** *(cont.)*

African agriculture is support for land reforms, especially for land restitution and redistribution, which includes investment assistance to producers.

Figure 1.15. **Total Support Estimate by country, 1995-97 and 2010-12**

Per cent of GDP

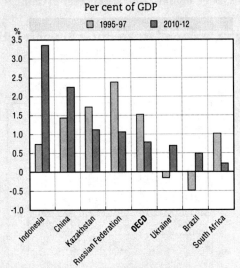

These estimates were published in 2013, thus the methodology in place at the time was used to calculate the General Services Support Estimate (GSSE) component of the Total Support Estimates (TSE).
1. For Ukraine, 1995-97 is replaced by 1996-97.
Source: OECD (2013c, 2014), Producer and Consumer Support Estimates, *OECD Agriculture Statistics Database,* http://dx.doi.org/10.1787/agr-pcse-data-en.

StatLink ⟦▨⟧ http://dx.doi.org/10.1787/888933109365

Despite strong GDP growth rates in China and Indonesia total support to agriculture as percentage of GDP for both countries has strongly increased. In recent years it is significantly higher than the OECD average. In Kazakhstan and Russia this share fell, but remained above the OECD average. In Ukraine it increased sharply, but from a low base and remains below the OECD average. In Brazil and South Africa it is much below the OECD average, reflecting low levels of agricultural support in both countries (Figure 1.15).

Assessing support and reforms

Progress in agricultural policy reform can be assessed by examining how the level of support and its composition have changed over time according to the policy indicators in the *PSE Database.*

Less and better support...

The last two decades of agricultural policy reform have led to less production and trade distorting policies, which are reflected in important changes in the level and the composition of agricultural support. The support level is shown by the %PSE and the composition of support by the share of the potentially most production and trade distorting categories in the PSE (market price support, payments based on output and payments based on non-constrained variable input use). Figure 1.16 juxtaposes these two dimensions of support, highlighting three periods: 1986-88, 1997-99 and 2011-13. The movement in the graph towards the south-west direction reveals progress in both

Figure 1.16. **OECD: Changes in level and composition of producer support**

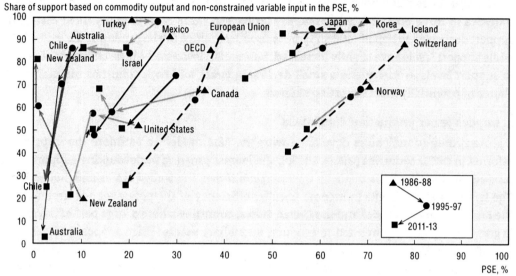

The level of support is presented by the percentage PSE. The composition of support is presented by the share in gross farm receipts of Market Price Support, Payments based on output and Payments based on non-constrained variable input use.

1. For Mexico, the change is measured between 1991-93, 1996-98 and 2011-13.
2. EU12 for 1986-88; EU15 for 1995-97; and EU27 for 2011-13.
3. For Chile, changes are given only between 1997-99 and 2011-13.
4. For Israel, changes are given only between 1997-99 and 2011-13. The statistical data for Israel are supplied by and under the responsibility of the relevant Israeli authorities. The use of such data by the OECD is without prejudice to the status of the Golan Heights, East Jerusalem and Israeli settlements in the West Bank under the terms of international law.
5. The OECD total does not include the non-OECD EU member states. Austria, the Czech Republic, Estonia, Finland, Hungary, Poland, the Slovak Republic, Slovenia and Sweden are included in the OECD total for all years. Chile and Israel are included in the OECD total from 1995.

Source: OECD (2014), "Producer and Consumer Support Estimates", *OECD Agriculture Statistics Database*, http://dx.doi.org/10.1787/agr-pcse-data-en.

StatLink ᴍ᠊ᔕᴘ http://dx.doi.org/10.1787/888933109384

dimensions. For the OECD area as a whole progress has been made both in bringing down the level of support and in the introduction of less distorting forms of support; the level of support was reduced by nearly half between 1986-88 and 2011-13, while the share of the most production and trade distorting support was reduced from 86% to 51%. A slight acceleration of the reform process has occurred since 1995-97, helped by the strong upward trend in world commodity prices since the early 2000s.

Support to producers in **New Zealand** has remained close to zero since the mid-1990s. **Australia** and **Chile** have followed similar reform paths leading to very low levels of support and significant improvement in its composition. The **European Union** and the **United States** have made substantial reforms to improve the composition of support, while also reducing the level; this is most striking in the European Union. **Norway** and **Switzerland** have also made progress in reducing the share of most distorting support to about half of total support in Norway and 40% in Switzerland. Levels of support were also significantly reduced, but remain among the five highest in the OECD area. **Iceland** has reduced the level of support but not changed its composition significantly. **Korea** and **Japan** have also reduced their level of support starting from very high levels, but improvements in the composition remain small. **Canada** reduced the level of support between 1986-88 and 1995-97, but it has varied around a stable trend since and the composition has not changed. It should be noted, however that most support in this country depends on variations in market conditions and farm income levels, and most distortions in markets are due to long-standing supply management schemes in three commodity sectors. In **Mexico**, the share of potentially most distorting support decreased to half of total support to producers since the beginning of the mid-1990s, while support levels have slightly increased, but remain low. Finally, little change is observed in support levels in **Turkey** and a small decline in **Israel**, and both countries maintain high shares of potentially most distorting support.

... implies fewer production distortions

According to indicators developed with the PEM model* to estimate the impacts of reforms in OECD countries (OECD, 2013b), the largest progress in decoupling support from production decisions was made by the **European Union**, the **United States** and **Switzerland**. The largest improvements in income transfer efficiency of the policy set occurred also in the **European Union, Mexico** and the **United States,** countries where a large part of payments is granted without requirement to produce, and where market price support has declined significantly (EU) or has been very low over the period (US). In **Canada**, there has been less progress, particularly in so far as income transfer efficiency is concerned. For **Japan** and **Korea**, the improvement in the degree of decoupling and income transfer efficiency occurred in the recent period from 1997-99.

Recent reforms generally take modest steps towards addressing long-term objectives, such as sustainability, innovation and risk management...

In the **European Union**, 30% of direct payments is made conditional on specific farming practices, with demonstrated benefits to the environment and the climate. More funds become available in Pillar II for a smaller number of specific actions bringing additional benefits to the environment, facilitating investment in farms and value chains, and helping develop the rural economy. And specific funding is dedicated to innovation in agriculture and agri-food, which bring long term benefits to the sector and the rural economy. The new set of direct payments in **Switzerland** is also better targeted to support specific agricultural practices and more decoupled from livestock production.

Canada's programming framework also puts an emphasis on longer term investments to strengthen the capacity of the sector to adapt and seize opportunities, including through the development and adoption of new products and technologies.

Japan's new plan focuses support on core (potentially viable) farmers. The re-orientation of the direct payments system gives farmers more flexibility in their choice of production, but continues to distort market signals. **Mexico**'s new policy framework re-links support to the adoption of farm practices to improve land productivity, with potential risk of distorting markets and reducing income transfer efficiency.

In the **United States**, the removal of untargeted income support and the strengthening of risk management support have both costs and benefits in terms of effectiveness, market distortion and income transfer efficiency.

---

* The PEM provides a stylised representation of agricultural markets and policies in the participating countries. It covers seven OECD countries or regions (Canada, the European Union, Japan, Korea, Mexico, Switzerland, the United States) and models six commodity markets (wheat, coarse grain, oilseeds, rice, milk and beef) and input market, and it represents policies according to the PSE classification. It is a partial equilibrium model that measures impacts in the medium term. OECD (2011b) presents the most updated documentation of the PEM, including the method of calculating the policy impact indicators.

... although in some countries, a large part of support remains unchanged

Agricultural policy continues to rely on market price support in Japan and Switzerland, as in some other OECD countries which did not introduce major reforms. In **Canada**, supply-management continues to generate significant levels of market price support, in particular in the dairy sector. Although market price support has been reduced significantly in the **European Union**, tariff quotas and domestic measures continue to protect some sectors significantly, and most direct payments are not linked to specific income criteria.

More efforts are needed to meet future challenges and to exploit new opportunities

There is evident progress across the OECD area towards agriculture support that is less distorting and more efficient in transferring income to farm households. Additional attention could now focus on addressing the policy priorities expressed by Ministers of Agriculture meeting at the OECD in 2010 (OECD, 2010). Reforms in producer support have allowed the development of conditions attached to payments and emergence of forms of support to producers more targeted to specific outcomes, populations or regions, reflecting specific circumstances. As a result of improved efficiency at transferring income and targeting of specific outcomes, lower levels of funding are necessary to meet objectives and public funds become available to invest in knowledge, education and strategic infrastructure, that can help improve the long-term productivity, sustainability, and profitability of the sector.

Increased focus on innovation will be necessary to improve agriculture productivity and sustainability in the long run. While mobilising public as well as private funds for innovation remains an important challenge, much can be achieved by better organisational set-up of the knowledge and innovation system to connect different stakeholders, make research and development more responsive to demand, and improve related collaboration across countries.

Sound policy making and sound business decisions require good information. The G20 initiative AMIS makes important contributions to enhancing transparency of market information for some key agricultural commodities. More could be done to develop and share information on the performance of agricultural technology and production systems, and information that is important for fundamental research on plant and animal breeding, as discussed at previous G20 Meetings of Agricultural Chief Scientists. Improving quality and accessibility of evidence-based information on innovative solutions for farmers and non-specialised users would also be important.

Improving the capacity of the agriculture sector to contribute to economic growth and jobs as well as to feeding an increasing global population reinforces the need to improve the wider policy environment in which the sector operates so as to attract financial and human resources and facilitate innovative business developments. A comprehensive approach to improve coherence with other policies (macroeconomic, trade, structural, social, environmental and others) and to reduce impediments to structural adjustment will in most countries be more effective than fine-tuning existing agricultural policies.

References

FAO (2014), FAO Food Price Index dataset, Rome: *www.fao.org/worldfoodsituation/foodpricesindex/en.*

IMF (2013), *Commodity Market Review* (from *World Economic Outlook*, October 2013), Washington: The International Monetary Fund, *www.imf.org/external/np/res/commod/pdf/cmr/cmr1013.pdf.*

OECD (2002), *Frascati Manual: Proposed Standard Practice for Surveys on Research and Experimental Development*, 6th edition, OECD publishing, Paris, available at: *http://dx.doi.org/10.1787/9789264199040-en.*

OECD (2008), *Agricultural Policy Design and Implementation. A Synthesis*, OECD Publishing, Paris, *http://dx.doi.org/10.1787/243786286663.*

OECD (2010), Communiqué from the Ministers, OECD Agriculture Ministerial, 25-26 February, Paris, *www.oecd.org/tad/communiquefromtheministers-meetingofthecommitteeforagricultureatministeriallevel.htm.*

OECD (2011a), "Long-Term Trends in Agricultural Policy Impacts", *OECD Food, Agriculture and Fisheries Papers*, No. 45, OECD Publishing, Paris, *http://dx.doi.org/10.1787/5kgdp5zw179q-en.*

OECD (2013a), *OECD Economic Outlook*, Vol. 2013/2, OECD Publishing, Paris, *http://dx.doi.org/10.1787/eco_outlook-v2013-2-en.*

OECD (2013b), *Agricultural Policy Monitoring and Evaluation 2013: OECD Countries and Emerging Economies*, OECD Publishing, Paris, *http://dx.doi.org/10.1787/agr_pol-2013-en.*

OECD (2013c), "Producer and Consumer Support Estimates", *OECD Agriculture Statistics Database*, *http://stats.oecd.org/Index.aspx?DataSetCode=MON20123_2.*

OECD/FAO (2013d), *OECD-FAO Agricultural Outlook 2013*, OECD Publishing, Paris, *http://dx.doi.org/10.1787/agr_outlook-2013-en.*

OECD (2014), "Producer and Consumer Support Estimates", *OECD Agriculture Statistics Database*, *http://dx.doi.org/10.1787/agr-pcse-data-en.*

OECD Dot.Stat: *Harmonized Unemployment Rates*, accessed 7 April 2014, *http://stats.oecd.org/index.aspx?queryid=21760.*

World Trade Organisation (2013), Bali Ministerial Declaration and Decisions, Geneva. *http://wto.org/english/thewto_e/minist_e/mc9_e/balipackage_e.htm.*

ANNEX 1.A1

Definition of OECD indicators of agricultural support

Nominal indicators used in this report

Producer Support Estimate (PSE): The annual monetary value of gross transfers from consumers and taxpayers to agricultural producers, measured at the farm gate level, arising from policy measures that support agriculture, regardless of their nature, objectives or impacts on farm production or income. It includes market price support, budgetary payments and budget revenue foregone, i.e. gross transfers from consumers and taxpayers to agricultural producers arising from policy measures based on: current output, input use, area planted/animal numbers/receipts/incomes (current, non-current), and non-commodity criteria.

Market price support (MPS): The annual monetary value of gross transfers from consumers and taxpayers to agricultural producers arising from policy measures that create a gap between domestic market prices and border prices of a specific agricultural commodity, measured at the farm gate level. MPS is also available by commodity.

Producer single commodity transfers (producer SCT): The annual monetary value of gross transfers from consumers and taxpayers to agricultural producers, measured at the farm gate level, arising from policies linked to the production of a single commodity such that the producer must produce the designated commodity in order to receive the payment. This includes broader policies where transfers are specified on a per-commodity basis. Producer SCT is also available by commodity.

Group commodity transfers (GCT): The annual monetary value of gross transfers from consumers and taxpayers to agricultural producers, measured at the farm gate level, arising from policies whose payments are made on the basis that one or more of a designated list of commodities is produced, i.e. a producer may produce from a set of allowable commodities and receive a transfer that does not vary with respect to this decision.

All commodity transfers (ACT): The annual monetary value of gross transfers from consumers and taxpayers to agricultural producers, measured at the farm gate level, arising from policies that place no restrictions on the commodity produced but require the recipient to produce some commodity of their choice.

Other transfers to producers (OTP): The annual monetary value of gross transfers from consumers and taxpayers to agricultural producers, measured at the farm gate level, arising from policies that do not require any commodity production at all.

Consumer single commodity transfers (consumer SCT): The annual monetary value of gross transfers from (to) consumers of agricultural commodities, measured at the farm gate level, arising from policies linked to the production of a single commodity. Consumer SCT is also available by commodity.

Consumer support estimate (CSE): The annual monetary value of gross transfers from (to) consumers of agricultural commodities, measured at the farm gate level, arising from policy measures that support agriculture, regardless of their nature, objectives or impacts on consumption of farm products. If negative, the CSE measures the burden (implicit tax) on consumers through market price support (higher prices), that more than offsets consumer subsidies that lower prices to consumers.

General services support estimate (GSSE): The annual monetary value of gross transfers arising from policy measures that create enabling conditions for the primary agricultural sector through development of private or public services, institutions and infrastructure, regardless of their objectives and impacts on farm production and income, or consumption of farm products. The GSSE includes policies where primary agriculture is the main beneficiary, but does not include any payments to individual producers. GSSE transfers do not directly alter producer receipts or costs or consumption expenditures. GSSE categories are defined in Box 1.A1.2.

Total support estimate (TSE): The annual monetary value of all gross transfers from taxpayers and consumers arising from policy measures that support agriculture, net of the associated budgetary receipts, regardless of their objectives and impacts on farm production and income, or consumption of farm products.

Ratio indicators and percentage indicators

Percentage PSE (%PSE): PSE transfers as a share of gross farm receipts (including support in the denominator).

Percentage SCT (%SCT): Is the commodity SCT expressed as a share of gross farm receipts for the specific commodity (including support in the denominator).

Share of SCT in total PSE (%): Share of Single Commodity Transfers in the total PSE. This indicator is also calculated by commodity.

Producer nominal protection coefficient (producer NPC): The ratio between the average price received by producers (at farm gate), including payments per tonne of current output, and the border price (measured at farm gate). The Producer NPC is also available by commodity.

Producer nominal assistance coefficient (producer NAC): The ratio between the value of gross farm receipts including support and gross farm receipts (at farm gate) valued at border prices (measured at farm gate).

Percentage CSE (%CSE): CSE transfers as a share of consumption expenditure on agricultural commodities (at farm gate prices), net of taxpayer transfers to consumers. The %CSE measures the implicit tax (or subsidy, if CSE is positive) placed on consumers by agricultural price policies.

Consumer nominal protection coefficient (consumer NPC): The ratio between the average price paid by consumers (at farm gate) and the border price (measured at farm gate). The Consumer NPC is also available by commodity.

Consumer nominal assistance coefficient (consumer NAC): The ratio between the value of consumption expenditure on agricultural commodities (at farm gate) and that valued at border prices.

Percentage TSE (%TSE): TSE transfers as a percentage of GDP.

Percentage GSSE (%GSSE): Share of expenditures on general services in the Total Support Estimate (TSE).

Box 1.A1.1. **Definitions of categories in the PSE classification**

Definitions of categories

Category A1, Market price support (MPS): Transfers from consumers and taxpayers to agricultural producers from policy measures that create a gap between domestic market prices and border prices of a specific agricultural commodity, measured at the farm gate level.

Category A2, Payments based on output: Transfers from taxpayers to agricultural producers from policy measures based on current output of a specific agricultural commodity.

Category B, Payments based on input use: Transfers from taxpayers to agricultural producers arising from policy measures based on on-farm use of inputs:

- *Variable input use* that reduces the on-farm cost of a specific variable input or a mix of variable inputs.

- *Fixed capital formation* that reduce the on-farm investment cost of farm buildings, equipment, plantations, irrigation, drainage, and soil improvements.

- *On-farm services* that reduce the cost of technical, accounting, commercial, sanitary and phyto-sanitary assistance and training provided to individual farmers.

Category C, Payments based on current A/An/R/I, production required: Transfers from taxpayers to agricultural producers arising from policy measures based on current area, animal numbers, revenue, or income, and requiring production.

Category D, Payments based on non-current A/An/R/I, production required: Transfers from taxpayers to agricultural producers arising from policy measures based on non-current (i.e. historical or fixed) area, animal numbers, revenue, or income, with current production of any commodity required.

Category E, Payments based on non-current A/An/R/I, production not required: Transfers from taxpayers to agricultural producers arising from policy measures based on non-current (i.e. historical or fixed) area, animal numbers, revenue, or income, with current production of any commodity not required but optional.

Category F, Payments based on non-commodity criteria: Transfers from taxpayers to agricultural producers arising from policy measures based on:

- *Long-term resource retirement:* Transfers for the long-term retirement of factors of production from commodity production. The payments in this subcategory are distinguished from those requiring short-term resource retirement, which are based on commodity production criteria.

- *A specific non-commodity output:* Transfers for the use of farm resources to produce specific non-commodity outputs of goods and services, which are not required by regulations.

- *Other non-commodity criteria:* Transfers provided equally to all farmers, such as a flat rate or lump sum payment.

Category G, Miscellaneous payments: Transfers from taxpayers to farmers for which there is a lack of information to allocate them among the appropriate categories.

Note: A (area), An (animal numbers), R (receipts) or I (income).

Definitions of labels

With or without current commodity production limits and/or limit to payments: Defines whether or not there is a specific limitation on current commodity production (output) associated with a policy providing transfers to agriculture and whether or not there are limits to payments in the form of limits to area or animal numbers eligible for those payments. Applied in categories A-F.

> ## Box 1.A1.1. **Definitions of categories in the PSE classification** (cont.)
>
> ***With variable or fixed payment rates:*** Any payments is defined as subject to a variable rate where the formula determining the level of payment is triggered by a change in price, yield, net revenue or income or a change in production cost. Applied in categories A-E.
>
> ***With or without input constraints:*** defines whether or not there are specific requirements concerning farming practices related to the programme in terms of the reduction, replacement, or withdrawal in the use of inputs or a restriction of farming practices allowed. Applied in categories A-F. The payments with input constrains are further broken down to:
>
> - payments conditional on compliance with basic requirements that are mandatory (*with mandatory*);
> - payments requiring specific practices going beyond basic requirements and voluntary (*with voluntary*):
>   - ❖ specific practices related to environmental issues;
>   - ❖ specific practices related to animal welfare;
>   - ❖ other specific practices.
>
> ***With or without commodity exceptions:*** defines whether or not there are prohibitions upon the production of certain commodities as a condition of eligibility for payments based on non-current A/An/R/I of commodity(ies). Applied in Category E.
>
> ***Based on area, animal numbers, receipts or income:*** defines the specific attribute (i.e. area, animal numbers, receipts or income) on which the payment is based. Applied in categories C-E.
>
> ***Based on a single commodity, a group of commodities or all commodities:*** defines whether the payment is granted for production of a single commodity, a group of commodities or all commodities. Applied in categories A-D.

Decomposition indicators

Decomposition of PSE

Per cent change in PSE: Per cent change in the nominal value of the PSE expressed in national currency. The per cent change is calculated using the two most recent years in the series.

Contribution of MPS to per cent change in PSE: Per cent change in nominal PSE if all variables other than MPS are held constant.

Contribution of price gap to per cent change in the PSE: Per cent change in nominal PSE if all variables other than gap between domestic market prices and border prices are held constant.

Contribution of quantity produced to per cent change in the PSE: Per cent change in nominal PSE if all variables other than quantity produced are held constant.

Contribution of budgetary payments (BP) to per cent change in PSE: Per cent change in nominal PSE if all variables other than BP are held constant.

Contribution of BP elements to per cent change in PSE: Per cent change in nominal PSE if all variables other than a given BP element are held constant. BP elements include *Payments based on output, Payments based on input use, Payments based on current A/An/R/I, production required, Payments based on non-current A/An/R/I, production required, Payments based on non-current A/An/R/I, production not required, Payments based on non-commodity criteria* and *Miscellaneous payments.*

Decomposition of price gap elements

Per cent change in producer price: Per cent change in producer price (at farm gate) expressed in national currency. The per cent change is calculated using the two most recent years in the series.

Per cent change in the border price: Per cent change in border price (at farm gate) expressed in national currency. The per cent change is calculated using the two most recent years in the series.

Contribution of exchange rate to per cent change in border price: Per cent change in the border price (at farm gate) expressed in national currency if all variables other than exchange rate between national currency and USD are held constant.

Contribution of border price expressed in USD to per cent change in border price: Per cent change in the border price (at farm gate) expressed in national currency if all variables other than border price (at farm gate) expressed in USD are held constant.

Definition of GSSE categories

The general GSSE definition is complemented in Annex 1.A2 by more specific implementation guidelines, provided under the different categories in the GSSE classification.

Box 1.A1.2. Definitions of categories in the GSSE classification

- **Agricultural knowledge and innovation system**

  ❖ *Agricultural knowledge generation:* Budgetary expenditure financing research and development (R&D) activities related to agriculture, and associated data dissemination, irrespective of the institution (private or public, ministry, university, research centre or producer groups) where they take place, the nature of research (scientific, institutional, etc.), or its purpose.

  ❖ *Agricultural knowledge transfer:* Budgetary expenditure financing agricultural vocational schools and agricultural programmes in high-level education, training and advice to farmers that is generic (e.g. accounting rules, pesticide application), not specific to individual situations, and data collection and information dissemination networks related to agricultural production and marketing.

- **Inspection and control**

  ❖ *Agricultural product safety and inspection:* Budgetary expenditure financing activities related to agricultural product safety and inspection. This includes only expenditures on inspection of domestically produced commodities at first level of processing and border inspection for exported commodities.

  ❖ *Pest and disease inspection and control:* Budgetary expenditure financing pest and disease control of agricultural inputs and outputs (control at primary agriculture level) and public funding of veterinary services (for the farming sector) and phytosanitary services.

  ❖ *Input control:* Budgetary expenditure financing the institutions providing control activities and certification of industrial inputs used in agriculture (e.g. machinery, industrial fertilisers, pesticides, etc.) and biological inputs (e.g. seed certification and control).

Box 1.A1.2. **Definitions of categories in the GSSE classification** (*cont.*)

● **Development and maintenance of infrastructure**

❖ *Hydrological infrastructure:* Budgetary expenditure financing public investments into hydrological infrastructure (irrigation and drainage networks).

❖ *Storage, marketing and other physical infrastructure:* Budgetary expenditure financing investments to off-farm storage and other market infrastructure facilities related to handling and marketing primary agricultural products (silos, harbour facilities – docks, elevators; wholesale markets, futures markets), as well as other physical infrastructure related to agriculture, when agriculture is the main beneficiary.

❖ *Institutional infrastructure:* Budgetary expenditure financing investments to build and maintain institutional infrastructure related to the farming sector (e.g. land cadastres; machinery user groups, seed and species registries; development of rural finance networks; support to farm organisations, etc.).

❖ *Farm restructuring:* Budgetary payments related to reform of farm structures financing entry, exit or diversification (outside agriculture) strategies.

● **Marketing and promotion**

❖ *Collective schemes for processing and marketing:* Budgetary expenditure financing investment in collective, mainly primary, processing, marketing schemes and marketing facilities, designed to improve marketing environment for agriculture.

❖ *Promotion of agricultural products:* Budgetary expenditure financing assistance to collective promotion of agro-food products (e.g. promotion campaigns, participation on international fairs).

● **Cost of public stockholding:** Budgetary expenditure covering the costs of storage, depreciation and disposal of public storage of agricultural products.

● **Miscellaneous:** Budgetary expenditure financing other general services that cannot be disaggregated and allocated to the above categories, often due to a lack of information.

ANNEX 1.A2

Revised General Services Support Estimate: Overview of main changes

Change in the definition of the general services support estimate

The revised general services support estimate (GSSE) is defined as "budgetary expenditure that creates enabling conditions for the primary agricultural sector through development of private or public services, institutions and infrastructure". This definition replaces the previous, broader, definition of the GSSE as "payments to eligible private or public services provided to agriculture generally".

The revised definition continues to apply the main distinction that: "Unlike the producer support estimate (PSE) and the consumer support estimate (CSE), the GSSE transfers are not destined to individual producers or consumers, and do not directly affect farm receipts (revenue) or consumption expenditure, although they may affect production or consumption of agricultural commodities in the longer term. While implementation criteria are used to distinguish whether the transfer is allocated to PSE or GSSE, the definition of the categories in the GSSE and the allocation of policy measures to these categories is according to the nature of the service" (PSE Manual).

The boundaries of the GSSEs have been re-defined to cover policies where primary agriculture is the main beneficiary. This definition is narrower because it excludes all payments to services for which primary agriculture is not the main beneficiary, such as rural infrastructure, and support to agro-industries further down the stream.

Change in GSSE categories

Table 1.A2.1 compares the different categories and subcategories under the previous and the revised methodology. Main changes include:

- *A narrowing of the concept to primary agriculture,* which results in the inclusion of support to the processing industry for the financing of collective initiatives, the move of support to primary processors in the CSE and the exclusion of support to processors further down the stream from the TSE.

- *The principle that farmers are the main beneficiaries* of the services, which results in the exclusion of some rural infrastructure services.

- *More detailed sub-categories,* which allow payments previously included under a general category to be grouped under a sub-category (e.g. hydrological infrastructure, farm restructuring and institutions under "development and maintenance of infrastructure"; distinction of the type of inspection and control).

Table 1.A2.1. **GSSE categories**

New classification		Previous classification
See definition in Box 1.A1.1		See definition in Box 1.A1.2
Agricultural knowledge and innovation system	A	
Agricultural knowledge generation	A1	**Research and development**
Agricultural knowledge transfer	A2	**Agricultural schools**
Inspection and control	B	**Inspection services**
Agricultural product safety and inspection	B1	
Pest and disease inspection and control	B2	
Input control	B3	
Development and maintenance of infrastructure	C	**Infrastructure**
Hydrological infrastructure	C1	
Storage, marketing and other physical infrastructure	C2	
Institutional infrastructure	C3	
Farm restructuring	C4	
Marketing and promotion	D	**Marketing and promotion**
Collective schemes for processing and marketing	D1	
Promotion of agricultural products	D2	
Public stockholding	E	**Public stockholding**
Miscellaneous	F	**Miscellaneous**

- *The addition of new measures,* such as the inspection and control of farm inputs under a new subcategory "Input control", and the collection and dissemination of knowledge under the category "Agricultural knowledge and innovation system".

- *Clarifying that GSSE measures policy efforts* and not policy effect, which results for example in all payments to agricultural schools being included, even if students do not end up working in or for primary agriculture.

  The definition of public stockholding and miscellaneous was not changed.

Guidelines for implementing the revised methodology

The headings of the different categories in new the GSSE classification provide an idea of their broad contents, but more specificity is needed to specify the scope of information to be included. The guiding principles for the implementation of the new GSSE classification are provided below.

Agricultural knowledge and innovation system

Agricultural knowledge generation

This sub-category includes budgetary expenditure financing research and development (R&D) activities related to agriculture, irrespective of the institution (private or public, ministry, university, research centre or producer groups); irrespective of where they take place, the nature of research (scientific, institutional, etc.), or its purpose. The focus is on R&D expenditures on applied research related to the primary agricultural sector (the definition in the Frascati manual[1] may be a guidance). Social sciences related to agriculture are included. To the extent possible R&D related to forestry, fisheries etc. should be excluded and, if the information is not readily available, the method used to estimate their share should be clearly stated in the documentation.

This expenditure includes also transfers to finance ex situ conservation of livestock and plant species (e.g. gene banks). Data dissemination when primarily associated with research and development (knowledge generation) e,g. reports from research and databases developed as an adjunct to research also belongs to this sub-category.

Agricultural knowledge transfer

This sub-category includes budgetary expenditure to finance agricultural vocational schools and agricultural programmes in high-level education. The entire expenditure on those education activities is considered as related to agriculture, as the indicator measures policy effort.

This sub-category also includes budgetary expenditure financing generic training and extension advice to farmers, such as accounting rules or pesticide application methods). Expenditure on advice that are specific to individual farms (e.g. a farm business plan) are included in the PSE category for payment based on services.

Public expenditures on data collection and information dissemination networks related to agricultural production and marketing (e.g. information on technologies and production methods, price and market information) are also included in this subcategory.

Inspection and control

Agricultural product safety and inspection

This sub-category includes budgetary expenditure financing activities related to agricultural product safety and inspection. This includes only expenditures on inspection of domestically produced commodities at first level of processing and border inspection for exported commodities. Import control activities are not included. Production and trade data may be used to make an approximate estimation of a differentiation between export and import inspections. In case that such a separation is not possible, the entire expenditure on food safety and inspection should be included and mention should be made in the documentation.

Pest and disease inspection and control

This sub-category includes budgetary expenditures financing pest and disease control of agricultural inputs and outputs (control at primary agriculture level) as well as public funding of veterinary and phytosanitary services (for the farming sector).

Input control

This sub-category includes budgetary expenditure financing the institutions providing control activities and certification of industrial inputs used in agriculture (e.g. machinery, industrial fertilisers, pesticides, etc.) and biological inputs (e.g. seed certification and control).

Development and maintenance of infrastructure

Hydrological infrastructure

This sub-category includes public investments into hydrological infrastructure (irrigation and drainage networks). Water subsidies granted to individual farmers and investment subsidies to on-farm irrigation infrastructure are included in the PSE. The expenditures related to hydrological network infrastructures are included according to the share which corresponds to farmer's participation in that network (e.g. share of water used by agriculture, as reported in OECD agri-environmental indicators).[2]

Flood prevention expenditures where agriculture is not the main beneficiary are not included. In the case of large investments, such as dams, with multiple outputs (irrigation, water retention, flood prevention, hydro-energy), the GSSE accounts only for the share of the outputs used by primary agriculture. Investment expenditure should be accounted in the year when it occurs.

Storage, marketing and other physical infrastructure

This sub-category includes budgetary expenditure financing investments and operating costs for off-farm storage and other market infrastructure facilities related to handling and marketing primary agricultural products (silos, harbour facilities – docks, elevators; wholesale markets, futures markets).

The item other physical infrastructure includes public investments to build and maintain other physical infrastructure related to agriculture. These are included in the GSSE only in cases when agriculture is the main beneficiary. In general the share of the primary agriculture should be above 50% of economic activity or regional employment or similar indicator. The choice of the indicator should be related to the nature of the policy and data available and should be clearly explained in the documentation.

Institutional infrastructure

This sub-category includes budgetary expenditure financing investments and operating costs to build and maintain institutional infrastructure related to the farming sector (e.g. land cadastres; machinery user groups, seed and species registries; development of rural finance networks; support to farm organisations, etc.).

As a rule, only the institutional infrastructure closely related to agriculture is included. The decision whether to include an institutional infrastructure should be clearly explained in the documentation.

Farm restructuring

This sub-category includes budgetary expenditure related to reform of farm structures. It includes measures related to "entry strategies" (such as assisting new farmers within the context of land reforms). Transfers provided directly to individual farmers within those programmes should be in PSE. It also includes measures related to "exit strategies" and diversification strategies outside agriculture used in some developed countries, such as certain programmes in the European Union. However, support to diversification into other commodity sectors is included in the PSE.

Marketing and promotion

Collective schemes for processing and marketing

This sub-category includes budgetary expenditure financing investments in downstream activities (mainly at the level of primary processing) designed to improve the marketing environment for agriculture. It captures support to collective processing, marketing schemes and marketing facilities, while support to on-farm investments in processing activities is classified in the PSE; and support to individual firms (first processors) is classified in the CSE.

Promotion of agricultural products

This sub-category includes budgetary expenditure financing assistance to collective promotion of agro-food products (e.g. promotion campaigns, participation on international fairs), as well as those promoting food quality schemes. It does not include public expenditure related to export subsidies.

Cost of public stockholding

This category includes budgetary expenditure to cover the costs of storage, depreciation of the stocks and disposal of public storage of agricultural products. It includes cost of public stockholding related to market interventions (intervention storage) and storage of strategic reserves (stockholding for food security purposes, state reserves). This category does not include public expenditure related to export subsidies or buying into intervention stocks.

Miscellaneous

This category includes budgetary expenditure financing other general services that cannot be disaggregated and allocated to the above categories, often due to a lack of information. In such cases all efforts should be made to get more information concerning the implementation of the policy which will allow classifying in the categories mentioned above.

Main changes in GSSE and TSE estimates

Table 1.A2.2 compares estimates for 2011 for which data expenditures were considered final in the 2013 edition of the M&E report. Changes between the 2013 and 2014 editions reflect two factors: a) changes in the methodology; and b) data improvements facilitated by the clarification of definitions. In addition, the estimates in the 2014 report contain updated information across all agriculture support categories, in particular for recent years.

Changes in the GSSE are reflected in the TSE, which is the sum of PSE, GSSE and transfers from taxpayers to consumers. The revision of the GSSE definition also results in support to individual first-stage processors being moved from the GSSE, which includes only support to collective schemes under the category marketing and promotion, to the CSE, which captures support to processors being considered as first-stage consumers. The detailed review of GSSE measures also resulted in some being reclassified as PSE measures in some countries.

Most frequent changes are found in the category sub-category labelled A2 in Table 1.A2.1 and Table 1.A2.2, which corresponds to expenditure on agricultural knowledge transfer. They reflect the fact that expenditure on agricultural education are now fully included in the measure of policy effort, while in the previous methodology, expenditure on students, which did not remain in the agri-food sector, was excluded. While new a expenditure item was added in the inspection and control category (for farm input), numbers change only marginally in most countries. This might indicate that information is not yet available. Expenditure on infrastructure development and maintenance and on marketing and promotion is generally lower due to the narrower definition, focusing on primary agriculture. In most countries the aggregate indicators of support do not change very much, but the case of the United States is a notable exception.

Table 1.A2.2. **Estimate of support to agriculture for 2011 published in the 2013 and the 2014 reports**

	Total Support Estimate	Producer Support Estimate	Consumer Support Estimate	General Services Support Estimate	GSSE categories[1]						
					A1	A2	B	C	D	E	F
Australia (Million AUD)											
2014 monitoring report	2 600	1 542	0	1 058	573	35	109	333	7	0	0
2013 monitoring report	2 447	1 445	0	1 003	576	5	109	305	7	0	0
%diff	6	7	-	5	-1	596	0	9	0	-	-
Canada (Million CAD)											
2014 monitoring report	10 026	7 435	-4 697	2 591	680	243	1 008	352	239	0	69
2013 monitoring report	10 139	7 581	-4 900	2 558	506	274	1 022	523	233	0	0
%diff	-1	-2	-4	1	34	-11	-1	-33	2	-	-
Chile (Million CLP)											
2014 monitoring report	363 554	170 959	-17 967	192 595	43 706	2 876	36 986	103 626	5 397	0	4
2013 monitoring report	362 360	169 688	-15 200	192 672	45 917	814	36 915	103 626	5 397	0	4
%diff	0	1	18	0	-5	253	0	0	0	-	0
European Union (Million EUR)											
2014 monitoring report	89 558	77 907	-9 513	10 585	1 878	2 774	650	3 052	2 157	27	48
2013 monitoring report	89 094	76 505	-7 770	11 045	2 074	1 530	540	3 190	3 640	30	41
%diff	1	2	22	-4	-9	81	20	-4	-41	-10	18
Iceland (Million ISK)											
2014 monitoring report	17 464	16 248	-5 613	826	89	0	347	5	21	364	0
2013 monitoring report	17 702	16 505	-5 923	808	89	0	329	5	21	364	0
%diff	-1	-2	-5	2	0	-	5	0	0	0	-
Israel (Million ILS)											
2014 monitoring report	4 324	3 697	-3 403	627	282	2	94	202	1	45	1
2013 monitoring report	4 364	3 737	-3 524	627	282	2	94	202	1	45	1
%diff	-1	-1	-3	0	0	0	0	0	0	0	0
Japan (Billion JPY)											
2014 monitoring report	5 818	4 813	-5 111	1 004	83	36	14	840	14	16	0
2013 monitoring report	5 824	4 820	-5 122	1 004	83	36	14	822	14	16	18
%diff	0	0	0	0	0	0	0	2	0	0	-100
Korea (Billion KRW)											
2014 monitoring report	26 050	23 243	-29 622	2 761	675	47	170	1 433	69	366	0
2013 monitoring report	25 706	22 864	-28 871	2 796	740	43	124	1 453	69	366	0
%diff	1	2	3	-1	-9	10	37	-1	0	0	-
Mexico (Million MXN)											
2014 monitoring report	100 455	86 593	-15 591	9 958	1 335	3 968	771	3 707	176	1	0
2013 monitoring report	101 945	88 083	-17 081	9 958	1 414	3 889	771	3 190	692	1	0
%diff	-1	-2	-9	0	-6	2	0	16	-75	0	-
New Zealand (Million NZD)											
2014 monitoring report	659	202	-158	457	131	25	208	93	0	0	0
2013 monitoring report	647	206	-157	442	112	25	208	96	0	0	0
%diff	2	-2	1	3	16	0	0	-3	-	-	-
Norway (Million NOK)											
2014 monitoring report	23 971	21 623	-9 738	1 911	251	752	644	211	54	0	0
2013 monitoring report	24 724	22 112	-9 905	2 174	933	0	284	290	89	0	578
%diff	-3	-2	-2	-12	-73	-	126	-27	-40	0	-100

Table 1.A2.2. **Estimate of support to agriculture for 2011 published in the 2013 and the 2014 reports** (*cont.*)

	Total Support Estimate	Producer Support Estimate	Consumer Support Estimate	General Services Support Estimate	GSSE categories[1]						
					A1	A2	B	C	D	E	F
Switzerland (Million CHF)											
2014 monitoring report	5 930	5 442	-2 260	483	102	12	11	83	55	40	180
2013 monitoring report	5 994	5 507	-2 321	482	102	12	11	83	55	40	179
%diff	-1	-1	-3	0	0	0	0	0	0	0	1
Turkey (Million TRY)											
2014 monitoring report	30 079	27 689	-18 239	2 390	34	0	76	0	2 280	0	0
2013 monitoring report	31 747	29 357	-17 236	2 390	34	0	76	0	2 280	0	0
%diff	-5	-6	6	0	0	-	0	-	0	-	-
United States (Million USD)											
2014 monitoring report	74 963	31 038	33 927	6 640	2 227	186	1 058	-233	1 250	1	2 151
2013 monitoring report	143 778	31 596	35 694	71 539	2 324	0	1 079	320	65 664	1	2 151
%diff	-48	-2	-5	-91	-4	-	-2	-173	-98	0	0
OECD (Million USD)											
2014 monitoring report	341 570	258 473	-91 578	43 888	8 319	5 289	3 846	17 206	6 104	635	2 489
2013 monitoring report	409 244	257 230	-86 305	108 943	8 695	3 238	3 681	17 577	72 353	656	2 742
%diff	-17	0	6	-60	-4	63	4	-2	-92	-3	-9

1. See Table 1.A2.1 for descriptive labels of the GSSE categories under the 2014 and 2013 monitoring report. The 2013 estimates utilise the previous GSSE methodology and definitions. The estimates from the 2014 report use the revised GSSE methodology and may contain updated information across all agriculture support categories.

Source: OECD (2013c, 2014), "Producer and Consumer Support Estimates", *OECD Agriculture Statistics Database*, http://dx.doi.org/10.1787/agr-pcse-data-en.

StatLink ᴍ⛽∎ http://dx.doi.org/10.1787/888933110220

The main changes for each country are described below:

- **Australia:** There have been only minor changes in programmes that have been reclassified. The main change is due to the need to allocate programmes under "Marketing and promotion" into two new sub-categories. Most of these programmes have both a collective processing and promotion component. The total expenditure has been provisionally allocated to each sub-category in equal amounts. New information is being collected with the view of improving this allocation in the next monitoring cycle. The change of the classification of measures within the General Services Support Estimate (GSSE) has no significant implications for the total GSSE or the Total Support Estimate (TSE).

- **Canada:** Canada was one of the pilot countries of new GSSE classification. Canada reviewed around 5 000 individual programmes under the current GSSE. The revisions were implemented for the whole period since 1986 and the programmes are aggregated by the level of new GSSE categories. The programmes providing support to downstream industry (such as subsidy to biofuel plants), general rural development measure and general R&D expenditure were removed. During the review process, some previous GSSE programmes went to PSE and CSE as well. Canada asked for a standard definition of "the primary processing" to maintain the consistency across countries. Overall, the change of the classification of measures within the GSSE resulted in a minor reduction of the total GSSE and the TSE.

- **Chile:** A programme on Forestry Research was removed. Two new programmes were added: one on market information implemented by ODEPA agency and classified as

GSSE C2; and another one on food quality and safety implemented by ACHIPIA agency and classified as GSSE B1. The change of the classification of measures within the GSSE has no significant implications for the total GSSE or the TSE.

- **European Union:** The new GSSE classification was implemented for the whole period starting in 1986. Generally, sufficient documentation is available to inform classification decisions. Schemes that related to the production of specific products were removed, so was international food aid. Work is on-going to classify expenditures for which documentation is insufficient, this relates to both national and EU expenditure. In most cases these measures came to an end in the earlier years of the period covered by the indicators. As an example some further investigation is needed for the classification of some measures under the EAGGF that were phased out in 2007. Knowledge transfer up because better coverage of national expenditures. Reclassification and better coverage, of some items, especially in the category knowledge transfer at member state level, leads to some shifts between categories of the GSSE and overall it declines by -4%, while the TSE is hardly affected. The CSE shows a bigger negative number due to a revised estimate of market price support for 2011.

- **Iceland:** The change of the classification of measures within the General Services Support Estimate (GSSE) has no significant implications for the total GSSE or the TSE.

- **Israel:** The only issue was how to classify one inspection payment which included a combination of three different inspection services, but provided by the same inspection institution. This payment is allocated to Pest and disease inspection and control (GSSE-B2) as it is the closest to the dominant part of the activity of this institution. The change in the classification of measures within the General Services Support Estimate (GSSE) has no significant implications for the total GSSE or the TSE.

- **Japan:** The change of the classification of measures within the GSSE has no significant implications for the total GSSE or the TSE.

- **Korea:** The change of the classification of measures within the GSSE has no significant implications for the total GSSE or the TSE.

- **Mexico:** There have been only minor changes in programmes that have been reclassified. The main change is due to the need to allocate programmes under Inspection Services and Marketing and promotion into new sub-categories. In particular the inspection and control programmes implemented by the inspection agency SENASICA include inspection, pest and diseases and input components. Good budgetary information for the allocation of this expenditure to different sub-categories was not available and allocation was provisionally done in equal amounts. New information is being collected with the view of improving this allocation in the next monitoring cycle. The change of the classification of measures within the GSSE has no significant implications for the total GSSE or the TSE.

- **New Zealand:** The change of the classification of measures within the GSSE has no significant implications for the total GSSE or the TSE.

- **Norway:** There have been only minor changes in programmes that have been reclassified. The existing programmes have been reallocated and more detailed information was provided to split the programmes into the new categories and sub-categories. In some cases there was not enough data to split the programmes for the early years in the time series. Support to production of potato spirit was moved to the CSE. The programmes classified in the category miscellaneous were removed as these were administration costs. Overall, the change of the classification of measures within the GSSE resulted in a minor reduction of the total GSSE and TSE.

- **Switzerland:** There have been only minor changes in programmes that have been reclassified. One programme was moved to the PSE and one to CSE. Outstanding issue: data on expenditure on agricultural universities were not available. The change of the classification of measures within the GSSE has no significant implications for the total GSSE or the TSE.

- **Turkey:** The change of the classification of measures within the GSSE has no significant implications for the total GSSE or the TSE

- **United States:** There have been major changes in the reclassification of some large US programmes and as a result a very significant reduction of the GSSE and TSE. For the year 2011, these indicators drop by -91% and -48% respectively. The reduction results from the clarification in the new methodology that the GSSE encompasses only general services to the domestic primary agriculture sector. For the US, that narrowing of the GSSE boundaries leads to removal of two major sources of previously reported expenditures from the GSSE: 1) the share of the US Supplemental Nutrition Assistance Program (SNAP) expenditures (USD 62 billion in 2013) attributable to the food supply chain beyond the farm; and 2) expenditures on international food assistance (USD 1.6 billion in 2013), both of which had been included under "Marketing and promotion" under the previous GSSE. The share of SNAP expenditures attributable to farm level production (USD 16 billion) continues to be reported in the CSE. In addition to these two major items, some small additional changes have been made, including moving reported expenditures for the Renewable Energy Program (USD 56 million for 2013) to the PSE under payments based on input use, fixed capital formation.

Notes

1. OECD (2002), *Frascati Manual: Proposed Standard Practice for Surveys on Research and Experimental Development*, 6th edition, OECD publishing. Available at: *www.oecd-ilibrary.org/science-and-technology/frascati-manual-2002_9789264199040-en*.

2. Available at: *www.oecd.org/tad/sustainable-agriculture/agri-environmentalindicators.htm*.

Developments in agricultural support by country

PART II

Chapter 2

Developments in agricultural support in the OECD area

This chapter contains the information concerning the short- and long-term developments of the level and structure of support in the OECD area.

This chapter provides an overview of agricultural support in the OECD area as a whole as measured by the OECD indicators of agricultural support. The main drivers behind the changes in support between 2012 and 2013, and a more detailed analysis and evaluation of policy developments and support across OECD countries, are provided in Chapter 1 and the following country chapters.

The level and composition of agricultural support in the OECD area

Support to agriculture in the OECD area, as measured by the %PSE has been declining continuously: from 37% at the beginning of the period under review to less than 20% in the most recent years. The way support is delivered to farmers is also evolving (Figure 2.1).

Figure 2.1. **OECD: Level and composition of Producer Support Estimate, 1986-2013**

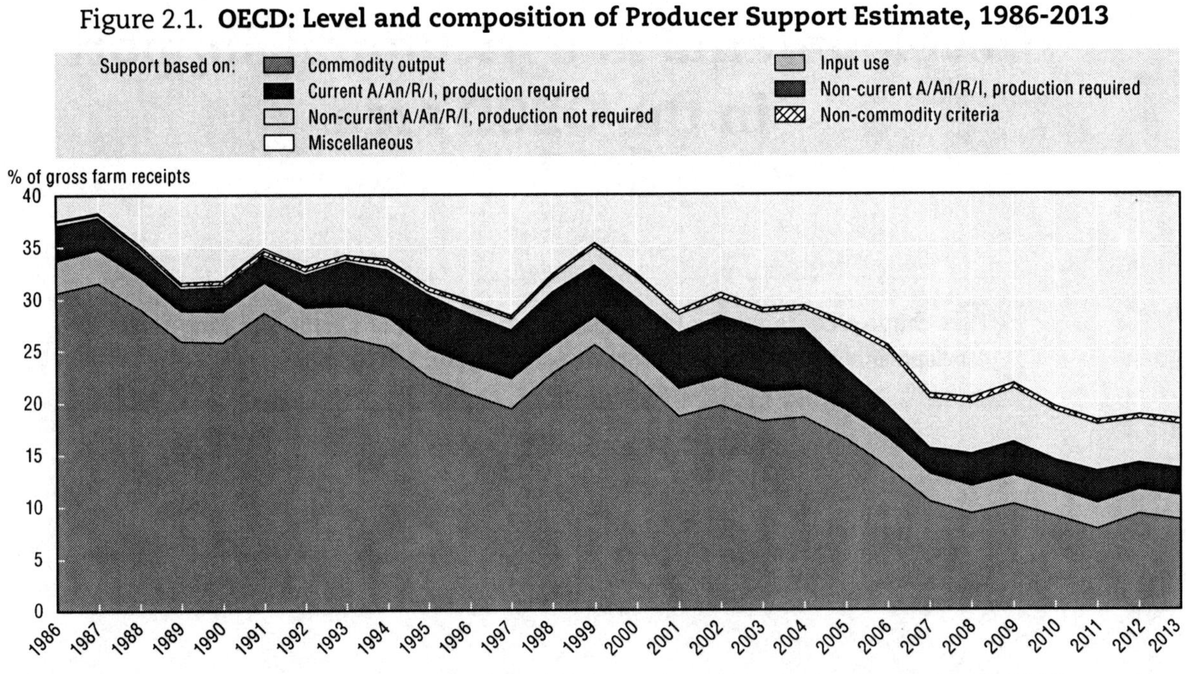

Source: OECD (2014), "Producer and Consumer Support Estimates", OECD Agriculture Statistics Database, http://dx.doi.org/10.1787/agr-pcse-data-en.
StatLink ⬛⬛ http://dx.doi.org/10.1787/888933109403

Support to agriculture in the OECD area is characterised by the long-term decline of support based on commodity output, mainly driven by reduced market price support. Support based on commodity output, comprising market price support and payments based on output is one of the most potentially production and trade distorting forms of support together with payments based on variable input use (without constraints). At the other end of the spectrum, the potentially less distorting forms of support, include payments based on parameters that are not linked to current production. Such payments can be based on non-current area or numbers of animals, receipts or income and do not require production in order to receive the payment. They can also be based on non-commodity criteria such as land set aside or payments for specific landscape features. These potentially less distorting forms of support have grown only in the most recent years, from a 1% share of the PSE in 1986-88 and 4% in 1995-97 to the second largest category of support representing 26% of support in 2011-13. Payments based on current areas and animal numbers were reduced slightly over the period since 1986-88. Today, they represent less than 3% of support (Figure 2.1, Tables 2.1 and 2.2).

Box 2.1. **Use of the %PSE indicator in evaluating annual changes in agricultural support**

The PSE, the total monetary value of the estimated policy transfers to producers, is expressed in the local currency of each country. It is converted into a common currency (USD, EUR) to allow aggregation into the total PSE for the OECD area as a whole. Consequently, the year-on-year variation in the total level of transfers denominated in a common currency will result from both changes in the level of transfers measured in each national currency and exchange rate movements against the currency used for the aggregation.

The OECD total value of agricultural policy transfers to producers, as measured by the nominal PSE, declined between 2012 and 2013 when expressed in USD – at USD 266 billion in 2012 and USD 258 billion in 2013 (Table 2.1). When expressed in Euros, the fall in the OECD total PSE was sharper from EUR 207 billion in 2012 to EUR 194 billion in 2013 (Table 2.2). How can these varying results expressed in different currencies be interpreted when the PSE is expressed in different currencies?

Exchange rate developments are the reason for the different movements, and consequently the best way to compare levels of support in the OECD as whole (as in individual countries) is to use relative indicators such as the %PSE, which expresses the value of policy transfers as a share of gross producer receipts. The latter represent the market value of agricultural output to which are added transfers to producers from taxpayers. The %PSE solves the problem of exchange rate choice because the same exchange rates are used to convert both the denominator and the numerator into a single currency. Consequently, the %PSE is the same regardless of the currency used (see Tables 2.1 and 2.2). Since the %PSE is a relative measure, it provides a sense of the importance of policy-induced transfers in the sector and is also appropriate for comparisons among OECD countries (as it eliminates the effects of the size of the agricultural sector) and over time (as it eliminates the effect of inflation).

Development of support to agriculture

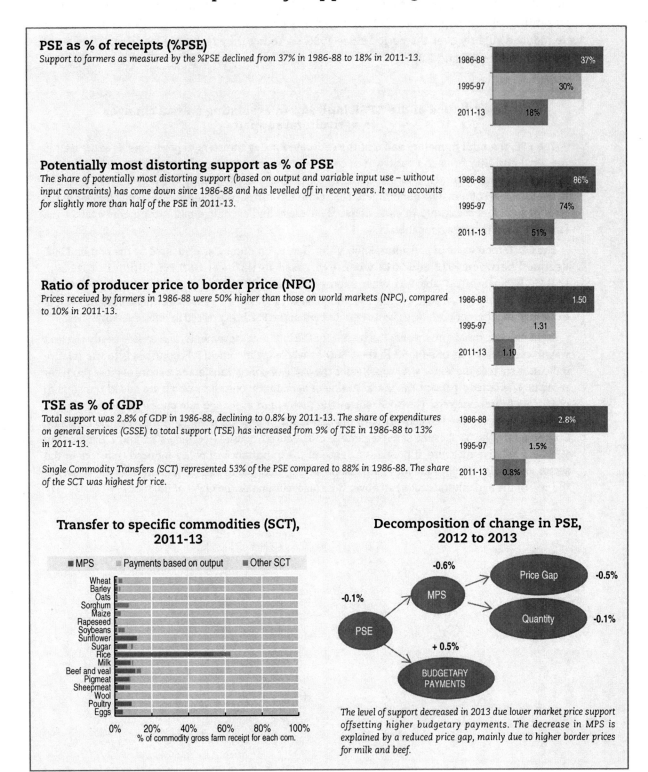

PSE as % of receipts (%PSE)

Support to farmers as measured by the %PSE declined from 37% in 1986-88 to 18% in 2011-13.

1986-88   37%
1995-97   30%
2011-13   18%

Potentially most distorting support as % of PSE

The share of potentially most distorting support (based on output and variable input use – without input constraints) has come down since 1986-88 and has levelled off in recent years. It now accounts for slightly more than half of the PSE in 2011-13.

1986-88   86%
1995-97   74%
2011-13   51%

Ratio of producer price to border price (NPC)

Prices received by farmers in 1986-88 were 50% higher than those on world markets (NPC), compared to 10% in 2011-13.

1986-88   1.50
1995-97   1.31
2011-13   1.10

TSE as % of GDP

Total support was 2.8% of GDP in 1986-88, declining to 0.8% by 2011-13. The share of expenditures on general services (GSSE) to total support (TSE) has increased from 9% of TSE in 1986-88 to 13% in 2011-13.

Single Commodity Transfers (SCT) represented 53% of the PSE compared to 88% in 1986-88. The share of the SCT was highest for rice.

1986-88   2.8%
1995-97   1.5%
2011-13   0.8%

Transfer to specific commodities (SCT), 2011-13

■ MPS   ▪ Payments based on output   ■ Other SCT

Wheat
Barley
Oats
Sorghum
Maize
Rapeseed
Soybeans
Sunflower
Sugar
Rice
Milk
Beef and veal
Pigmeat
Sheepmeat
Wool
Poultry
Eggs

0%   20%   40%   60%   80%   100%
% of commodity gross farm receipt for each com.

Decomposition of change in PSE, 2012 to 2013

-0.6%   Price Gap   -0.5%
-0.1%   MPS
PSE   Quantity   -0.1%
         + 0.5%
         BUDGETARY
         PAYMENTS

The level of support decreased in 2013 due lower market price support offsetting higher budgetary payments. The decrease in MPS is explained by a reduced price gap, mainly due to higher border prices for milk and beef.

Table 2.1. **OECD: Estimates of support to agriculture (USD)**

Million USD

	1986-88	1995-97	2011-13	2011	2012	2013p
Total value of production (at farm gate)	592 135	771 656	1 269 093	1 262 274	1 273 578	1 271 427
of which: share of MPS commodities (%)	72.1	70.6	67.4	66.7	67.7	67.7
Total value of consumption (at farm gate)	559 273	760 864	1 181 432	1 185 605	1 193 449	1 165 242
Producer Support Estimate (PSE)	239 543	253 959	260 935	258 473	266 382	257 950
Support based on commodity output	196 678	178 504	120 385	110 060	130 649	120 447
Market Price Support[1]	184 080	171 469	114 247	104 136	124 358	114 249
Payments based on output	12 599	7 035	6 138	5 924	6 292	6 198
Payments based on input use	20 197	24 050	33 606	34 927	32 829	33 061
Based on variable input use	9 763	11 004	13 087	13 420	12 954	12 887
with input constraints	743	417	647	602	675	665
Based on fixed capital formation	6 870	7 385	12 645	13 503	12 185	12 248
with input constraints	1 235	743	2 369	2 305	2 404	2 397
Based on on-farm services	3 563	5 661	7 873	8 004	7 690	7 926
with input constraints	439	1 056	1 263	1 260	1 231	1 297
Payments based on current A/An/R/I, production required	18 734	41 774	38 284	42 892	35 824	36 135
Based on Receipts / Income	2 051	1 432	5 005	5 182	5 340	4 494
Based on Area planted / Animal numbers	16 683	40 342	33 278	37 710	30 484	31 641
with input constraints	3 719	15 476	23 707	25 635	22 321	23 167
Payments based on non-current A/An/R/I, production required	533	459	977	1 037	925	970
Payments based on non-current A/An/R/I, production not required	2 080	6 626	61 657	63 738	60 075	61 159
With variable payment rates	181	639	368	404	321	378
with commodity exceptions	0	0	205	237	155	223
With fixed payment rates	1 899	5 988	61 289	63 334	59 754	60 780
with commodity exceptions	1 561	4 917	27 773	29 253	27 862	26 205
Payments based on non-commodity criteria	1 077	3 135	5 570	5 388	5 611	5 712
Based on long-term resource retirement	1 076	2 951	3 214	3 298	3 150	3 193
Based on a specific non-commodity output	1	183	2 169	1 861	2 297	2 350
Based on other non-commodity criteria	0	1	187	229	163	169
Miscellaneous payments	244	-589	456	432	468	467
Percentage PSE (%)	37.0	29.7	18.4	18.2	18.8	18.2
Producer NPC (coeff.)	1.50	1.31	1.10	1.09	1.11	1.10
Producer NAC (coeff.)	1.59	1.42	1.23	1.22	1.23	1.22
General Services Support Estimate (GSSE)[2]	25 621	43 464	43 919	43 888	44 192	43 675
Agricultural knowledge and innovation system	4 842	8 400	13 509	13 608	13 451	13 467
Inspection and control	1 072	1 504	3 861	3 846	3 882	3 854
Development and maintenance of infrastructure	10 264	22 757	17 938	17 206	18 926	17 683
Marketing and promotion	2 192	5 475	5 318	6 104	4 677	5 173
Cost of public stockholding	5 872	3 518	759	635	781	860
Miscellaneous	1 379	1 809	2 534	2 489	2 474	2 638
Percentage GSSE (% of TSE)	9.0	13.5	12.7	12.8	12.6	12.7
Consumer Support Estimate (CSE)	-159 865	-171 139	-94 833	-91 578	-105 929	-86 992
Transfers to producers from consumers	-169 187	-167 732	-110 242	-101 729	-119 756	-109 243
Other transfers from consumers	-22 093	-30 309	-25 473	-29 388	-26 276	-20 754
Transfers to consumers from taxpayers	19 875	24 761	40 524	39 208	39 756	42 608
Excess feed cost	11 540	2 141	358	330	347	397
Percentage CSE (%)	-29.7	-23.2	-8.3	-8.0	-9.2	-7.7
Consumer NPC (coeff.)	1.52	1.35	1.13	1.12	1.14	1.13
Consumer NAC (coeff.)	1.42	1.30	1.09	1.09	1.10	1.08
Total Support Estimate (TSE)	285 040	322 184	345 378	341 570	350 329	344 234
Transfers from consumers	191 280	198 041	135 715	131 116	146 032	129 997
Transfers from taxpayers	115 853	154 452	235 135	239 841	230 573	234 992
Budget revenues	-22 093	-30 309	-25 473	-29 388	-26 276	-20 754
Percentage TSE (% of GDP)	2.8	1.5	0.8	0.8	0.8	0.8

Notes: p: provisional. NPC: Nominal Protection Coefficient. NAC: Nominal Assistance Coefficient. A/An/R/I: Area planted/Animal numbers/Receipts/Income. The OECD total for 1986-88 includes all countries, except Chile, Israel and Slovenia, for which data is not available. TSE as a share of GDP for 1986-88 for the OECD is an estimate based on available data.

1. Market Price Support (MPS) is net of producer levies and excess feed cost. MPS commodities: see notes to individual country tables in Part II.
2. A revised GSSE definition with new categories was introduced in 2014. When possible, the revision was implemented for the whole time series. The GSSE series and the resulting TSE are not comparable with the series published previously (for more details, see Annex 1.A2)

Source: OECD (2014), "Producer and Consumer Support Estimates", OECD *Agriculture Statistics Database*, doi: *http://dx.doi.org/10.1787/agr-pcse-data-en.*

StatLink ⚙️ *http://dx.doi.org/10.1787/888933110239*

Table 2.2. **OECD: Estimates of support to agriculture (EUR)**

Million EUR

	1986-88	1995-97	2011-13	2011	2012	2013p
Total value of production (at farm gate)	**536 394**	**625 221**	**952 130**	**907 775**	**990 852**	**957 763**
of which: share of MPS commodities (%)	72.1	70.6	67.4	66.7	67.7	67.7
Total value of consumption (at farm gate)	**506 239**	**615 795**	**886 308**	**852 638**	**928 511**	**877 774**
Producer Support Estimate (PSE)	**217 332**	**205 293**	**195 814**	**185 883**	**207 246**	**194 314**
Support based on commodity output	178 364	144 142	90 510	79 151	101 646	90 733
Market Price Support[1]	166 876	138 450	85 902	74 890	96 751	86 064
Payments based on output	11 489	5 692	4 608	4 260	4 895	4 669
Payments based on input use	18 293	19 510	25 188	25 118	25 541	24 904
Based on variable input use	8 863	8 900	9 812	9 651	10 078	9 708
with input constraints	683	334	486	433	525	501
Based on fixed capital formation	6 214	5 974	9 472	9 710	9 480	9 226
with input constraints	1 124	596	1 778	1 658	1 871	1 806
Based on on-farm services	3 217	4 636	5 903	5 756	5 983	5 971
with input constraints	397	869	947	906	958	977
Payments based on current A/An/R/I, production required	17 101	33 763	28 646	30 846	27 871	27 220
Based on Receipts / Income	1 906	1 169	3 755	3 726	4 155	3 385
Based on Area planted / Animal numbers	15 195	32 594	24 890	27 120	23 717	23 835
with input constraints	3 300	12 518	17 751	18 436	17 365	17 451
Payments based on non-current A/An/R/I, production required	505	371	732	746	719	731
Payments based on non-current A/An/R/I, production not required	1 900	5 467	46 216	45 838	46 739	46 071
With variable payment rates	161	498	275	291	250	285
with commodity exceptions	0	0	153	171	121	168
With fixed payment rates	1 739	4 969	45 941	45 547	46 489	45 786
with commodity exceptions	1 417	4 099	20 818	21 037	21 677	19 740
Payments based on non-commodity criteria	942	2 526	4 181	3 875	4 365	4 303
Based on long-term resource retirement	941	2 376	2 409	2 372	2 451	2 406
Based on a specific non-commodity output	1	149	1 632	1 338	1 787	1 770
Based on other non-commodity criteria	0	0	140	164	127	127
Miscellaneous payments	227	-486	342	310	364	352
Percentage PSE (%)	**37.0**	**29.7**	**18.4**	**18.2**	**18.8**	**18.2**
Producer NPC (coeff.)	**1.50**	**1.31**	**1.10**	**1.09**	**1.11**	**1.10**
Producer NAC (coeff.)	**1.59**	**1.42**	**1.23**	**1.22**	**1.23**	**1.22**
General Services Support Estimate (GSSE)[2]	**23 119**	**35 153**	**32 948**	**31 563**	**34 382**	**32 901**
Agricultural knowledge and innovation system	4 383	6 819	10 132	9 787	10 465	10 145
Inspection and control	972	1 226	2 896	2 766	3 020	2 903
Development and maintenance of infrastructure	9 241	18 314	13 473	12 373	14 725	13 320
Marketing and promotion	1 975	4 451	3 975	4 390	3 639	3 897
Cost of public stockholding	5 294	2 876	571	457	607	648
Miscellaneous	1 254	1 467	1 901	1 790	1 925	1 988
Percentage GSSE (% of TSE)	**9.0**	**13.5**	**12.7**	**12.8**	**12.6**	**12.7**
Consumer Support Estimate (CSE)	**-144 680**	**-137 960**	**-71 268**	**-65 859**	**-82 413**	**-65 531**
Transfers to producers from consumers	-153 312	-135 388	-82 874	-73 159	-93 171	-82 292
Other transfers from consumers	-19 953	-24 382	-19 071	-21 134	-20 443	-15 634
Transfers to consumers from taxpayers	18 030	20 100	30 408	28 197	30 930	32 097
Excess feed cost	10 555	1 710	269	238	270	299
Percentage CSE (%)	**-29.7**	**-23.2**	**-8.3**	**-8.0**	**-9.2**	**-7.7**
Consumer NPC (coeff.)	**1.52**	**1.35**	**1.13**	**1.12**	**1.14**	**1.13**
Consumer NAC (coeff.)	**1.42**	**1.30**	**1.09**	**1.09**	**1.10**	**1.08**
Total Support Estimate (TSE)	**258 481**	**260 546**	**259 171**	**245 643**	**272 558**	**259 311**
Transfers from consumers	173 265	159 770	101 945	94 294	113 614	97 926
Transfers from taxpayers	105 169	125 159	176 297	172 484	179 388	177 019
Budget revenues	-19 953	-24 382	-19 071	-21 134	-20 443	-15 634
Percentage TSE (% of GDP)	**2.8**	**1.5**	**0.8**	**0.8**	**0.8**	**0.8**

Notes: p: provisional. NPC: Nominal Protection Coefficient. NAC: Nominal Assistance Coefficient. A/An/R/I: Area planted/Animal numbers/Receipts/Income. The OECD total for 1986-88 includes all countries except Chile, Israel and Slovenia, for which data is not available. TSE as a share of GDP for 1986-88 for the OECD is an estimate based on available data.

1. Market Price Support (MPS) is net of producer levies and excess feed cost. MPS commodities: see notes to individual country tables in Part II.
2. A revised GSSE definition with new categories was introduced in 2014. When possible, the revision was implemented for the whole time series. The GSSE series and the resulting TSE are not comparable with the series published previously (for more details, see Annex 1.A2).

Source: OECD (2014), "Producer and Consumer Support Estimates", OECD *Agriculture Statistics Database, doi: http://dx.doi.org/10.1787/agr-pcse-data-en.*

StatLink ⟶ *http://dx.doi.org/10.1787/888933110258*

PART II

Chapter 3

Developments in agricultural policies and support in Australia

The Australia country chapter includes a brief evaluation of policy developments and related support to agriculture, contextual information on the framework in which agricultural policies are implemented and the main characteristics of the agricultural sector, an evaluation of support in 2012-13 and in the longer term perspective, and a brief description of the main policy developments in 2013-14.

Evaluation of policy developments

- Since 1986-88, Australia has reduced the level of support to agriculture as measured by the %PSE to just 2% and removed the potentially most distorting forms of support in the early 2000s. This constitutes a continuous and significant progress. The remaining support programmes are targeted to risk management, environmental conservation and provision of general services to the sector.

- The Exceptional Circumstances (EC) programmes for droughts experienced a peak of expenditure in 2006-08. The ongoing reform of Drought Policy has been refocusing this support towards risk management and preparedness. In February 2014, a drought assistance package including concessional loans was introduced in response to prolonged severe dry conditions in some areas of the country.

- The overall challenge for the future is for farms to continue to prepare for extreme climatic conditions and to use resources, in particular water, sustainably.

- Australia should continue using its partnership arrangement through rural research and development corporations to foster innovation and the adoption of new technologies and practices, in order to improve total factor productivity growth.

Figure 3.1. **Australia: PSE level and composition by support categories, 1986-2013**

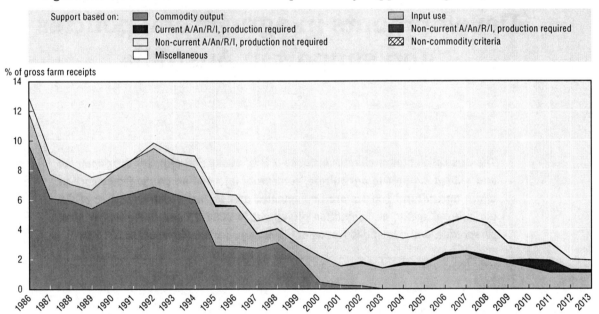

Source: OECD (2014), "Producer and Consumer Support Estimates", OECD *Agriculture Statistics Database*, http://dx.doi.org/10.1787/agr-pcse-data-en.
StatLink ⬛ᵐˢ⬛ http://dx.doi.org/10.1787/888933109422

Contextual information

Australia is the world's 12th largest economy and the sixth largest country by land area. However, the largest share of total land constitutes desert or semi-arid land, with the oldest and least fertile soils. Nevertheless, Australia is an important producer and exporter of agricultural products and maintains a consistently positive and sizeable agro-food trade balance. The share of agriculture in water consumption is high and lack of water, accentuated by climate change, is a principal limiting factor.

Table 3.1. **Australia: Contextual indicators, 1995, 2012[1]**

	1995	2012[1]
Economic context		
GDP (billion USD)	393	1 576
Population (million)	18	23
Land area (thousand km^2)	7 682	7 682
Population density (inhabitants/km^2)	2	3
GDP per capita, PPP (USD)	22 312	44 407
Trade as % of GDP	14.1	16.1
Agriculture in the economy		
Agriculture in GDP (%)	3.7	2.4
Agriculture share in employment (%)	4.7	2.8
Agro-food exports (% of total exports)	24.6	14.3
Agro-food imports (% of total imports)	4.7	4.7
Characteristics of the agricultural sector		
Agro-food trade balance (million USD)	10 356	24 822
Crop in total agricultural production (%)	54	57
Livestock in total agricultural production (%)	46	43
Agricultural area (AA) (thousand ha)	463 348	409 673
Share of arable land in AA (%)	9	12
Share of irrigated land in AA (%)	0.4	0.5
Share of agriculture in water consumption (%)	63	52
Nitrogen balance, kg/ha	15	14

1. Or latest available year.
Sources: OECD Statistical Databases, ITCS, World Development Indicators and national data.

StatLink 🔗 http://dx.doi.org/10.1787/888933110277

Figure 3.2. **Australia: Main macroeconomic indicators, 1995-2013**

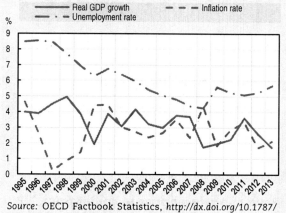

Source: OECD Factbook Statistics, *http://dx.doi.org/10.1787/data-00590-en.*

StatLink 🔗 http://dx.doi.org/10.1787/888933109441

Figure 3.3. **Australia: Agro-food trade, 1995-2012**

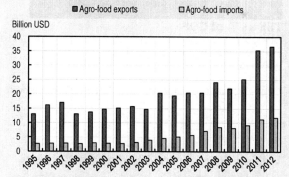

Source: International Trade by Commodity Statistics (ITCS) Database.

StatLink 🔗 http://dx.doi.org/10.1787/888933109460

Note: Detailed definitions of contextual indicators and their sources are provided in Annex II.A1.

Development of support to agriculture

Support to producers in Australia has been reduced from already relatively low levels in 1986-88 to the point that it is now the second lowest in OECD. Reform of support is also reflected in its composition, with a reduction of market price support to zero, a shift towards more targeted direct payments and an increase of the share of the support to general services. Producer support is currently down to less than 2%.

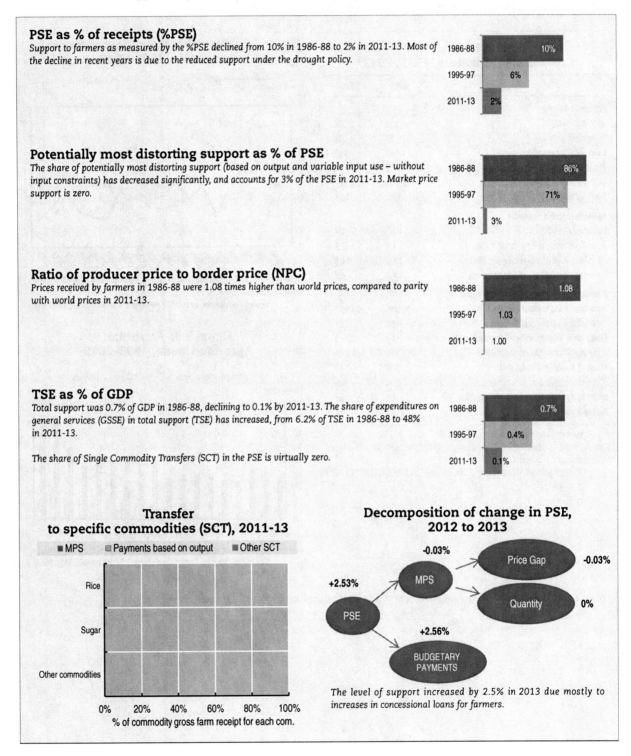

PSE as % of receipts (%PSE)
Support to farmers as measured by the %PSE declined from 10% in 1986-88 to 2% in 2011-13. Most of the decline in recent years is due to the reduced support under the drought policy.

1986-88   10%
1995-97   6%
2011-13   2%

Potentially most distorting support as % of PSE
The share of potentially most distorting support (based on output and variable input use – without input constraints) has decreased significantly, and accounts for 3% of the PSE in 2011-13. Market price support is zero.

1986-88   86%
1995-97   71%
2011-13   3%

Ratio of producer price to border price (NPC)
Prices received by farmers in 1986-88 were 1.08 times higher than world prices, compared to parity with world prices in 2011-13.

1986-88   1.08
1995-97   1.03
2011-13   1.00

TSE as % of GDP
Total support was 0.7% of GDP in 1986-88, declining to 0.1% by 2011-13. The share of expenditures on general services (GSSE) in total support (TSE) has increased, from 6.2% of TSE in 1986-88 to 48% in 2011-13.

The share of Single Commodity Transfers (SCT) in the PSE is virtually zero.

1986-88   0.7%
1995-97   0.4%
2011-13   0.1%

Transfer to specific commodities (SCT), 2011-13

■ MPS   ▨ Payments based on output   ■ Other SCT

Rice
Sugar
Other commodities

0%   20%   40%   60%   80%   100%
% of commodity gross farm receipt for each com.

Decomposition of change in PSE, 2012 to 2013

-0.03%
+2.53%   MPS
PSE
+2.56%
BUDGETARY PAYMENTS

Price Gap   -0.03%
Quantity   0%

The level of support increased by 2.5% in 2013 due mostly to increases in concessional loans for farmers.

Table 3.2. **Australia: Estimates of support to agriculture**

Million AUD

	1986-88	1995-97	2011-13	2011	2012	2013p
Total value of production (at farm gate)	**19 888**	**28 441**	**48 946**	**48 049**	**47 892**	**50 896**
of which: share of MPS commodities (%)	86.4	75.3	67.0	67.4	66.8	66.8
Total value of consumption (at farm gate)	**7 364**	**11 644**	**21 399**	**21 397**	**19 092**	**23 709**
Producer Support Estimate (PSE)	**2 022**	**1 694**	**1 170**	**1 542**	**971**	**996**
Support based on commodity output	1 447	834	0	0	0	0
Market Price Support[1]	1 447	834	0	0	0	0
Payments based on output	0	0	0	0	0	0
Payments based on input use	324	614	544	540	533	558
Based on variable input use	306	376	33	32	19	49
with input constraints	0	0	0	0	0	0
Based on fixed capital formation	5	33	296	276	308	303
with input constraints	0	0	156	139	164	164
Based on on-farm services	13	205	214	231	206	206
with input constraints	0	0	0	0	0	0
Payments based on current A/An/R/I, production required	0	19	202	413	98	96
Based on Receipts / Income	0	19	201	411	96	96
Based on Area planted / Animal numbers	0	0	1	2	2	0
with input constraints	0	0	1	2	2	0
Payments based on non-current A/An/R/I, production required	0	0	0	0	0	0
Payments based on non-current A/An/R/I, production not required	250	227	407	559	330	333
With variable payment rates	250	137	330	382	302	307
with commodity exceptions	0	0	178	230	150	155
With fixed payment rates	0	90	77	177	29	27
with commodity exceptions	0	0	0	0	0	0
Payments based on non-commodity criteria	0	1	16	31	10	8
Based on long-term resource retirement	0	0	6	15	2	0
Based on a specific non-commodity output	0	0	11	16	8	8
Based on other non-commodity criteria	0	1	0	0	0	0
Miscellaneous payments	0	0	0	0	0	0
Percentage PSE (%)	**10.1**	**5.8**	**2.3**	**3.1**	**2.0**	**1.9**
Producer NPC (coeff.)	**1.08**	**1.03**	**1.00**	**1.00**	**1.00**	**1.00**
Producer NAC (coeff.)	**1.11**	**1.06**	**1.02**	**1.03**	**1.02**	**1.02**
General Services Support Estimate (GSSE)[2]	**132**	**511**	**1 053**	**1 058**	**1 061**	**1 040**
Agricultural knowledge and innovation system	132	385	624	608	633	631
Inspection and control	0	26	102	109	98	98
Development and maintenance of infrastructure	0	72	319	333	321	302
Marketing and promotion	0	27	8	7	9	9
Cost of public stockholding	0	0	0	0	0	0
Miscellaneous	0	0	0	0	0	0
Percentage GSSE (% of TSE)	**6.2**	**23.6**	**48.0**	**40.7**	**52.2**	**51.1**
Consumer Support Estimate (CSE)	**-848**	**-386**	**0**	**0**	**0**	**0**
Transfers to producers from consumers	-848	-386	0	0	0	0
Other transfers from consumers	0	0	0	0	0	0
Transfers to consumers from taxpayers	0	0	0	0	0	0
Excess feed cost	0	0	0	0	0	0
Percentage CSE (%)	**-11.6**	**-3.3**	**0.0**	**0.0**	**0.0**	**0.0**
Consumer NPC (coeff.)	**1.13**	**1.03**	**1.00**	**1.00**	**1.00**	**1.00**
Consumer NAC (coeff.)	**1.13**	**1.03**	**1.00**	**1.00**	**1.00**	**1.00**
Total Support Estimate (TSE)	**2 154**	**2 204**	**2 223**	**2 600**	**2 032**	**2 035**
Transfers from consumers	848	386	0	0	0	0
Transfers from taxpayers	1 306	1 818	2 223	2 600	2 032	2 035
Budget revenues	0	0	0	0	0	0
Percentage TSE (% of GDP)	**0.7**	**0.4**	**0.1**	**0.2**	**0.1**	**0.1**
GDP deflator (1986-88=100)	**100**	**133**	**219**	**219**	**219**	**221**

Note: p: provisional. NPC: Nominal Protection Coefficient. NAC: Nominal Assistance Coefficient. A/An/R/I: Area planted/Animal numbers/ Receipts/Income.

1. Market Price Support (MPS) is net of producer levies and excess feed cost. MPS commodities for Australia are: wheat, barley, oats, sorghum, rice, soybean, rapeseed, sunflower, sugar, cotton, milk, beef and veal, sheep meat, wool, pigmeat, poultry and eggs.

2. A revised GSSE definition with new categories was introduced in 2014. When possible, the revision was implemented for the whole time series. The GSSE series and the resulting TSE are not comparable with the series published previously (for more details, see Annex 1.A2).

Source: OECD (2014), "Producer and Consumer Support Estimates", OECD *Agriculture Statistics Database, doi: http://dx.doi.org/10.1787/agr-pcse-data-en.*

StatLink ᵃᵖᵍᵉ *http://dx.doi.org/10.1787/888933110296*

Description of policy developments

Main policy instruments

Australia's agriculture sector remains strongly market oriented. It receives no market price support, with domestic and international prices closely aligned. Agricultural support is mainly provided by budgeted programmes as well as through regulatory arrangements and tax concessions. Budget-financed programmes are mainly used for structural adjustment and drought, and for natural resources and environmental management and services. With a low level of direct government support to farmers and no farm subsidy scheme, research and development (R&D) programmes are a major component of Australian support to agriculture. *Rural research and development corporations* (RDCs) are the Australian Government's primary vehicle for supporting rural innovation. RDCs are a partnership between the government and industry created to share the funding and strategic direction setting for primary industry R&D, investment in R&D and the subsequent adoption of R&D outputs. A levy system provides for the collection of contributions from farmers to finance RDCs, while research project funding can be matched with supplementary funds from the federal budget.

Efficient management of often scarce water resources is important for agriculture and for environmental sustainability. Australia is working towards a system of clear and secure water access entitlements which can be traded on open water markets subject to water market boundaries. Such trading systems aid the transfer of scarce water resources to the users that value them most. These objectives are key components of the National Water Initiative, Australia's enduring blueprint for water reform. The purpose is to have a system that is consistent across the different states and territories.

Domestic policy developments in 2013-14

In the face of an increasingly variable climate, the Australian Government has continued to pursue reform of drought assistance to help farm households prepare for the future by focusing on risk management and preparedness. In 2013, the Australian state and territory primary industries ministers signed the Intergovernmental Agreement on National Drought Program Reform (IGA). The IGA formalises the commitment of Australian federal, state and territory governments to implement a new approach to drought programmes from 1 July 2014. The new approach replaces the Exceptional Circumstances arrangements and recognises that farm households can experience hardship for a range of reasons, not only drought. The IGA includes: a farm household support payment; continued access to Farm Management Deposits Scheme and taxation measures; a national approach to farm business training; a coordinated, collaborative approach to providing social support services; tools and technologies to inform farmer decision making.

The IGA retains flexibility for governments to introduce additional support measures if needed in a drought. It contains an agreed set of principles and a process to guide governments in determining support in difficult times so that any in-drought support measures remain consistent with the intent of reform. In February 2014, the Australian Government announced a drought assistance package worth AUD 320 million (USD 309 million) to support those farm businesses, farm families and rural communities facing hardship brought on by drought. Key components of the drought package include: more generous criteria for accessing *income support* for farmers; drought concessional loans totalling AUD 280 million (USD 270 million) will be allocated to help eligible farm businesses cope with and recover from the effects of drought; assistance of up to AUD 12 million (USD 11.6 million) to assist drought-affected farm businesses to install water-related infrastructure; AUD 10 million(USD 9.6 million) in assistance will be available to help reduce the impact of pest animals in drought-affected areas; AUD 10.7 million (USD 10.3 million) to increase access to social and mental health services in communities affected by this drought.

The Australian Government also developed in 2013 the *Farm Finance* package to improve the financial resilience of viable farm businesses under pressure from high levels of debt. The package consists of four measures: provision of concessional loans for debt restructuring or productivity enhancement activities; funding of AUD 420 million (USD 406 million) for the for additional counsellors with the Rural Financial Counselling Service; enhancements to the Farm Management Deposits Scheme giving farmers greater flexibility in managing their finances; and pursuing a common approach to farm debt in different states and territories.

Throughout 2013, the Australian Government continued work on biosecurity reform, with the objective of moving towards a system that manages biosecurity risks offshore, at the border and onshore. New biosecurity legislation to replace the *Quarantine Act 1908*, comprising the Biosecurity Bill and the Inspector-General of Biosecurity Bill, was introduced into Parliament in late 2012. Due to the dissolution of the Australian Parliament for the September 2013 election, both bills lapsed. The Australian Government will determine the next steps for the legislation.

Australia is in the process of consolidating its state-operated genebanks into a National Genetic Resources Centre with an integrated national approach. It will consist of two nodes: one for grains – being developed as the Australian Grains Genebank (AGG) – and one for pastures – being developed as the Australian Pastures Genebank (APG). The AGG officially opened its new facilities on 28 March 2014, holding more than 180 000 samples from Australia and around the world. The APG is expected to become operational in 2014.

The Australian Government is developing an Agricultural Competitiveness White Paper, due for completion at the end of 2014, which will drive the long-term agricultural policies of the government. It will consider issues on food security, improving farm gate returns, debt, supply chain competitiveness, investment, job creation, infrastructure, skills and training, research and development, regulatory effectiveness and market access. It will also provide the opportunity to review, in consultation with industry, whether guidelines relating to drought preparedness and in-event drought measures are adequate.

Trade policy developments in 2013-14

Australia has seven comprehensive Free Trade Agreements (FTAs) in force, both regional and bilateral. These account for 28% of Australia's total trade. Australia has signed FTAs with **New Zealand** (ANZCERTA 1983), **Singapore** (SAFTA 2003), **Thailand** (TAFTA 2005), the **United States** (AUSFTA 2005), **Chile** (Australia-Chile FTA 2009), the **ASEAN**-Australia-New Zealand Free Trade Area (AANZFTA 2010) and **Malaysia** (2013). Australia and the **Republic of Korea** concluded negotiations on the Korea-Australia Free Trade Agreement (KAFTA) in December 2013. The agreement was signed in April 2014 and will enter into force following domestic approval processes in both countries. In terms of agricultural products, Korea will gradually eliminate import tariffs, over time frames of up to 20 years, on a wide range of Australian agricultural exports, in particular beef and dairy with the elimination of tariffs of 40% and 36% respectively. Australia will give immediate tariff free access to all agricultural products from Korea, and will eliminate tariffs in other sectors such as car components and electronics in three years.

After seven years of negotiations, **Japan** and Australia have concluded the Japan-Australia Economic Partnership Agreement (EPA) in April 2014. The agreement includes i) an increase of the TRQ of Japan for selected Australian dairy products such as processed cheese, and tariff reductions for several Australian agricultural products including beef (from current 38.5% to 19.5% for frozen beef in 18 years, and to 23.5% for fresh beef in 15 years); and ii) elimination of Australian tariffs on Japanese automobiles (from current 5 to 0%). Rice is excluded from the agreement.

Australia is engaged in six other FTA negotiations. There are three individual bilateral FTA negotiations with **China**, **India** and **Indonesia.** Three plurilateral FTA negotiations are ongoing under the **Trans-Pacific Partnership Agreement** (TPP), the **Pacific Trade and Economic Agreement** (PACER Plus), and the Regional Comprehensive Economic Partnership Agreement (RCEP).

PART II

Chapter 4

Developments in agricultural policies and support in Canada

The Canada country chapter includes a brief evaluation of policy developments and related support to agriculture, contextual information on the framework in which agricultural policies are implemented and the main characteristics of the agricultural sector, an evaluation of support in 2012-13 and in the longer term perspective, and a brief description of the main policy developments in 2013-14.

Evaluation of policy developments

- Overall, producer support has significantly decreased since 1986-88, and the majority of agricultural markets are competitive. The monopoly of the Canadian Wheat Board on marketing wheat and barley in western Canada was removed in 2012. Most reforms in the past decade have involved fine-tuning existing programmes, although the current five-year policy framework for 2013-18 stresses a renewed focus on competitiveness and sustainability.

- The dairy, poultry and egg sectors continue to receive high price support, distorting production and trade and establishing high rents capitalised in the quotas required to produce under the supply-management system. As a gradual step to eliminate production quota, increasing the amount of quota available would improve market orientation and reduce these rents which currently act as a barrier to entry into supply-managed sectors.

- Budgetary policies have become tightly focused on risk management for farm operations, resulting in several programmes with potentially overlapping mandates and impacts. The reforms implemented in 2013 aim to reduce the overlap (i.e. reduction of margin coverage by AgriStability).

- The implementation of *ad hoc* programmes should be governed by stricter protocols and disciplines that mitigate potential pressure for additional support in situations in which existing programmes suffice.

Figure 4.1. **Canada: PSE level and composition by support categories, 1986-2013**

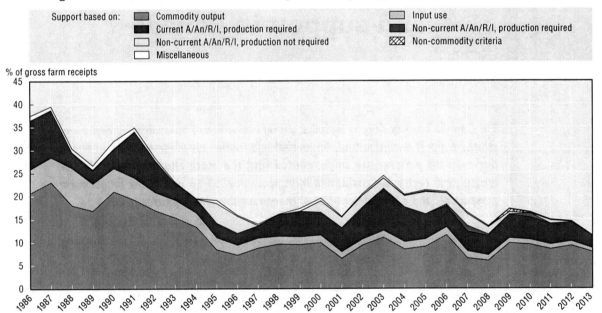

Source: OECD (2014), "Producer and Consumer Support Estimates", OECD *Agriculture Statistics Database, http://dx.doi.org/10.1787/agr-pcse-data-en.*
StatLink ⏋ *http://dx.doi.org/10.1787/888933109479*

Contextual information

Canada is a large country with a small population relative to its area. Canada is ranked 7th in the OECD in GDP per capita. Agriculture remains an important part of the economy regionally, but overall primary agriculture represents less than 2% of GDP. Canada is a net exporter of agricultural products and agriculture exports are important, accounting for 10% of exports. More than half of Canadian agricultural exports are destined to the United States; market access is a significant issue for the sector. The typical farm in the western prairies is twice larger than the national average in terms of land use, highly productive and produces largely for export markets. Most milk production is located in Eastern Canada, which has relatively smaller farm sizes and a larger variety of crops, including fruits and vegetables. The red meat industries (i.e. hog and beef cattle) maintain a significant presence across Canada, especially in Western Canada, Ontario and Quebec.

Table 4.1. **Canada: Contextual indicators, 1995, 2012[1]**

	1995	2012[1]
Economic context		
GDP (billion USD)	590	1 780
Population (million)	29	35
Land area (thousand km^2)	9 094	9 094
Population density (inhabitants/km^2)	3	3
GDP per capita, PPP (USD)	22 789	41 150
Trade as % of GDP	30.1	25.7
Agriculture in the economy		
Agriculture in GDP (%)	2.9	1.9
Agriculture share in employment (%)	3.8	2.0
Agro-food exports (% of total exports)	6.8	9.8
Agro-food imports (% of total imports)	5.5	7.2
Characteristics of the agricultural sector		
Agro-food trade balance (million USD)	3 817	10 858
Crop in total agricultural production (%)	51	..
Livestock in total agricultural production (%)	49	..
Agricultural area (AA) (thousand ha)	67 994	62 597
Share of arable land in AA (%)	67	69
Share of irrigated land in AA (%)	1.2	..
Share of agriculture in water consumption (%)	10	6
Nitrogen balance, kg/ha	18	24

1. Or latest available year.
Sources: OECD Statistical Databases, ITCS, World Development Indicators and national data.

StatLink ᵐˢ⁴ http://dx.doi.org/10.1787/888933110315

Figure 4.2. **Canada: Main macroeconomic indicators, 1995-2013**

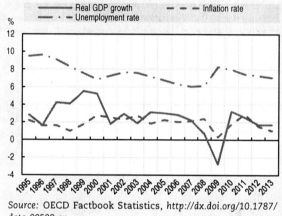

Source: OECD Factbook Statistics, *http://dx.doi.org/10.1787/data-00590-en.*

StatLink ᵐˢ⁴ http://dx.doi.org/10.1787/888933109498

Figure 4.3. **Canada: Agro-food trade, 1995-2012**

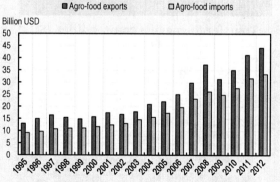

Source: International Trade by Commodity Statistics (ITCS) Database.

StatLink ᵐˢ⁴ http://dx.doi.org/10.1787/888933109517

Note: Detailed definitions of contextual indicators and their sources are provided in Annex II.A1.

Development of support to agriculture

Agricultural support in Canada has been reduced significantly since 1986-88, but has been stable since the mid-1990s as federal-provincial programme frameworks became established. Support is focussed on payments aiming at mitigating farm income fluctuations. The share of potentially most production and trade distorting support, the NPC, and the share of SCT transfers in the PSE are largely determined by market price support, delivered through longstanding supply-management systems for milk, poultry and eggs.

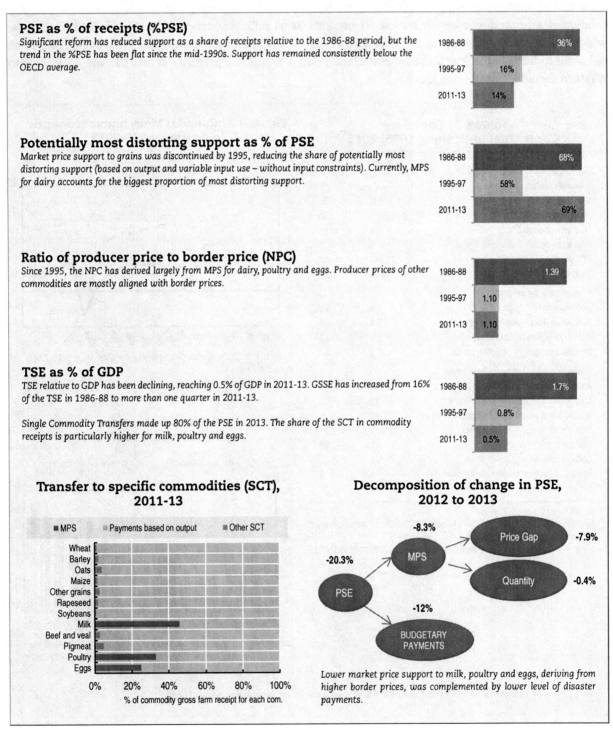

PSE as % of receipts (%PSE)
Significant reform has reduced support as a share of receipts relative to the 1986-88 period, but the trend in the %PSE has been flat since the mid-1990s. Support has remained consistently below the OECD average.

1986-88 — 36%
1995-97 — 16%
2011-13 — 14%

Potentially most distorting support as % of PSE
Market price support to grains was discontinued by 1995, reducing the share of potentially most distorting support (based on output and variable input use – without input constraints). Currently, MPS for dairy accounts for the biggest proportion of most distorting support.

1986-88 — 68%
1995-97 — 58%
2011-13 — 69%

Ratio of producer price to border price (NPC)
Since 1995, the NPC has derived largely from MPS for dairy, poultry and eggs. Producer prices of other commodities are mostly aligned with border prices.

1986-88 — 1.39
1995-97 — 1.10
2011-13 — 1.10

TSE as % of GDP
TSE relative to GDP has been declining, reaching 0.5% of GDP in 2011-13. GSSE has increased from 16% of the TSE in 1986-88 to more than one quarter in 2011-13.

Single Commodity Transfers made up 80% of the PSE in 2013. The share of the SCT in commodity receipts is particularly higher for milk, poultry and eggs.

1986-88 — 1.7%
1995-97 — 0.8%
2011-13 — 0.5%

Transfer to specific commodities (SCT), 2011-13

■ MPS ■ Payments based on output ■ Other SCT

Wheat, Barley, Oats, Maize, Other grains, Rapeseed, Soybeans, Milk, Beef and veal, Pigmeat, Poultry, Eggs

0% 20% 40% 60% 80% 100%
% of commodity gross farm receipt for each com.

Decomposition of change in PSE, 2012 to 2013

PSE -20.3%
MPS -8.3%
Price Gap -7.9%
Quantity -0.4%
BUDGETARY PAYMENTS -12%

Lower market price support to milk, poultry and eggs, deriving from higher border prices, was complemented by lower level of disaster payments.

Table 4.2. **Canada: Estimates of support to agriculture**

Million CAD

	1986-88	1995-97	2011-13	2011	2012	2013p
Total value of production (at farm gate)	**18 458**	**27 549**	**49 815**	**46 900**	**50 893**	**51 653**
of which: share of MPS commodities (%)	85.6	84.2	85.0	84.5	85.3	85.1
Total value of consumption (at farm gate)	**16 601**	**21 504**	**34 124**	**32 756**	**35 516**	**34 098**
Producer Support Estimate (PSE)	**7 982**	**4 910**	**7 147**	**7 435**	**7 795**	**6 210**
Support based on commodity output	4 591	2 465	4 517	4 264	4 967	4 320
Market Price Support[1]	4 116	2 296	4 517	4 264	4 967	4 320
Payments based on output	476	169	0	0	0	0
Payments based on input use	1 396	692	472	501	503	414
Based on variable input use	795	345	356	374	393	301
with input constraints	0	0	0	0	0	0
Based on fixed capital formation	575	328	83	83	78	90
with input constraints	0	0	2	0	1	5
Based on on-farm services	26	19	33	44	32	23
with input constraints	0	0	0	0	0	0
Payments based on current A/An/R/I, production required	1 787	840	1 945	2 225	2 188	1 422
Based on Receipts / Income	632	459	898	1 037	1 043	615
Based on Area planted / Animal numbers	1 155	382	1 047	1 188	1 145	807
with input constraints	0	0	0	0	0	0
Payments based on non-current A/An/R/I, production required	0	0	1	2	0	0
Payments based on non-current A/An/R/I, production not required	0	790	137	365	46	1
With variable payment rates	0	733	0	0	0	0
with commodity exceptions	0	0	0	0	0	0
With fixed payment rates	0	58	137	365	46	1
with commodity exceptions	0	0	0	0	0	0
Payments based on non-commodity criteria	10	0	5	15	0	0
Based on long-term resource retirement	10	0	5	15	0	0
Based on a specific non-commodity output	0	0	0	0	0	0
Based on other non-commodity criteria	0	0	0	0	0	0
Miscellaneous payments	197	123	70	63	93	53
Percentage PSE (%)	**35.8**	**16.3**	**13.7**	**14.8**	**14.5**	**11.6**
Producer NPC (coeff.)	**1.39**	**1.10**	**1.10**	**1.10**	**1.11**	**1.09**
Producer NAC (coeff.)	**1.56**	**1.20**	**1.16**	**1.17**	**1.17**	**1.13**
General Services Support Estimate (GSSE)[2]	**1 493**	**1 694**	**2 543**	**2 591**	**2 467**	**2 571**
Agricultural knowledge and innovation system	621	694	938	922	955	936
Inspection and control	372	355	997	1 008	993	989
Development and maintenance of infrastructure	365	244	275	352	249	226
Marketing and promotion	111	363	201	239	196	168
Cost of public stockholding	0	0	0	0	0	0
Miscellaneous	24	38	132	69	74	253
Percentage GSSE (% of TSE)	**15.8**	**25.7**	**26.4**	**25.8**	**24.0**	**29.3**
Consumer Support Estimate (CSE)	**-3 758**	**-2 415**	**-5 010**	**-4 697**	**-5 477**	**-4 857**
Transfers to producers from consumers	-4 062	-2 405	-4 511	-4 255	-4 961	-4 317
Other transfers from consumers	-48	-25	-501	-443	-517	-542
Transfers to consumers from taxpayers	42	6	1	0	2	2
Excess feed cost	310	9	0	0	0	1
Percentage CSE (%)	**-22.8**	**-11.2**	**-14.7**	**-14.3**	**-15.4**	**-14.2**
Consumer NPC (coeff.)	**1.33**	**1.13**	**1.17**	**1.17**	**1.18**	**1.17**
Consumer NAC (coeff.)	**1.30**	**1.13**	**1.17**	**1.17**	**1.18**	**1.17**
Total Support Estimate (TSE)	**9 518**	**6 610**	**9 691**	**10 026**	**10 264**	**8 782**
Transfers from consumers	4 111	2 430	5 012	4 698	5 478	4 859
Transfers from taxpayers	5 455	4 205	5 180	5 771	5 303	4 465
Budget revenues	-48	-25	-501	-443	-517	-542
Percentage TSE (% of GDP)	**1.7**	**0.8**	**0.5**	**0.6**	**0.6**	**0.5**
GDP deflator (1986-88=100)	**100**	**126**	**178**	**176**	**178**	**181**

Note: p: provisional. NPC: Nominal Protection Coefficient. NAC: Nominal Assistance Coefficient. A/An/R/I: Area planted/Animal numbers/Receipts/Income.

1. Market Price Support (MPS) is net of producer levies and excess feed cost. MPS commodities for Canada are: wheat, maize, barley, oats, soybean, rapeseed, flax, potatoes, lentils, dry beans, dry peas, milk, beef and veal, pigmeat, poultry and eggs.
2. A revised GSSE definition with new categories was introduced in 2014. When possible, the revision was implemented for the whole time series. The GSSE series and the resulting TSE are not comparable with the series published previously (for more details, see Annex 1.A2).

Source: OECD (2014), "Producer and Consumer Support Estimates", OECD *Agriculture Statistics Database, doi: http://dx.doi.org/10.1787/agr-pcse-data-en.*

StatLink ⟨⟨⟨ *http://dx.doi.org/10.1787/888933110334*

Description of policy developments

Main policy instruments

Market price support is provided for dairy products, poultry and eggs through tariffs and production quotas that are tradable only within provinces combined with a system of domestic price-setting.

Under the Canadian Constitution responsibility for agriculture is shared by the federal and provincial governments. Since 2003, the main policy instruments have been delivered through joint Federal, Provincial, and Territorial (FPT) agreements. A new FPT multilateral agricultural policy framework, called *Growing Forward 2* (GF2), was implemented on 1 April 2013. The new policy framework builds on previous frameworks, but stresses three broad priority areas: innovation, competitiveness and market development, and adaptability and industry capacity.

Major support policies are delivered through the business risk management (BRM) heading. The four BRM programmes are *AgriStability* (whole-farm margin programme providing support in years of significant income declines); *AgriInvest* (government-matched producer savings account for moderate income declines or to make investments in farming operations to mitigate risk); *AgriInsurance* (coverage for production losses due to natural perils); and *AgriRecovery* (FPT co-ordinated disaster relief framework).

GF2 introduces three new federal non-BRM programmes, *AgriInnovation*, *AgriMarketing* and *AgriCompetitiveness*, based on a renewed focus on competitiveness and sustainability, with the recognition that enabling innovation and providing the right institutional and physical infrastructure are critical to the sector's success. GF2 continues to allow flexibility for provinces and territories to design and deliver non-BRM programmes that responded to regional priorities in support of shared national outcomes. Provinces can also determine the level of resources to be expended in the overall programme area of support within the agreed limits of the Framework Agreement.

Most farm-level environmental programmes are designed and administered by provincial governments. Common examples include environmental risk assessments and support for adoption of Beneficial Management Practices. The federal government complements these programmes through the Sustainable Science and Technology Advancement programme, which supports biophysical research and other activities. GF2 emphasizes new policy directions of more efficient and responsible use of resources; more targeted, collaborative and result-oriented approaches, and enabling market-based solutions (i.e., increased use of group farm plans based on watersheds).

Domestic policy developments in 2013-14

Reforms to BRM programmes were negotiated in 2012 and took effect in 2013. Under GF2, margin coverage of the *AgriStability* was reduced from 85% to 70% (i.e. increasing the payment trigger from 15% to a 30% margin decline), and compensation rates under the programme will be harmonized at a flat 70% of a producer's loss (previously there were three different compensation rates depending on the degree of loss). In addition, government contributions under *AgriInvest* was reduced from 1.5% allowable net sales (ANS) to 1% of a producer's ANS up to CAD 15 000 (USD 14 561) annually. However, the maximum amount of account balance has been increased from 25% to 400% of ANS to encourage producer savings. These changes are intended to address concerns about overlapping programme coverage, and enhance producer's proactive risk management strategies.

As a new BRM programme under GF2, *AgriRisk* Initiatives (ARI), was introduced to support the private sector to expand its role in agricultural risk management and develop new industry-led risk management tools. The ARI programme supports research and development as well as the implementation and pilot implementation of new risk management tools.

In 2013, producers received CAD 0.81 million (USD 0.79 million) through six *AgriRecovery* Initiatives, which is 97% lower than the CAD 27.5 million (USD 27.5 million) in 2012 due to fewer events of natural disasters in 2013. Three of these initiatives were new for 2013 and combined they provided producers with approximately CAD 0.46 million (USD 0.44 million). The *Canada-Ontario Forage and Livestock Transportation Assistance Initiative* and the *Canada-Quebec Drought Livestock and Forage Transportation Assistance Initiative* assisted livestock producers with the extraordinary costs of feeding their breeding herds, due to severe pasture and forage shortages resulting from excessive drought. The third Initiative in 2013, the *Canada-Nova Scotia Strawberry Assistance Initiative*, assisted strawberry growers with the extraordinary costs they incurred to destroy and replant strawberries infected with a production limiting virus complex. The remaining three AgriRecovery Initiatives were initially implemented in 2012 to assist producers with disasters resulting from severe weather including: the *Canada-Manitoba Agricultural Recovery Program*, *Canada-New Brunswick Excess Moisture Initiative* and the *Canada-Manitoba Forage Shortfall and Restoration Assistance Initiative*.

The Government introduced the Safe Food for Canadians Act in November 2012 to modernise, simplify and strengthen rules for food commodities, which will come into force once new regulations are in place, which is expected to be in 2015. The Safe Food for Canadians Act focuses on three important areas: 1) improved food safety oversight to better protect consumers; 2) streamlined and strengthened legislative authorities; and 3) enhanced international market opportunities for Canadian industry. The legislation provides clearer and more consistent rules for food commodity importers to assure that imported foods meet domestic food safety requirements. The legislation strengthens import controls by including powers to register or license importers and prohibits the importation of food commodities considered unsafe. It also provides the CFIA (Canadian Food Inspection Agency) with the authority to certify all food commodities for export, allowing for a consistent approach to Canadian export certification. As well, the legislation is an important step in aligning Canada's food safety system, such as with the Food Safety Modernization Act in the United States.

In addition, the Safe Food for Canadians Act provides the CFIA with strengthened authorities to develop regulations related to tracing and recalling food, and the tools to take action on potentially unsafe food commodities. A component of Agriculture and Agri-food Canada's AgriMarketing Program supports industry-government collaboration and investment in the development of national assurance systems and standards, including traceability systems such as animal identification, premises identification, and movement reporting for priority livestock species.

Trade policy developments in 2013-14

In 2013, Canada implemented the Canada-**Panama** FTA, signed the Canada-**Honduras** FTA, and on 18 October 2013, Canada reached an Agreement in Principle with the **European Union** toward a Comprehensive Economic and Trade Agreement. In March 2014, Canada concluded its FTA negotiation with Korea. Canada is also engaged in FTA negotiations with several countries including the **Trans-Pacific Partnership** (TPP), **Japan, India**, **Morocco**, **CARICOM** (Caribbean Community), and **Israel** (modernisation of existing FTA), and is pursuing exploratory discussions with **Turkey**, **Mercosur** and **Thailand**.

In December 2008, Canada requested consultations on the **United States** mandatory country of origin labelling (COOL) provisions in the Food, Conservation, and Energy Act 2008 (2008 Farm Bill). These measures contain an obligation to inform consumers at the retail level of the country of origin of covered commodities, including beef and pork. Upon Canada's request, a WTO panel was established in November 2009. In June 2012, the Appellate Body upheld the Panel's finding that mandatory COOL discriminates against Canadian exports of cattle and hogs. The US Department of Agriculture issued a new COOL regulation on 23 May 2013. On 15 June 2013, Canada published in the *Canada Gazette* a list of products that are imported into Canada from the United States which may be targeted for retaliation. At the request of Canada and Mexico, a WTO Compliance Panel was established on 25 September 2013, to determine whether the new regulation brings COOL into conformity with the WTO obligations.

PART II

Chapter 5

Developments in agricultural policies and support in Chile

The Chile country chapter includes a brief evaluation of policy developments and related support to agriculture, contextual information on the framework in which agricultural policies are implemented and the main characteristics of the agricultural sector, an evaluation of support in 2012-13 and in the longer term perspective, and a brief description of the main policy developments in 2013-14.

Evaluation of policy developments

- Agricultural markets in Chile are open and there are virtually no policy induced market distortions. PSE averaged 3% of gross farm receipts in 2011-13 and general services (GSSE) accounted for 50% of total support to the sector.

- Total budgetary outlays to the sector increased by 9% between 2012 and 2013. Direct payments are mostly targeted at small-scale agriculture and aim to improve productivity, competiveness, recovery of degraded soils, and on-farm irrigation systems. Most expenditures on general services are allocated to irrigation infrastructure, inspection and control, and agricultural knowledge and innovation systems.

- Developments in 2013 relate to improvements of market information systems and institutional changes. A bill was sent to Congress to reform the Ministry of Agriculture by incorporating food safety and food quality under its mandate. The bill, still in Congress, is likely to eliminate differences between food safety and quality regulations for domestic consumption, exports and imports.

- Even when most support is targeted to small-scale agriculture and indigenous farmers, careful attention should be paid to the increment of input use support.

Figure 5.1. **Chile: PSE level and composition by support categories, 1995-2013**

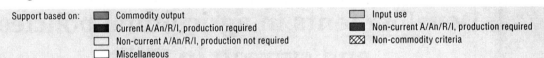

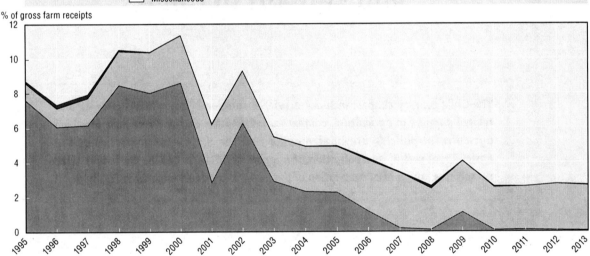

Source: OECD (2014), "Producer and Consumer Support Estimates", *OECD Agriculture Statistics Database, http://dx.doi.org/10.1787/agr-pcse-data-en.*
StatLink ᵹᵔᵍᵖ *http://dx.doi.org/10.1787/888933109536*

Contextual information

Over the past nine years, the Chilean economy grew at an average rate of 4.8% and at 4% in 2013. Chile had in 2013 the lowest unemployment rate in thirty years with only 5.7%. This economic situation has helped Chile to become an upper middle income country with a GDP per capita of USD 21 519 in 2012. Agriculture contributes with 3.6% to the national GDP and 10% of the total employment. Chile is a net exporter of agro-food products (excluding fish and forestry) with a surplus of USD 5 billion in 2012 and accounting for 14% of total exports in the same year.

Table 5.1. **Chile: Contextual indicators, 1995, 2012[1]**

	1995	2012[1]
Economic context		
GDP (billion USD)	74	269
Population (million)	14	17
Land area (thousand km^2)	744	744
Population density (inhabitants/km^2)	19	23
GDP per capita, PPP (USD)	7 507	21 519
Trade as % of GDP	20.9	29.4
Agriculture in the economy		
Agriculture in GDP (%)	8.0	3.6
Agriculture share in employment (%)	15.7	10.3
Agro-food exports (% of total exports)	18.0	14.3
Agro-food imports (% of total imports)	7.2	7.4
Characteristics of the agricultural sector		
Agro-food trade balance (million USD)	1 787	5 279
Crop in total agricultural production (%)	63	63
Livestock in total agricultural production (%)	37	37
Agricultural area (AA) (thousand ha)	15 330	15 789
Share of arable land in AA (%)	14	8
Share of irrigated land in AA (%)	..	7.0
Share of agriculture in water consumption (%)	..	..
Nitrogen balance, kg/ha	..	..

1. Or latest available year.
Sources: OECD Statistical Databases, ITCS, World Development Indicators and national data.

StatLink ⟨⟨⟨ http://dx.doi.org/10.1787/888933110353

Figure 5.2. **Chile: Main macroeconomic indicators, 1995-2013**

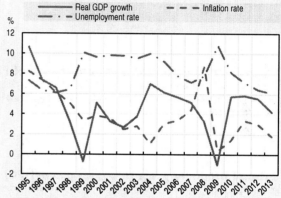

Source: OECD Factbook Statistics, http://dx.doi.org/10.1787/data-00590-en.

StatLink ⟨⟨⟨ http://dx.doi.org/10.1787/888933109555

Figure 5.3. **Chile: Agro-food trade, 1995-2012**

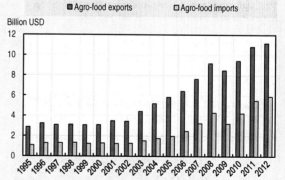

Source: International Trade by Commodity Statistics (ITCS) Database.

StatLink ⟨⟨⟨ http://dx.doi.org/10.1787/888933109574

Note: Detailed definitions of contextual indicators and their sources are provided in Annex II.A1.

Development of support to agriculture

Chile continues to provide low levels of support to its agricultural sector reflected by a PSE of 3% of gross farm receipts, one of the lowest in the OECD area, with almost no Market Price Support (MPS) and with prices aligned with world market levels. Government spending on agriculture has been focusing on boosting competitiveness and productivity with an emphasis on improving the performance of small-scale agriculture. Around 49% of budgetary outlays are allocated to support general services and 51% on payments to farmers. Support to farmers is based mostly on input use particularly on fixed capital formation.

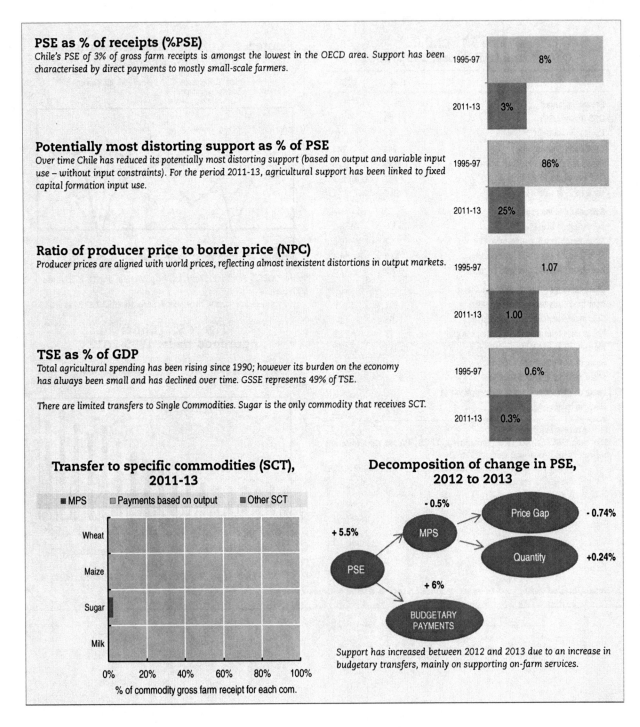

PSE as % of receipts (%PSE)
Chile's PSE of 3% of gross farm receipts is amongst the lowest in the OECD area. Support has been characterised by direct payments to mostly small-scale farmers.

1995-97   8%
2011-13   3%

Potentially most distorting support as % of PSE
Over time Chile has reduced its potentially most distorting support (based on output and variable input use – without input constraints). For the period 2011-13, agricultural support has been linked to fixed capital formation input use.

1995-97   86%
2011-13   25%

Ratio of producer price to border price (NPC)
Producer prices are aligned with world prices, reflecting almost inexistent distortions in output markets.

1995-97   1.07
2011-13   1.00

TSE as % of GDP
Total agricultural spending has been rising since 1990; however its burden on the economy has always been small and has declined over time. GSSE represents 49% of TSE.

There are limited transfers to Single Commodities. Sugar is the only commodity that receives SCT.

1995-97   0.6%
2011-13   0.3%

Transfer to specific commodities (SCT), 2011-13

■ MPS   ▨ Payments based on output   ■ Other SCT

Wheat
Maize
Sugar
Milk

0%   20%   40%   60%   80%   100%
% of commodity gross farm receipt for each com.

Decomposition of change in PSE, 2012 to 2013

- 0.5%
+ 5.5%   MPS   Price Gap   - 0.74%
PSE   Quantity   +0.24%
+ 6%
BUDGETARY PAYMENTS

Support has increased between 2012 and 2013 due to an increase in budgetary transfers, mainly on supporting on-farm services.

Table 5.2. **Chile: Estimates of support to agriculture**

Million CLP

	1995-97	2011-13	2011	2012	2013p
Total value of production (at farm gate)	**2 098 835**	**6 860 088**	**6 401 525**	**6 849 632**	**7 329 106**
of which: share of MPS commodities (%)	64.6	60.3	59.9	59.3	61.7
Total value of consumption (at farm gate)	**2 110 811**	**6 085 765**	**5 960 329**	**5 938 789**	**6 358 178**
Producer Support Estimate (PSE)	**170 102**	**189 733**	**170 959**	**193 802**	**204 438**
Support based on commodity output	140 034	5 752	7 331	5 447	4 477
Market Price Support[1]	140 034	5 752	7 331	5 447	4 477
Payments based on output	0	0	0	0	0
Payments based on input use	25 910	182 200	163 327	187 935	195 338
Based on variable input use	6 697	41 754	38 056	42 943	44 263
with input constraints	0	0	0	0	0
Based on fixed capital formation	9 825	97 205	87 858	100 955	102 803
with input constraints	6 909	54 210	52 230	54 619	55 782
Based on on-farm services	9 389	43 241	37 413	44 038	48 272
with input constraints	307	13 363	12 189	13 964	13 937
Payments based on current A/An/R/I, production required	4 158	1 781	301	419	4 623
Based on Receipts / Income	0	0	0	0	0
Based on Area planted / Animal numbers	4 158	1 781	301	419	4 623
with input constraints	4 158	1 781	301	419	4 623
Payments based on non-current A/An/R/I, production required	0	0	0	0	0
Payments based on non-current A/An/R/I, production not required	0	0	0	0	0
With variable payment rates	0	0	0	0	0
with commodity exceptions	0	0	0	0	0
With fixed payment rates	0	0	0	0	0
with commodity exceptions	0	0	0	0	0
Payments based on non-commodity criteria	0	0	0	0	0
Based on long-term resource retirement	0	0	0	0	0
Based on a specific non-commodity output	0	0	0	0	0
Based on other non-commodity criteria	0	0	0	0	0
Miscellaneous payments	0	0	0	0	0
Percentage PSE (%)	**8.0**	**2.7**	**2.6**	**2.8**	**2.7**
Producer NPC (coeff.)	**1.07**	**1.00**	**1.00**	**1.00**	**1.00**
Producer NAC (coeff.)	**1.09**	**1.03**	**1.03**	**1.03**	**1.03**
General Services Support Estimate (GSSE)[2]	**32 672**	**187 581**	**192 595**	**173 360**	**196 788**
Agricultural knowledge and innovation system	9 085	47 272	46 583	47 275	47 957
Inspection and control	400	36 879	36 986	36 015	37 636
Development and maintenance of infrastructure	20 888	95 227	103 626	80 554	101 501
Marketing and promotion	2 078	8 202	5 397	9 516	9 693
Cost of public stockholding	0	0	0	0	0
Miscellaneous	220	1	4	0	0
Percentage GSSE (% of TSE)	**15.6**	**49.7**	**53.0**	**47.2**	**49.0**
Consumer Support Estimate (CSE)	**-172 494**	**-14 223**	**-17 967**	**-14 834**	**-9 867**
Transfers to producers from consumers	-141 015	-5 752	-7 331	-5 447	-4 477
Other transfers from consumers	-33 146	-8 471	-10 636	-9 387	-5 390
Transfers to consumers from taxpayers	0	0	0	0	0
Excess feed cost	1 667	0	0	0	0
Percentage CSE (%)	**-8.2**	**-0.2**	**-0.3**	**-0.2**	**-0.2**
Consumer NPC (coeff.)	**1.09**	**1.00**	**1.00**	**1.00**	**1.00**
Consumer NAC (coeff.)	**1.09**	**1.00**	**1.00**	**1.00**	**1.00**
Total Support Estimate (TSE)	**202 774**	**377 314**	**363 554**	**367 161**	**401 226**
Transfers from consumers	174 161	14 223	17 967	14 834	9 867
Transfers from taxpayers	61 759	371 562	356 223	361 714	396 749
Budget revenues	-33 146	-8 471	-10 636	-9 387	-5 390
Percentage TSE (% of GDP)	**0.6**	**0.3**	**0.3**	**0.3**	**0.3**
GDP deflator (1995-97=100)	**100**	**212**	**209**	**212**	**215**

Note: p: provisional. NPC: Nominal Protection Coefficient. NAC: Nominal Assistance Coefficient. A/An/R/I: Area planted/Animal numbers/Receipts/Income.

1. Market Price Support (MPS) is net of producer levies and excess feed cost. MPS commodities for Chile are: wheat, maize, apples, grapes, sugar, tomatoes, milk, beef and veal, pigmeat and poultry.

2. A revised GSSE definition with new categories was introduced in 2014. When possible, the revision was implemented for the whole time series. The GSSE series and the resulting TSE are not comparable with the series published previously (for more details, see Annex 1.A2).

Source: OECD (2014), "Producer and Consumer Support Estimates", OECD *Agriculture Statistics Database,* doi: *http://dx.doi.org/10.1787/agr-pcse-data-en.*

StatLink ⧉ *http://dx.doi.org/10.1787/888933110372*

Description of policy developments

Main policy instruments

Agricultural policies in Chile continue to emphasise agricultural productivity and competitiveness as well as the development of small-scale agriculture. Chilean agricultural policy involves few distortions on agricultural markets and does not have policy instruments to support prices. **Budgetary allocations** increased 9% from CLP 361 billion (USD 743 million) in 2012 to CLP 394 billion (USD 797 million) in 2013. In Chile only 2% of total support to agriculture is given through market price support the rest 98% is given through budgetary expenditures. For the year 2013, around 50% of total expenditures were allocated on general services support (**GSSE**), the other half was allocated on support to farmers (**PSE**) through programmes targeted to mostly small-scale farmers and used considerably (51%) for fixed capital formation.

Different programmes with the objective of improving **productivity** and **competitiveness** accounted for 28% of total budget expenditures, the equivalent to CLP 110 billion (USD 222 million) in 2013. The majority of these programmes were targeted to small-scale agriculture under the auspices of the National Institute for Agricultural Development (INDAP), and include a whole range of support from variable input use, fixed capital formation programmes to on-farm services.

Irrigation investment continues to be an important area of budgetary allocations. In 2013, it amounted to 22% of total outlays in the sector equivalent to CLP 88 billion (USD 178 million). Irrigation investment has both on-farm and off-farm components. The off-farm component represents 50% of the GSSE.

The **Soil** Recovery Programme accounted for 8% of expenditures in 2013 with CLP 30 billion (USD 62 million). This programme is administered jointly by the inspection agency Agriculture and Livestock Service (SAG), INDAP and by the Office of Agricultural Policies, Trade and Information (ODEPA). This programme aims to improve degraded soils used in agriculture.

INDAP is a provider of **credit** to small-scale agriculture at preferential rates. INDAP lending in 2013 was CLP 60 billion (USD 121 million), an increase of 5% from 2012. Support through preferential interest rates, and agricultural **insurance** subsidies (i.e. subsidies to insurance premium) accounted for only 1.4% and 1.1% respectively of total expenditures.

The agricultural **knowledge and innovation** system accounts for 13% of government expenditures on agriculture, CLP 50 billion (USD 101 million), representing 25% of GSSE. **Inspection and control** accounted for 10% of all government spending in 2013 and represents 20% of GSSE.

Domestic policy developments in 2013-14

A new government took office on March 2014. Its strategy will focus on helping small-scale agriculture, improving productivity, competitiveness and infrastructure, protection of natural resources and market access, among others.

In September 2013, the central zone of the country was affected by severe **frosts** that caused significant damage to the prune, nectarine and peach sub-sectors; vineyards were also seriously damaged, particularly the Chardonnay variety. Exports for 2014 were projected to drop by 22% and are estimated at USD 60 million.

The country also had a severe **drought** that damaged the fruit export sector in the central zone as well as vegetables for domestic market. Authorities have implemented a rural support mechanism in 38 districts that were declared to be in a state of emergency. About CLP 17 billion

(USD 34 million) were redistributed to mitigate the social impact. More than 17 000 producers were assisted in terms of water distribution for human and animal consumption and well deepening.

In 2013, a bill was sent to the Congress that sought to modernise and transform the current Ministry of Agriculture into the Ministry of Agriculture, Food, Fisheries and Forestry. This **new institution** will allow the food sector to be under a single ministry. This decision seeks to align regulations on food safety and quality for domestic consumption, exports and imports. The project will monitor the entire supply chain of food production and processing through permanent systems of quality assurance and certification. The bill is still in Congress for approval.

The Ministry of Agriculture has enhanced the **business partnerships programme** with the goal of achieving transparent and sustainable business relationships between small-scale producers and consolidated marketing chains. This programme seeks to provide technical assistance to small producers on market requirements to allow them to have a direct marketing channel, without intermediaries. In 2013, the programme benefited 7 247 users and the budget executed corresponded to CLP 5 852 million. Currently there are over 180 productive partnerships between small producers and producer associations and large exporters, retail and industry.

The Office of Agricultural Policies, Trade and Information (ODEPA) has improved **market information** systems for a better decision-making of domestic producers. ODEPA has created new websites (e.g. *Agroatiende* which gathers all institutional services), and monthly newsletters (e.g. *Infodepa*). ODEPA has improved the processes of data collection of relevant market information, such as trade statistics, consumer, wholesale, and input prices, among others.

The national commission in charge of investigating the existence of **price distortions** on imported goods was involved in a series of investigations to determine the existence of such distortions. In 2013, there were investigations related to possible safeguards in the pork industry and grain maize imports, and an eventual dumping in cracked maize, poultry meat and other animal feed preparations containing at least 20% corn.

In 2013, the **wine zoning** and origin denomination regulation had two modifications in order to give more transparency and information to consumers about the kind and origin of wine being purchased. The first modification was in late 2012; this amendment includes new terms as origin denomination such as "Andes", "Entre Cordilleras" or "Costa". The second amendment, made in 2013 but which has not yet entered into force, is related to distinguishing when wine is made of "table grapes".

The Commercial Transactions Law came into force in January 2013. It seeks to provide more precise mechanisms and tools to standardise the quality and quantity measurement of agricultural products, including equipment certification and sampling and counter sampling rules. During 2013, specific regulations for maize, wheat, wine grapes, fresh milk and sugar beet were published.

Trade policy developments in 2013-14

Chile has kept its strategy of economic integration with the rest of the world through bilateral trade agreements. The Chilean government has concluded the negotiation of FTAs with **Viet Nam**, **Hong Kong (China)** and **Thailand**. The FTA with **Viet Nam** has been in force as of February 2014. In September 2012, an investment chapter for the FTA with **China**, in force since 2006, was signed and is waiting for the exchange of notifications to come into force. Negotiations with India to broaden the coverage of the current Partial Scope Agreement are concluded.

During 2013, Chile participated in five negotiating sessions of the **Trans-Pacific Partnership** (TPP). Chile has also been negotiating a comprehensive agreement called Pacific Alliance (*Alianza del Pacífico*) that aims to create a Free Trade Area among Chile, **Mexico**, **Peru** and **Colombia**.

PART II

Chapter 6

Developments in agricultural policies and support in the European Union*

> The European Union chapter includes a brief evaluation of policy developments and related support to agriculture, contextual information on the framework in which agricultural policies are implemented and the main characteristics of the agricultural sector, an evaluation of support in 2012-13 and in the longer term perspective, and a brief description of the main policy developments in 2013-14.

* This report covers the European Union of 27 member states.

Evaluation of policy developments

- Overall, policy reforms since 1986-88 have considerably improved the sector's market orientation. There has been a gradual and consistent move away from high levels of market price support and output payments and reduction in the level of support. With reduced market intervention and protection from 1992, the implementation of reforms initiated in 2003 gradually increased the share of payments granted with no requirement to produce, thus allowing producers to better respond to market signals. The end of the milk production quota in 2015 and the sugar quota in 2017 are important further steps in this direction.

- After a continuous decline up until 2011, production and trade distorting measures increased and now account for 29% of support to producers as measured by the PSE. This increase is not caused by a change in policies, but is a consequence of existing policy instruments that have kept prices paid to producers in some sectors above world market prices since 2011.

- The share of payments requiring production increased as some European Union member states increasingly use the flexibility to grant payments requiring specific production or specific types of farming (Article 68). Although these payments are limited to 10% of the overall direct payments envelope, they can distort competition across member states.

- Market access for agricultural products has improved through bilateral agreements and lower applied tariffs. However, Tariff Rate Quotas (TRQs) and special safeguards continue to apply to a number of products.

- Substantial progress has been made in reducing the level of support and the share of production and trade distorting support. However, in the last two years, the effects of such distorting measures have been more visible. Member states should seize the flexibility offered by the CAP 2014-20 to anchor market orientation more deeply and better target support to improve the long-term productivity, sustainability and efficiency of the sector.

Figure 6.1. **European Union: PSE level and composition by support categories, 1986-2013**

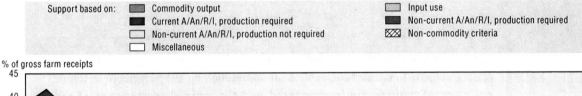

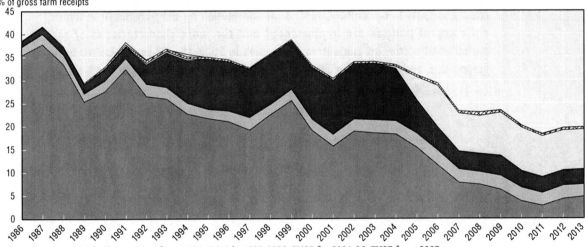

1. EU12 in 1986-94 including ex-GDR from 1990; EU15 in 1995-2003; EU25 for 2004-06; EU27 from 2007.

Source: OECD (2014), "Producer and Consumer Support Estimates", *OECD Agriculture Statistics Database, http://dx.doi.org/10.1787/agr-pcse-data-en.*

StatLink ⟶ *http://dx.doi.org/10.1787/888933109593*

Contextual information

The European Union is the largest economic region in the OECD area. Its average GDP per capita is below the OECD average, with wide differences across member countries. Agriculture accounts for 1.7% of GDP and 4.5% of employment in the EU27, with significant differences across member states. The European Union was a net exporter of agro-food products in 2012. It is the second largest exporter and the largest importer of agro-food products in the world. In 2012, agro-food products accounted for 6.6% of all EU exports and 5.8% of all EU imports. There is a large diversity of farm structures and production systems in EU regions. Agriculture occupies more than half of the territory and accounts for about a quarter of water consumption. In July 2013, Croatia joined the European Union as its 28th member state.

Table 6.1. **European Union: Contextual indicators, 1995, 2012[1]**

	1995	2012[1]
Economic context		
GDP (billion USD)	9 246	16 616
Population (million)	371	501
Land area (thousand km^2)	3 128	4 182
Population density (inhabitants/km^2)	112	114
GDP per capita, PPP (USD)	20 158	34 091
Trade as % of GDP	8.8	14.1
Agriculture in the economy		
Agriculture in GDP (%)	2.9	1.7
Agriculture share in employment (%)	4.7	4.5
Agro-food exports (% of total exports)	8.3	6.6
Agro-food imports (% of total imports)	9.6	5.8
Characteristics of the agricultural sector		
Agro-food trade balance (million USD)	-8 588	1 769
Crop in total agricultural production (%)	53	56
Livestock in total agricultural production (%)	47	44
Agricultural area (AA) (thousand ha)	142 453	187 882
Share of arable land in AA (%)	53	58
Share of irrigated land in AA (%)	..	3.7
Share of agriculture in water consumption (%)	..	26
Nitrogen balance, kg/ha	102	58

1. Or latest available year.
Sources: OECD Statistical Databases, ITCS, World Development Indicators and national data.

StatLink ⟡ http://dx.doi.org/10.1787/888933110391

Figure 6.2. **European Union: Main macroeconomic indicators, 1995-2013**

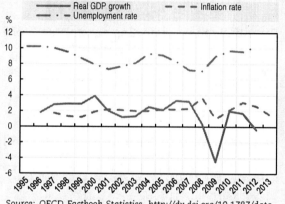

Source: OECD Factbook Statistics, http://dx.doi.org/10.1787/data-00590-en.

StatLink ⟡ http://dx.doi.org/10.1787/888933109612

Figure 6.3. **European Union: Agro-food trade, 1995-2012**

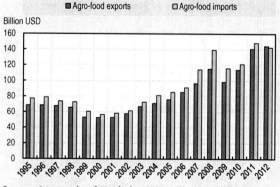

Source: International Trade by Commodity Statistics (ITCS) Database.

StatLink ⟡ http://dx.doi.org/10.1787/888933109631

Note: Detailed definitions of contextual indicators and their sources are provided in Annex II.A1.
EU15 in 1995-2003; EU25 for 2004-06; EU27 from 2007. 2012 figures for the Share of agriculture in water consumption relate to the EU15, and to the EU members of the OECD for the Nitrogen balance.

Development of support to agriculture

The European Union has gradually reduced its support to agriculture since the mid-1990s, in particular the potentially most production and trade distorting forms of support, which have stabilised at about a quarter of support to producers in the past three years. The level of price distortions has been significantly reduced as illustrated by changes in the Nominal Protection Coefficient (NPC). Nearly half of producer support is granted with no requirement to produce, however this share has declined since 2011. The share of payments targeted to environmentally and animal friendly practices has also increased.

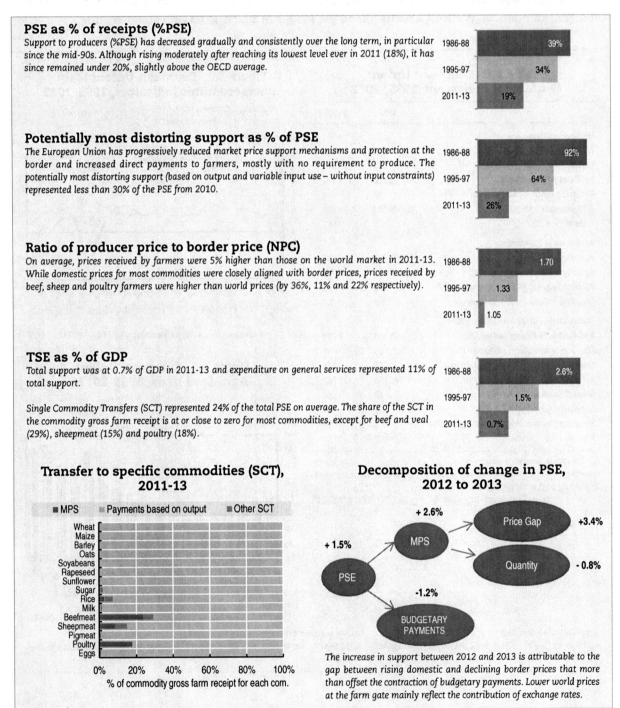

PSE as % of receipts (%PSE)

Support to producers (%PSE) has decreased gradually and consistently over the long term, in particular since the mid-90s. Although rising moderately after reaching its lowest level ever in 2011 (18%), it has since remained under 20%, slightly above the OECD average.

1986-88   39%
1995-97   34%
2011-13   19%

Potentially most distorting support as % of PSE

The European Union has progressively reduced market price support mechanisms and protection at the border and increased direct payments to farmers, mostly with no requirement to produce. The potentially most distorting support (based on output and variable input use – without input constraints) represented less than 30% of the PSE from 2010.

1986-88   92%
1995-97   64%
2011-13   26%

Ratio of producer price to border price (NPC)

On average, prices received by farmers were 5% higher than those on the world market in 2011-13. While domestic prices for most commodities were closely aligned with border prices, prices received by beef, sheep and poultry farmers were higher than world prices (by 36%, 11% and 22% respectively).

1986-88   1.70
1995-97   1.33
2011-13   1.05

TSE as % of GDP

Total support was at 0.7% of GDP in 2011-13 and expenditure on general services represented 11% of total support.

Single Commodity Transfers (SCT) represented 24% of the total PSE on average. The share of the SCT in the commodity gross farm receipt is at or close to zero for most commodities, except for beef and veal (29%), sheepmeat (15%) and poultry (18%).

1986-88   2.6%
1995-97   1.5%
2011-13   0.7%

Transfer to specific commodities (SCT), 2011-13

■ MPS   ■ Payments based on output   ■ Other SCT

Wheat, Maize, Barley, Oats, Soyabeans, Rapeseed, Sunflower, Sugar, Rice, Milk, Beefmeat, Sheepmeat, Pigmeat, Poultry, Eggs

0%   20%   40%   60%   80%   100%
% of commodity gross farm receipt for each com.

Decomposition of change in PSE, 2012 to 2013

+ 2.6%   Price Gap   +3.4%
+ 1.5%   MPS
PSE   Quantity   - 0.8%
-1.2%
BUDGETARY PAYMENTS

The increase in support between 2012 and 2013 is attributable to the gap between rising domestic and declining border prices that more than offset the contraction of budgetary payments. Lower world prices at the farm gate mainly reflect the contribution of exchange rates.

Table 6.2. **European Union: Estimates of support to agriculture**

Million EUR

	1986-88	1995-97	2011-13	2011	2012	2013p
Total value of production (at farm gate)	**211 380**	**239 230**	**368 256**	**358 731**	**371 000**	**375 037**
of which: share of MPS commodities (%)	75.0	73.7	74.8	74.5	74.9	74.8
Total value of consumption (at farm gate)	**188 226**	**230 175**	**359 290**	**348 083**	**365 515**	**364 272**
Producer Support Estimate (PSE)	**88 006**	**94 287**	**83 935**	**77 907**	**86 321**	**87 576**
Support based on commodity output	79 854	57 676	17 191	11 739	18 750	21 084
Market Price Support[1]	74 791	54 160	16 397	10 906	18 007	20 278
Payments based on output	5 063	3 516	794	833	742	806
Payments based on input use	4 565	6 512	12 032	11 843	12 632	11 622
Based on variable input use	872	2 292	4 692	4 573	4 964	4 540
with input constraints	0	0	32	31	33	31
Based on fixed capital formation	2 685	2 565	5 973	6 036	6 189	5 694
with input constraints	0	86	140	160	151	109
Based on on-farm services	1 008	1 655	1 367	1 234	1 479	1 389
with input constraints	82	427	9	6	12	8
Payments based on current A/An/R/I, production required	3 195	29 775	14 473	14 560	14 433	14 426
Based on Receipts / Income	132	64	1 009	874	1 229	925
Based on Area planted / Animal numbers	3 063	29 711	13 464	13 686	13 204	13 501
with input constraints	849	11 363	11 619	11 488	11 604	11 765
Payments based on non-current A/An/R/I, production required	0	0	91	107	80	87
Payments based on non-current A/An/R/I, production not required	0	24	37 952	37 555	38 066	38 234
With variable payment rates	0	0	0	0	0	0
with commodity exceptions	0	0	0	0	0	0
With fixed payment rates	0	24	37 952	37 555	38 066	38 234
with commodity exceptions	0	0	15 286	15 493	15 321	15 045
Payments based on non-commodity criteria	428	988	2 062	1 792	2 216	2 178
Based on long-term resource retirement	426	882	475	508	466	453
Based on a specific non-commodity output	1	106	1 496	1 193	1 659	1 636
Based on other non-commodity criteria	0	0	91	92	91	89
Miscellaneous payments	-35	-687	134	312	145	-54
Percentage PSE (%)	**39.2**	**33.8**	**19.2**	**18.3**	**19.6**	**19.8**
Producer NPC (coeff.)	**1.70**	**1.33**	**1.05**	**1.03**	**1.05**	**1.06**
Producer NAC (coeff.)	**1.65**	**1.51**	**1.24**	**1.22**	**1.24**	**1.25**
General Services Support Estimate (GSSE)[2]	**8 309**	**8 669**	**10 620**	**10 585**	**10 720**	**10 555**
Agricultural knowledge and innovation system	1 636	3 150	4 709	4 652	4 703	4 772
Inspection and control	176	232	649	650	655	641
Development and maintenance of infrastructure	1 241	1 701	3 104	3 052	3 207	3 054
Marketing and promotion	1 119	1 674	2 100	2 157	2 100	2 043
Cost of public stockholding	4 114	1 865	15	27	11	9
Miscellaneous	22	47	43	48	44	35
Percentage GSSE (% of TSE)	**8.2**	**8.1**	**11.2**	**11.8**	**11.0**	**10.7**
Consumer Support Estimate (CSE)	**-65 589**	**-47 130**	**-15 782**	**-9 513**	**-17 536**	**-20 298**
Transfers to producers from consumers	-75 427	-51 952	-16 131	-10 536	-17 769	-20 088
Other transfers from consumers	-1 501	-486	-436	-42	-377	-889
Transfers to consumers from taxpayers	4 442	3 932	785	1 065	610	679
Excess feed cost	6 897	1 376	0	0	0	0
Percentage CSE (%)	**-35.7**	**-20.8**	**-4.4**	**-2.7**	**-4.8**	**-5.6**
Consumer NPC (coeff.)	**1.70**	**1.30**	**1.05**	**1.03**	**1.05**	**1.06**
Consumer NAC (coeff.)	**1.56**	**1.26**	**1.05**	**1.03**	**1.05**	**1.06**
Total Support Estimate (TSE)	**100 756**	**106 888**	**95 340**	**89 558**	**97 652**	**98 811**
Transfers from consumers	76 928	52 438	16 567	10 578	18 147	20 977
Transfers from taxpayers	25 329	54 935	79 209	79 022	79 882	78 723
Budget revenues	-1 501	-486	-436	-42	-377	-889
Percentage TSE (% of GDP)	**2.6**	**1.5**	**0.7**	**0.7**	**0.8**	**0.8**
GDP deflator (1986-88=100)	**100**	**139**	**185**	**181**	**186**	**189**

Note: p: provisional. NPC: Nominal Protection Coefficient. NAC: Nominal Assistance Coefficient. A/An/R/I: Area planted/Animal numbers/ Receipts/Income.
  EU12 for 1986-88; EU15 for 1995-97; and EU27 from 2007.
1. Market Price Support (MPS) is net of producer levies and excess feed cost. MPS commodities for the European Union are: wheat, maize, barley, oats, rice, rapeseed, sunflower, soybean, sugar, milk, beef and veal, sheep meat, pigmeat, poultry, eggs, potatoes, tomatoes, plants and flowers, and wine.
2. A revised GSSE definition with new categories was introduced in 2014. When possible, the revision was implemented for the whole time series. The GSSE series and the resulting TSE are not comparable with the series published previously (for more details, see Annex 1.A2).
Source: OECD (2014), "Producer and Consumer Support Estimates", OECD *Agriculture Statistics Database, doi: http://dx.doi.org/10.1787/agr-pcse-data-en.*

StatLink ⟜⟝ *http://dx.doi.org/10.1787/888933110410*

Description of policy developments

Main policy instruments

The Common Agricultural Policy (CAP) is composed of two pillars. Pillar I defines and funds market measures under the **Common Market Organisation**, and includes the **Single Payment Scheme** (SPS) and the **Single Area Payment Scheme** (SAPS). It is funded by the European Agricultural Guarantee Fund (EAGF). Pillar II, or **Rural Development Regulation**, contains various measures co-financed by EU member states, including agri-environmental schemes, payments to less favoured areas (LFA), rural development and investment assistance. Pillar II funds come from the European Agricultural Fund for Rural Development (EAFRD). The two pillars continue to structure the CAP during the 2014-20 period. A transitional regulation applies in 2014 to bridge the gap between the existing legal framework and the elements of the CAP 2014-20 that will be implemented only from 2015. Starting in budget year 2015, it will be possible for member states to transfer funds between the two pillars within specific limits and conditions.

The EU budget on agriculture and rural development (title 05) decreased from EUR 58 billion (USD 77 billion) in 2012 to EUR 57 billion (USD 76 billion) in 2013, of which 5% was for market price support measures, 72% for Pillar I payments and 23% for Pillar II measures. The overall budget for the CAP for the 2014-20 period is set at 2011 prices to EUR 363 billion (USD 505 billion[2]); of which EUR 278 billion (USD 387 billion) are allocated to Pillar I market related expenditure and direct payments and EUR 85 billion (USD 118 billion) to Pillar II. The annual allocation will decline by 10% over the 2014-20 period. During this period, greater convergence in payments between countries (external convergence) and within countries and regions (internal convergence) is pursued. Under external convergence, Pillar I national envelopes are adjusted to reduce the gap in payments per hectare between countries. Countries receiving less than 90% of the EU average payment per hectare, will gradually receive more from 2015 onwards, and those receiving more than the EU average payment per hectare will see a cut in payments. In 2020, a minimum average payment of EUR 196 (USD 260) per hectare would be reached in all countries. Internal convergence requires all member states to progress towards flatter payment rates per hectare at national or regional level. All farmers receiving less than 90% of regional/national average per hectare payment would receive increased payments reaching at least 60% of the average per hectare payment in that member state by 2019. Per hectare payments exceeding the regional/national average will be gradually reduced, while member states may choose to limit the reduction of above average payments to 30%.

Most Pillar I payments are implemented as a single payment granted with no requirement to produce. Under the **Single Payment Scheme** (SPS) applying in the EU15, in Malta, Slovenia and Croatia, payment entitlements are based on historical references, either at individual farm level (historical model), at regional level (regional model) or as a combination of the two (hybrid model).[3] The **Single Area Payment Scheme** (SAPS), an optional scheme that applies in other member states for a transition period initially planned to end in 2008, subsequently extended to 2013, is prolonged to 2020 as part of the new CAP 2014-20.[4] Under the SAPS, each hectare in a member state receives the same payment rate. However, payments relating to the reform of the sugar regime and the fruit and vegetable regime are paid on a historical basis and will be progressively included in the Basic Payment Scheme starting in 2015. The **Complementary National Direct payments** (CNDPs) are paid from national funds as complements during the phasing-in of direct payments in the member states that apply the SAPS The new Transitional National Aid (TNA) permit member states to grant aids from national funds in certain sectors. As was the case with the CNDP, the level of these aids is planned to decrease. In cases where these payments are linked to commodity production, they may distort competition among member states.

Under the CAP 2014-20, the **Basic Payment Scheme** (BPS) prolongs the SPS. Together with a number of other measures, some of which are new, it uses 70% of Pillar I direct payments. A new compulsory top-up payment to **young farmers** applies in all member states. It will use a maximum of 2% of the national envelope. Also, for up to 10% from the same envelope, member states may opt to offer **small farms** whose support does not exceed EUR 1 250 (USD 1 660) a single and simplified payment setup that waives the compliance to greening and cross-compliance requirements. A supplementary payment using up to 5% of the national envelope may be allocated to farmers in **Areas with Natural Constraints** (replacing Less Favoured Areas). Member states may choose to grant a higher amount to the first hectares, under the so-called **redistributive payment**. A new **crisis reserve** measure is created, as part of the **financial discipline**, with an annual budget of EUR 400 million (USD 531 million) withdrawn from the direct payments budget. The so-called financial discipline ensures that the amounts financing the CAP remain contained within annual ceilings for expenditure in all circumstances. The level of direct support can thus be reduced accordingly. However, farmers whose direct income support does not exceed EUR 2 000 (USD 2 655) are exempt from financial discipline.

From 2015, the remaining 30% of Pillar I payments is conditional on three farming practices designated by the term **Greening**, paid in addition to the BPS or the SAPS: 1) the establishment of a minimum share of **Ecological Focus Areas** (EFA); 2) crop diversification on arable land; and 3) maintenance of permanent grassland. The definition and conditions of the EFA were not yet defined in April 2014. Alternatively, member states have flexibility to implement national certification schemes instead. **Cross-compliance** requirements are redefined and continue to apply to direct payments. Under so-called **degressivity**, a mandatory minimum 5% reduction will apply to support amounts above EUR 150 000 (USD 199 000) per recipient, adjusted for salaries paid. Member states may choose to apply a higher percentage reduction that can be as high as 100%, resulting in a full capping of the BPS.

In EU15 countries, most **payments for specific commodities** are integrated into the single payment as of 2012, with some exceptions: member states can chose to maintain the ewe premium, the suckler cow premium, and payments for cotton. Moreover, member states can introduce commodity-specific payments as part of **Article 68** of the Health Check Regulation, which gives them the option to use up to 10% of their national budget ceilings under EAGF for specific purposes.[5] This flexibility has been used increasingly as shown by the growing share of commodity-specific payments in the PSE in the recent period.

Under the CAP 2014-20, the ceiling to such payments is increased to 8% or even 13% of the national ceilings based on previous levels of commodity-specific payments under Article 68 in each member state. An additional 2% can be allocated to **protein crops**. No major change is foreseen to the **POSEI** scheme that supports farming in the European Union's outermost regions.[6]

Pillar I also funds market price support measures. There is public intervention for **cereals,** namely common and durum wheat, barley and maize. Purchase at the cereal intervention price is limited to 3 million tonnes of **common wheat**, beyond which purchase is by tender. Public intervention for **durum wheat, barley** and **maize** can be opened under special circumstances by means of tendering. **Sugar** is supported through production quotas and support to private storage. After the end of the sugar quota regime, in September 2017, existing provisions for agreements between sugar factories and growers will be maintained, and white sugar will remain eligible for private storage aid. The support regime for cereals and sugar also comprises trade protection through tariffs, tariff rate quotas (TRQs), and, under certain markets circumstances, export subsidies. **Fruits and vegetables** are supported through various measures to which producers contribute increasingly. These include crisis intervention measures managed by producer organisations, an entry price system (minimum import price) for some products, *ad valorem* duties but no export subsidies. Member state co-financed aids also apply to the fruit and vegetables sector as well as the **olive oil and table olives** sector. These support, through producer organisations of the fruit and vegetables sector, a wide range of actions from production planning, quality measures, market withdrawal and harvest insurance to training, promotion and communication. Some of these measures apply at farm level while others are provided to professional organisations or to the sector at large. Also directed to the fruit and vegetables sector, a consumer support system targeted to school children is expanded in the CAP 2014-20 to cover the consumption of fresh fruits and vegetables, processed fruits and vegetables, and banana. The scheme's EUR 150 million (USD 199 million) cover the supply and costs related to logistics and distribution. It is co-financed up to 25% by member states, or 10% in less developed and outermost regions. The **wine** planting rights system will be phased out at the end of 2015 and a system of authorisations for new vine planting introduced from 2016 that allows growth of up to 1% per year.

Intervention prices are used for **butter** and **skimmed milk powder** together with import protection and export subsidies. As of 1 January 2014, intervention purchase for butter was raised from 30 000 to 50 000 tonnes, while the volume for skimmed milk powder (SMP) was unchanged at 109 000 tonnes. Above those limits, purchase is made by tender. Milk production quotas expire by 31 March 2015. The consumption of milk and milk products by school children is supported. This aid is set to EUR 18.15 per 100 kg (USD 24) for all milk and limited to 0.25 litre of milk per child and per school day. The support system is maintained in the new CAP. The **beef** market is supported by floor prices, tariffs, TRQs and export subsidies. Support for **pigmeat** is provided by import protection and export subsidies. For **sheepmeat**, the market support regime comprises tariffs and TRQs, with most country-specific TRQs subject to a zero customs duty, and provisions for private storage. For **poultry and eggs**, there are TRQs and export subsidies. As a result of these measures, prices paid to domestic producers were 4% above world market prices in 2011-13, and the support they generated (Market Price Support) represented 20% of the estimated support to agricultural producers.

The **Common Organisation of Markets** for 2014-20 maintains the ability to use existing instruments for market intervention, including public intervention and aid for private storage. Public intervention at a fixed price and for determined quantities for common wheat, butter and skimmed milk powder (SMP) is continued, while intervention may be opened for durum wheat, barley, maize, paddy rice, beef and veal. Private storage may be activated as an optional scheme for white sugar, olive oil, flax fibre, beef, butter, SMP, certain cheeses, pigmeat, sheep meat and goat meat. Furthermore, specific provisions are made for sugar, wine, milk and milk products. Third-country trade, for specific commodities, is subject to import and export licences and import duties and tariff quota management. Although export refunds are set to zero, provisions are made that allow their future use under certain market circumstances. In the CAP 2014-20, the rules on recognition of Producer organisations and interbranch organisations are expanded beyond fruits and vegetables, this without any associated financial support.

Pillar II funds are implemented through National (or Regional) Development Programmes, which define the list of measures chosen by the country and their funding with a focus on three "thematic axes": 1) improving the competitiveness of the agricultural and forestry sectors; 2) improving the environment and the countryside; 3) improving the quality of life in rural areas and encouraging diversification of the rural economy. Axis 1 includes measures for farm modernisation, the setting-up of young farmers, early retirement, semi-subsistence farms undergoing restructuring, vocational training, producer groups, adding value to farm and forestry products, and restoring production potential damaged by natural disasters. Axis 2 includes agri-environmental and animal welfare payments, payments to farmers in areas with natural handicaps, payments for afforestation, payments for protecting biodiversity in specific sites, and support to non-productive investments. Axis 3 supports the diversification into non-agricultural activities, tourism activities, the creation and development of micro-enterprises, rural services, and the conservation of rural heritage. Rural Development Programmes also support projects using the "LEADER approach" (Liaison Entre Actions de Développement de l'Économie Rurale") – i.e. relying on a multi-sectoral approach and local partnerships to address specific local problems; as well as technical assistance for the implementation of Pillar II measures.

Pillar II of the CAP 2014-20 identifies six priority areas. Member states can choose from a menu of measures to meet these priorities. Two conditions apply: a minimum 30% of rural development funding from the EU budget is spent on measures related to the environment and climate change adaptation, including forestry and investments in physical assets; and another 5% is spent on the LEADER approach. The six priority areas are as follows: 1) fostering knowledge transfer and innovation; 2) enhancing competitiveness of all types of agriculture and the sustainable management of forests; 3) promoting food chain organisation, including processing and marketing, and risk management; 4) restoring, preserving and enhancing ecosystems; 5) promoting resource efficiency and the transition to a low-carbon economy; and 6) promoting social inclusion, poverty reduction and economic development in rural areas. Under Pillar II, member states can grant additional payments to Less Favoured Areas (LFAs), redefined on the basis of eight biophysical criteria and renamed as Areas of Natural Constraints (ANCs). Member states have until 2018 to implement the new delimitation. Rural Development is part of the EU-level Common Strategic Framework covering all support from European Structural and Investment (ESI) funds (the EAFRD, ERDF, Cohesion Fund, ESF and EMFF) in member states through partnership agreements.

The implementation of the **CAP 2014-20** started in January 2014 with full entry into force planned in January 2015. Transitional provisions have been made from the EU budgetary period 2007-13 to 2014-20.

Domestic policy developments in 2013-14

The combination of EU, national and regional payments to producers represents 80% of the PSE. The PSE increase of 1.5% was due to the rise in market price support (2.6%), explained by a rise in producer prices in conjunction with a drop in border prices at the farm gate, mainly reflecting the contribution of exchange rates.

The implementation in **France** of an action plan to help the **poultry sector** to adapt to the removal of export subsidies was started at the end of 2013. It includes cash flow emergency assistance to intermediary firms, EUR 7.5 million (USD 10 million) investment subsidies to abattoirs and coupled payments to producers of EUR 15 million (USD 20 million).

Part of the **sugar** market management system, the levy that applies to over quota production was fixed at EUR 148 (USD 196) per tonne for a maximum quantity of 150 000 tonnes of sugar and 8 000 tonnes of isoglucose sugar. Out-of-quota sugar exports were almost totally suspended throughout 2013, resuming for two short periods from 1 to 4 October and 2 to 6 December. They were subsequently suspended up to 30 September 2014. Import duties for industrial sugar were suspended for a quantity of 400 000 tonnes from 1 October 2013 to 30 September 2014. A fixed export limit of 1 350 000 tonnes of out-of-quota sugar without refund and the release of 70 000 tonnes of out-of-quota isoglucose were announced.

Member states implemented measures to adapt to the end of the **milk** quota in 2015. As part of the Milk Package, implemented in **Portugal** and a number of other countries, there is an obligation to establish written contracts for the purchase of raw milk.

Flexibility is offered to countries to maintain commodity-specific direct payments. This is the case for the ewe premium in **Finland** and **Portugal** (50% of historical reference levels), the suckler cow premium delivered in **Austria**, **Belgium**, **France**, **Portugal** and **Spain** (at 100% of the historical reference level for all respectively except France 75%) and cotton aid in **Spain**, **Portugal** and **Greece** (at 50%, 100% and 35% of the historical reference level, respectively). Other commodity-specific payments have been gradually discontinued. Member states also have the flexibility to introduce assistance to sectors with specific situations as part of the so-called **Article 68** measures.[7] These are mostly used in the livestock sectors for dairy and sheep and goat. France, Spain, Slovenia and Denmark opted out of the sheepmeat payment. In 2013, it was planned to discontinue Article 68 measures supporting durum wheat, rice, protein crops, starch potatoes, nuts and beef and veal, as well as the transitional fruit and vegetables payments, while payments to improve the quality of production extended to tobacco, olive oil and sugar were continued.

Phasing-in the **Single Area Payment Scheme** was continued in 2013 and the ten-year transition period following accession was extended by another seven years to end in 2020. Member states applying the SAPS have achieved different levels of direct payment rates, based on the criteria, whether agricultural area, budgetary ceiling or maximum quantities on which the historical envelope of direct payments is based. Single payments increased in 2013 by 11% compared to the previous year. In the **Czech Republic**, **Hungary** and the **Slovak Republic**, SAPS reached 100% of the payment to the EU15 in 2013.

Financial Discipline was applied to confine CAP direct payments and market measures within the reduced limits foreseen for 2013 in the Multi-annual Financial Framework (MFF). For example, payments above EUR 2 000 (USD 2 655) were reduced in the **Czech Republic** and **Estonia** by 2.45% and in the **Slovak Republic** by 4%. The Financial Discipline concept, established in 2003, is a structuring element of the CAP 2014-20. It allows the gradual reduction of the overall budget allocated to the CAP, in line with the MFF agreement reached in 2013. Under modulation of direct payments, total payments entitlements in excess of EUR 300 000 (USD 398 000) per recipient were reduced by 4%; this was the case for example in the **Czech Republic** and **Slovenia**.

In **Portugal**, a computerised platform was setup in the **horticulture** sector to manage programmes and keep track of producer organisations engaged. The share of government spending was scaled down from 60% of costs in 2012, to 50% in 2013. When farmers had had recourse to the harvest insurance the share was further reduced to 40% of costs. **Wine** restructuring and reorganisation was continued in **Romania** and the wine grape crop supported overall with about RON 900 000 (USD 270 000). In **France**, assistance measures were announced that are targeted to new comers and new investors in the **dairy** and **beef meat** sectors. They consist of 1) EUR 20 million (USD 27 million) to fund payments to the first 100 000 litres of milk produced by farmers holding a quota on a per 1 000 litres payment of EUR 10 (USD 13); 2) EUR 12 million (USD 16 million) for suckler cows; 3) EUR 8 million (USD 11 million) to fund payments for fattening young bovine animals, with a limit of EUR 60 (USD 79) per animal and 24 animals per farm. In **Austria**, a seven-year programme to support on-farm **investment** was allocated an annual envelope of EUR 100 million (USD 133 million). The programme contributes 20% of the incurred investment cost estimated at EUR 3.5 billion (USD 4.65 billion) for the whole period.

As part of animal welfare measures, **Denmark**'s Veterinary Agreement II sets targets for the use of antibiotics, improved animal welfare, performance of the control and a veterinary alert system for the 2013-16 period. **Hungary** spent EUR 42 billion (USD 56 billion) in 2013 as an investment subsidy related to the pigmeat and poultry sector. **Sweden** implemented an animal health and wellbeing programme for sows. Farmers can apply for EUR 110 (USD 146) per head for extra care for sows.

Emergency measures were taken in several countries. In response to drought-related damages, the government of **Austria** allocated EUR 50 million (USD 66 million) to a provincially co-financed disaster fund. The Austrian hail insurance estimated damages caused in the first half of 2013 by hail and floods at EUR 36 million (USD 48 million). Producers received advanced CAP payments mid-October, rather than 1 December, in **France**. Farmers affected by natural disasters received compensations from the national fund for the management of agricultural risks and will benefit from reductions or delays in the payment of social charges as well as exemption from cross compliance conditions. In the **United Kingdom**, the Farming Recovery Fund was attributed GBP 10 million (USD 16 million) to support uninsured flood losses. Farmers can apply for GBP 5 000 (USD 7 800) covering up to 100% of their business costs.

The European Union's 2014-16 programme for **bee keeping** was deployed. In **Estonia**, this resulted in a three-year programme that includes technical assistance measures as well as disease control; support to research and to the restocking of hives. In **France**, consistent with this programme, a wider national plan includes 17 axis and 115 specific actions to improve bee health and engage beekeeping on a sustainable path. The bee keeping programme was also implemented in **Latvia**. In **Portugal**, the programme includes marketing and promotion and the reinforcement of producer groups as well as a new digitalisation platform was reacted to manage the programme. On 1 December 2013, a two-year moratorium was imposed at EU level on the use of three neonicotinoids on bee-attractive crops and plants, including maize, due to risks to bee health.

A number of measures were taken to improve the functioning of the **food chain**. In **France**, an agreement was signed to improve and simplify the traceability system for the transportation of bovine animals using a computerised platform. The cost of the programme is estimated at EUR 1.5 million (USD 2 million), of which the government will pay 80%. Campaigns to promote the marketing of agricultural products through **short supply chains** were continued in several countries (**France**, the **Flemish Region of Belgium**). Member states are preparing for the entry into force in December 2014 of the mandatory indication of the nutrition values on food labels.

Progress is made with the implementation of the European **Innovation Partnership for Agriculture**. The **United Kingdom** launched the GBP 160 million (USD 250 million) Agri-tech strategy that supports development and adoption of innovation and sustainability of agricultural technology. In **Denmark**, a partnership was launched to encourage innovation and mitigate the negative effects of intensive pig production on the environment by the use of improved technology.

Latvia disbursed EUR 13.7 million (USD 18 million) on programmes covering economic and environmental sustainability, maintenance of genetic resources, improved productivity, access to credit, advisory systems and risk management. The risk insurance will benefit from a subsidised harvest premium as part of **Portugal**'s Rural development plan for 2014-20. In **Romania**, RON 27 000 (USD 8 000) support agricultural producers joining insurance schemes for the first time

Existing agro-environmental programmes were refined in several member states. France launched a national programme with Pillar II funds of EUR 160 million (USD 212 million) over 2014-20 to aid the conversion and maintenance of organic practices by combining marketing and promotion measures with R&D and training and adaptation. The **Walloon Region of Belgium** implemented a strategic plan for organic farming and an agricultural methanisation plan. Certification of organic farms continued in **Latvia** and organic farming was promoted in **Italy** and

Romania. Seven years into implementation, **Estonia**'s Organic Farming Development Plan has achieved partial success in meeting its targets. The organic agricultural area and the number of processing facilities have increased. However, the number of active farmers (1 550) and the share of Estonian-grown organic products on the domestic market (0.75%) were below target. The programme will be continued in 2014-20.

The European Union's farm and forestry emission rules were expanded to include emissions from crops and grazing as of 2013. The national pact against **food waste** was launched in **France** in June 2013. Similar programmes were also launched in **Spain** and **Austria** where the objective is to reduce food waste by 20% by 2016.

France's Law for the Future of Agriculture, Food and Forestry is going through the legislative adoption process. The Law aims for more competitive agro-food chains, innovative practices for agro-ecology, young farmers and renewed dialogue between agriculture and society.

Consultations were organised in member states to contribute to the transition to the CAP 2014-20. Implementation plans have been developed and some have been announced, for example in the **United Kingdom (England)**, **Slovenia** and **Sweden**. In several member states, the implementation will be carried out at regional level. Rural development priorities of the CAP 2014-20 were identified and conditions of the transition between the CAP 2007-13 and the CAP 2014-20 were defined so as to avoid payment breaks.

Institutional changes implemented in member states in 2013, include **Portugal**'s reorganisation of the Ministry of Agriculture, Sea, Environment and Territorial Management that was split into a Ministry of Agriculture and the Sea (MAM) and a Ministry of Environment, Territorial Management and Energy (MAOTE). The implementation of agricultural policy, food security and safety falls under MAM while the two ministries will share agro environmental policies.

Trade policy developments in 2013-14

In 2013, **export subsidy** spending was about EUR 86 million (USD 114 million), compared to EUR 156 million (USD 200 million) in 2012 and EUR 3.7 billion (USD 5 billion) in 2004. This gradual decline is due to reforms of the sugar, fruit and vegetable, wine and dairy regimes and to the rise in world prices. More recently, export refunds for frozen whole chickens were reduced (October 2012 and January 2013 and set to zero in July 2013) and those for beef were cut to zero (May 2012) while refunds for eggs and processed pigmeat were phased out. According to the most recent EU notifications to the WTO on export subsidies commitments (February 2014), the European Union remained below its WTO commitment level for the marketing year 2011/12. According to this notification, export subsidies were used for meat products and eggs, representing less than 10% of the outlay allowed for most commodities except for poultry (41%). Sugar exports represented 98% of the annual commitment quantity level, poultry meat 54% and eggs 42%.

The European Union's simple average MFN applied rate for agricultural products, as published by the WTO, was 13.2 per cent in 2012, as compared with 4.2 for non-agricultural products. **Market access** was improved as in-quota import duties on **wheat**, **rye**, **maize** and **sorghum** were suspended in 2012, in 2013 and again into 2014. The hormone-free beef import quota was extended for two years, 48 200 tonnes are open for imports from Australia, Canada, New Zealand, the United States and Uruguay.

According to the most recent EU notifications to the WTO (November 2013), **import tariff quotas** during the marketing year 2011/12 were filled at 80-100% for about one-fourth of quotas, notably for chicken carcasses, and zero to 5% of quota for 45% of them, notably for live bovines, meat of swine and most dairy products except cheddar cheese, eggs in shell and most cereals.

In 2012, 44% of quotas were filled at 80-100%, notably for poultry cuts and wine while 35% of them had a fill-rate of zero to 5%. The latter was the case for live sheep, preserved fruits, orange juice, manioc and sweet potatoes.

The most recent EU notifications to the WTO (June 2013), states that the price-based **special safeguard system** has been made operational for some **frozen poultry meat**, **egg** and **sugar** products in marketing year 2011/12. During the same period, the volume-based special safeguard action has not been invoked. However, the system has been made operational at the level of calculation of figures for the trigger volumes for some fruit and vegetable products.

On 19 November 2013, the European Union imposed definitive anti-dumping duties on biodiesel imports from **Indonesia**, ranging from EUR 76.94 to EUR 178.85 per tonne [USD 102 to USD 236.29 per tonne], and from **Argentina** from EUR 216.64 to EUR 245.67 per tonne [USD 287.59 to USD 326.13 per tonne]. The duties are renewable after five years. These followed provisional anti-dumping duties that were imposed from 27 May 2013. As part of an anti-subsidy proceeding, imports were subject to registration from 10 April 2013. The anti-subsidy proceeding was terminated on 26 November 2013 and the registration of imports, imposed since 28 January 2013, discontinued.

The European Commission's new import preference scheme entered into force in January 2014. Under the new scheme, the **Generalised System of Preferences (GSP)** offers reduced import duties and tariff-free quotas to 89 developing countries including 49 least developed countries for a large number of agricultural and industrial products. The new scheme limits the number of countries that will receive preferential treatment on an expanded number of products and a longer transition period. Specific safeguards under the scheme include ethanol.

In August 2013, the Free Trade Agreement[8] with **Colombia** came into force and at the same time the trade provisions of the Association Agreement with Central American countries took effect for **Honduras**, **Nicaragua** and **Panama**. The agreement that also covers **Costa Rica**, **El Salvador** and **Guatemala** will enter into force when these countries have completed their domestic implementation procedures. A political agreement on a Comprehensive Economic and Trade Agreement (CETA) was reached on 18 October 2013 between the EU and **Canada.**

Negotiation talks on the **Transatlantic Trade and Investment Partnership** (TTIP) were initiated in July 2013. By March 2014, four rounds had taken place between the European Union and the **United States**. Other free trade agreement negotiations are on-going between the European Union and **Japan**, **Thailand**, **Canada**, **India**, **Malaysia**, **Viet Nam** and the **Mercosur**. Negotiations with **Morocco** on a Deep and Comprehensive Free Trade Agreement (DCFTA) are progressing. The DCFTAs with **Moldova**, **Armenia** and **Georgia** are awaiting initiation and the signature of a similar agreement reached with **Ukraine** was halted. The European Union and **Singapore** concluded a Free Trade Agreement in December 2012, to be endorsed.

A number of countries have applied to join the European Union: **Montenegro** in December 2008, **Albania** in May 2009; **Iceland** in July 2009; and **Serbia** in December 2009. In 2012, accession negotiations with **Montenegro** were launched and those with **Turkey** were continued. In May 2013, the government of Iceland decided to put the accession negotiations on hold. **Serbia** was granted candidate status in March 2012.

Notes

1. This report covers the European Union of 27 member states.

2. The 2011 exchange rate is used for this specific conversion.

3. *http://ec.europa.eu/agriculture/markets/sfp/pdf/2008_01_dp_capFVrev.pdf.*

4. Of the 12 member states that joined the European Union in 2004 and 2007, six (the Czech Republic, Estonia, Hungary, Poland, the Slovak Republic and Slovenia) are members of the OECD. The other six, as well as Croatia that joined the European Union in July 2013, which are not members of the OECD, are covered in this report, in particular in EU aggregate indicators, but not in indicators for the OECD area.

5. According to the general rules of Article 68, member states may grant specific support to farmers: a) for: i) specific types of farming which are important for the protection or enhancement of the environment; ii) improving the quality of agricultural products; iii) improving the marketing of agricultural products; iv) practicing enhanced animal welfare standards; v) specific agricultural activities entailing additional agri-environmental benefits; b) to address specific disadvantages affecting farmers in the dairy, beef and veal, sheepmeat and goatmeat and rice sectors in economically vulnerable or environmentally sensitive areas, or, in the same sectors, for economically vulnerable types of farming; c) in areas subject to restructuring and/or development programmes in order to ensure against land being abandoned and/or to address specific disadvantages for farmers in those areas; d) in the form of contributions to crop, animal and plant insurance premiums in accordance with the conditions set out in Article 70; e) by way of mutual funds for animal and plant diseases and environmental incidents in accordance with the conditions set out in Article 71.

6. The POSEI covers the Canary Islands (Spain); the Azores and Madeira (Portugal); the Réunion, Guadeloupe, Martinique, French Guyana (France); the Aegean Islands (Greece), and from 2014 the French Island of Mayotte.

7. More details on Article 68 measures are provided under the Main policy instruments section and in note 5 above.

8. An update on EU bilateral trade and investment agreements and negotiations is available at *http://ec.europa.eu/agriculture/bilateral-relations/index_en.htm*.

PART II

Chapter 7

Developments in agricultural policies and support in Iceland

The Iceland country chapter includes a brief evaluation of policy developments and related support to agriculture, contextual information on the framework in which agricultural policies are implemented and the main characteristics of the agricultural sector, an evaluation of support in 2012-13 and in the longer term perspective, and a brief description of the main policy developments in 2013-14.

Evaluation of policy developments

- Overall, policy reform in Iceland has been limited since 1986-88. Iceland's level of support remains well above those of most other OECD countries, although it has declined significantly between 2005 and 2010 due to higher world prices and a strong devaluation of the Icelandic Króna. Higher reference prices for dairy products again led to a declining support level in 2013 despite unchanged market and trade policies in Iceland.

- Agricultural support in Iceland remains dominated by production and trade distorting measures, although the mid-1990s saw some shift towards more decoupled payments in the sheepmeat sector. More recently, the establishment of a market for dairy quotas has helped to reduce efficiency losses, but has not significantly altered the level of market distortions.

- Induced by budget constraints, the renewal of the agricultural agreements in 2012 has brought about small reductions in government outlays for agriculture in 2013, without however changing the principles of agricultural support in Iceland. To sustainably reduce the level of support and its distortive effects, policies need to be changed in favor of measures less linked to production and away from border protection. The focus should be on efficiently targeting explicit policy objectives, including environmental protection and the conservation of natural resources, while reducing market distortions.

Figure 7.1. **Iceland: PSE level and composition by support categories, 1986-2013**

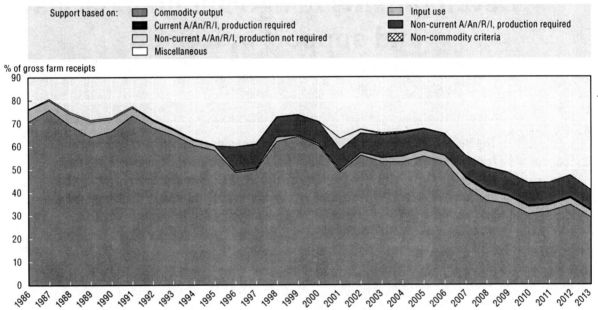

Source: OECD (2014), "Producer and Consumer Support Estimates", OECD Agriculture Statistics Database, http://dx.doi.org/10.1787/agr-pcse-data-en.
StatLink ⭑⭑⭑ http://dx.doi.org/10.1787/888933109650

Contextual information

Iceland is a relatively small economy with a GDP per capita close to the OECD average, slightly higher than the OECD average inflation, and low unemployment rates. The economic downturn after 2007 resulted in a significant worsening of the economy with lower per capita GDP and higher inflation and unemployment rates. Both GDP growth and inflation rates have come back closer to trend levels since 2011. With about 8% and 6%, respectively, the shares of agriculture (including fish) in both GDP and employment are relatively high, caused by an important fishing sector. Iceland has been a consistent net importer of agro-food products (excluding fishery), with a total agro-food trade balance of USD -135 million in 2012. Agriculture in Iceland mainly consists of livestock production, with milk and sheepmeat being the most important products, together accounting for almost half the agricultural production. Horticulture, much of which is under glass, is an important sector too, and together with a few other crops represented some 16% of total agricultural production in 2012.

Table 7.1. Iceland: Contextual indicators, 1995, 2012[1]

	1995	2012[1]
Economic context		
GDP (billion USD)	7	14
Population (million)	0.27	0.32
Land area (thousand km^2)	100	100
Population density (inhabitants/km^2)	3	3
GDP per capita, PPP (USD)	23 195	39 097
Trade as % of GDP	25.3	36.2
Agriculture in the economy		
Agriculture in GDP (%)	11.6	8.3
Agriculture share in employment (%)	9.5	5.6
Agro-food exports (% of total exports)	6.8	5.5
Agro-food imports (% of total imports)	10.0	8.7
Characteristics of the agricultural sector		
Agro-food trade balance (million USD)	-53	-135
Crop in total agricultural production (%)	22	16
Livestock in total agricultural production (%)	78	84
Agricultural area (AA) (thousand ha)	2 280	1 591
Share of arable land in AA (%)	0.3	7.7
Share of irrigated land in AA (%)	..	..
Share of agriculture in water consumption (%)	42	42
Nitrogen balance, kg/ha	7	9

1. Or latest available year.
Sources: OECD Statistical Datbases, ITCS, World Development Indicators and national data. a

StatLink ⟐ *http://dx.doi.org/10.1787/888933110429*

Figure 7.2. Iceland: Main macroeconomic indicators, 1995-2013

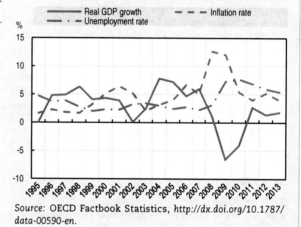

Source: OECD Factbook Statistics, http://dx.doi.org/10.1787/data-00590-en.

StatLink ⟐ *http://dx.doi.org/10.1787/888933109669*

Figure 7.3. Iceland: Agro-food trade, 1995-2012

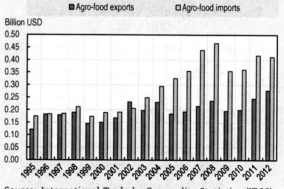

Source: International Trade by Commodity Statistics (ITCS) Database.

StatLink ⟐ *http://dx.doi.org/10.1787/888933109688*

Note: Detailed definitions of contextual indicators and their sources are provided in Annex II.A1.

Development of support to agriculture

Support to agriculture in Iceland dropped in 2013 after having picked up again in 2012. The longer trend shows a decline in support levels and market distortions. Direct payments, largely based on historical livestock production, have replaced some of the former price support in the sheepmeat sector. Together with movements of international prices and exchange rates this has reduced the level of price distortions as measured by the NPC. Nonetheless, support levels and the share of most production and trade distorting forms of support remain high in comparison to most other OECD countries.

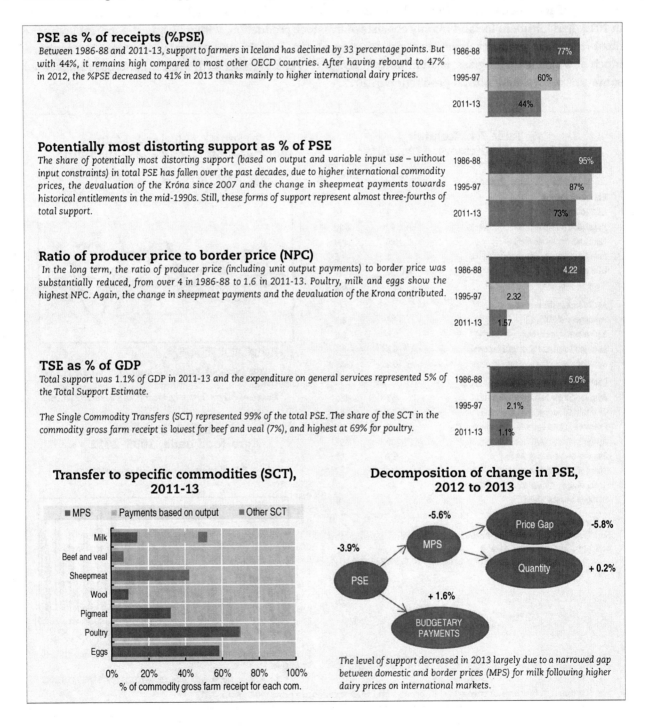

PSE as % of receipts (%PSE)
Between 1986-88 and 2011-13, support to farmers in Iceland has declined by 33 percentage points. But with 44%, it remains high compared to most other OECD countries. After having rebound to 47% in 2012, the %PSE decreased to 41% in 2013 thanks mainly to higher international dairy prices.

1986-88 77%
1995-97 60%
2011-13 44%

Potentially most distorting support as % of PSE
The share of potentially most distorting support (based on output and variable input use – without input constraints) in total PSE has fallen over the past decades, due to higher international commodity prices, the devaluation of the Króna since 2007 and the change in sheepmeat payments towards historical entitlements in the mid-1990s. Still, these forms of support represent almost three-fourths of total support.

1986-88 95%
1995-97 87%
2011-13 73%

Ratio of producer price to border price (NPC)
In the long term, the ratio of producer price (including unit output payments) to border price was substantially reduced, from over 4 in 1986-88 to 1.6 in 2011-13. Poultry, milk and eggs show the highest NPC. Again, the change in sheepmeat payments and the devaluation of the Krona contributed.

1986-88 4.22
1995-97 2.32
2011-13 1.57

TSE as % of GDP
Total support was 1.1% of GDP in 2011-13 and the expenditure on general services represented 5% of the Total Support Estimate.

The Single Commodity Transfers (SCT) represented 99% of the total PSE. The share of the SCT in the commodity gross farm receipt is lowest for beef and veal (7%), and highest at 69% for poultry.

1986-88 5.0%
1995-97 2.1%
2011-13 1.1%

Transfer to specific commodities (SCT), 2011-13

■ MPS   ▨ Payments based on output   ■ Other SCT

Milk
Beef and veal
Sheepmeat
Wool
Pigmeat
Poultry
Eggs

0%   20%   40%   60%   80%   100%
% of commodity gross farm receipt for each com.

Decomposition of change in PSE, 2012 to 2013

-3.9% PSE
-5.6% MPS
-5.8% Price Gap
+0.2% Quantity
+1.6% BUDGETARY PAYMENTS

The level of support decreased in 2013 largely due to a narrowed gap between domestic and border prices (MPS) for milk following higher dairy prices on international markets.

Table 7.2. **Iceland: Estimates of support to agriculture**

Million ISK

	1986-88	1995-97	2011-13	2011	2012	2013p
Total value of production (at farm gate)	**9 644**	**10 326**	**29 497**	**27 008**	**28 978**	**32 506**
of which: share of MPS commodities (%)	80.3	73.5	81.8	84.2	83.7	77.5
Total value of consumption (at farm gate)	**8 388**	**9 706**	**25 195**	**22 811**	**25 048**	**27 725**
Producer Support Estimate (PSE)	**7 909**	**8 825**	**17 570**	**16 248**	**18 597**	**17 866**
Support based on commodity output	7 374	7 645	12 641	11 625	13 587	12 711
Market Price Support[1]	7 307	4 533	7 263	6 471	8 176	7 143
Payments based on output	66	3 112	5 378	5 154	5 411	5 568
Payments based on input use	536	337	1 111	1 031	1 108	1 195
Based on variable input use	129	0	223	213	224	233
with input constraints	0	0	0	0	0	0
Based on fixed capital formation	233	126	443	409	430	490
with input constraints	0	0	0	0	0	0
Based on on-farm services	174	210	445	409	454	472
with input constraints	0	0	0	0	0	0
Payments based on current A/An/R/I, production required	-49	-181	220	143	282	236
Based on Receipts / Income	-49	-181	-389	-442	-334	-392
Based on Area planted / Animal numbers	0	0	610	586	616	628
with input constraints	0	0	3	5	6	0
Payments based on non-current A/An/R/I, production required	0	1 011	3 598	3 449	3 621	3 724
Payments based on non-current A/An/R/I, production not required	48	14	0	0	0	0
With variable payment rates	0	0	0	0	0	0
with commodity exceptions	0	0	0	0	0	0
With fixed payment rates	48	14	0	0	0	0
with commodity exceptions	48	14	0	0	0	0
Payments based on non-commodity criteria	0	0	0	0	0	0
Based on long-term resource retirement	0	0	0	0	0	0
Based on a specific non-commodity output	0	0	0	0	0	0
Based on other non-commodity criteria	0	0	0	0	0	0
Miscellaneous payments	0	0	0	0	0	0
Percentage PSE (%)	**77.2**	**60.4**	**44.2**	**44.2**	**47.2**	**41.3**
Producer NPC (coeff.)	**4.22**	**2.32**	**1.57**	**1.57**	**1.65**	**1.50**
Producer NAC (coeff.)	**4.44**	**2.52**	**1.80**	**1.79**	**1.89**	**1.70**
General Services Support Estimate (GSSE)[2]	**731**	**927**	**876**	**826**	**879**	**923**
Agricultural knowledge and innovation system	187	327	84	89	77	87
Inspection and control	37	88	367	347	374	380
Development and maintenance of infrastructure	91	187	14	5	15	23
Marketing and promotion	58	75	30	21	31	40
Cost of public stockholding	359	249	380	364	382	393
Miscellaneous	0	0	0	0	0	0
Percentage GSSE (% of TSE)	**6.8**	**9.1**	**4.7**	**4.7**	**4.4**	**4.8**
Consumer Support Estimate (CSE)	**-4 566**	**-4 012**	**-6 408**	**-5 613**	**-7 256**	**-6 353**
Transfers to producers from consumers	-6 421	-4 340	-6 815	-6 003	-7 666	-6 775
Other transfers from consumers	-51	-35	0	0	0	0
Transfers to consumers from taxpayers	1 906	363	407	390	410	422
Excess feed cost	0	0	0	0	0	0
Percentage CSE (%)	**-70.4**	**-42.9**	**-25.9**	**-25.0**	**-29.5**	**-23.3**
Consumer NPC (coeff.)	**4.44**	**1.82**	**1.37**	**1.36**	**1.44**	**1.32**
Consumer NAC (coeff.)	**3.50**	**1.75**	**1.35**	**1.33**	**1.42**	**1.30**
Total Support Estimate (TSE)	**10 546**	**10 115**	**18 854**	**17 464**	**19 886**	**19 211**
Transfers from consumers	6 472	4 375	6 815	6 003	7 666	6 775
Transfers from taxpayers	4 124	5 775	12 039	11 461	12 220	12 436
Budget revenues	-51	-35	0	0	0	0
Percentage TSE (% of GDP)	**5.0**	**2.1**	**1.1**	**1.1**	**1.2**	**1.1**
GDP deflator (1986-88=100)	**100**	**211**	**471**	**457**	**470**	**486**

Note: p: provisional. NPC: Nominal Protection Coefficient. NAC: Nominal Assistance Coefficient. A/An/R/I: Area planted/Animal numbers/ Receipts/Income.

1. Market Price Support (MPS) is net of producer levies and excess feed cost. MPS commodities for Iceland are: milk, beef and veal, sheep meat, wool, pigmeat, poultry and eggs.

2. A revised GSSE definition with new categories was introduced in 2014. When possible, the revision was implemented for the whole time series. The GSSE series and the resulting TSE are not comparable with the series published previously (for more details, see Annex 1.A2).

Source: OECD (2014), "Producer and Consumer Support Estimates", OECD *Agriculture Statistics Database, doi: http://dx.doi.org/10.1787/agr-pcse-data-en.*

StatLink ᵃᵐᵗˢ *http://dx.doi.org/10.1787/888933110448*

Description of policy developments

Main policy instruments

Agricultural policies in Iceland are determined by renewable multi-year agreements between the Government of Iceland and the Farmer's Association, which provide the general framework for support and production control for farmers in the covered sectors. The three agreements currently in force, all of which have been renewed in fall 2012, include the Agreement on Dairy Production (due to expire in 2016), the Agreement on Sheep Production (due to expire in 2017) and the Agreement on Horticultural Production (due to expire in 2015). Each of the agreements contains a precautionary clause allowing necessary changes to be made in case that Iceland might join the European Union during the term of the agreements.

Iceland's agricultural support continues to be provided through market price support, maintained by border measures, and through direct payments, which are based on payment entitlements, directly or indirectly coupled with production factors. Direct support is paid to **cattle** (mainly dairy) and **sheep** producers and, on a smaller scale, to certain **greenhouse** producers, while market price support is provided for all livestock products and some horticultural products.

Wholesale prices continue to be managed for approximately half of the dairy products. A government-chaired committee, representing both the Farmers' Association and – on behalf of the consumer side – the labour union, annually determines **guaranteed minimum prices** for milk delivered within production quotas. Both production quotas and entitlements for support payments are tradable between farmers.

Iceland maintains prices above world market levels for a range of livestock products, including the **poultry** and **eggs** sectors, **milk products** as well as, to a lesser extent, the **pigmeat** sector. MFN tariffs for most meat and egg products are at 30%, and additional specific tariffs apply depending on the product. In addition, imports into Iceland are prohibited for uncooked meat and meat products, uncooked milk and uncooked eggs. However, products originating in partner countries of the European Economic Area or in one of the more than 20 countries with which Iceland has free trade agreements may carry lower tariffs.

Payments based on historical entitlements have replaced output payments for sheep meat in the mid-1990s, and payment entitlements have become tradable among farmers. Keeping a minimum of winter-fed sheep on the farm is, however, required for being eligible to receive the payments. Additional payments to sheep farmers are related to a **quality control scheme** for lamb meat, based on animal welfare, product quality and traceability, and sustainability criteria. The Sheep Farmers' Association is allowed to publish reference prices for sheep meat, although these have no binding effect on slaughter companies' pricing policies.

Agricultural revenues are subject to a **levy** which is distributed within and between various agricultural bodies. Among these bodies is the **Emergency Relief Fund**: it grants compensation payments to farmers who suffer major financial losses after national disasters or because of extreme weather conditions, animal diseases or accidents for which there are no insurances available on the market. **Agri-environmental policies** particularly focus on soil conservation and forestry: related payments aim at the reduction of desertification and sand encroachment, the promotion of sustainable land use, the reclamation and restoration of degraded land and new afforestation.

Domestic policy developments in 2013-14

The only change in Iceland's agricultural policies relates to its support for domestic **wool processing**. Since November 2012, most of the support (84%) for the collection and processing of domestic sheep wool is paid directly to the producers. Up to 15% of the subsidies is paid to wool buyers who have to collect the wool from each farm in Iceland. 1% of the subsidies goes to the Farmers Association to cover administration costs.

Trade policy developments in 2013-14

Iceland is a Member of the **European Free Trade Association** (EFTA) and of the **European Economic Area** (EEA). While the EEA Agreement does not apply to most trade in agricultural goods, it opens trade in a number of processed agricultural products and encourages bilateral agreements on primary commodities. Such a bilateral agreement between Iceland and the **EU** has been in force since 2007, extending the EU-Iceland Free Trade Agreement from 1972. It reduces or eliminates agricultural tariffs and establishes quotas in bilateral trade. Furthermore, EFTA has a number of Free Trade Agreements with countries in South-East Europe, North Africa and the Middle East, Latin America, and Asia, as well as with the **South African Customs Union**. In addition, Iceland is Party to a bilateral Free Trade Agreement with the **Faroe Islands**.

After Iceland's application to join the European Union, dating from 2009, accession negotiations had started in July 2010, with a Screening Report on agriculture published in June 2011.* In May 2013, the Icelandic government decided to put the accession negotiations on hold. At that time, negotiations on 27 chapters had been opened, of which 11 provisionally closed. Other chapters, including agriculture and rural development and fisheries had not been opened yet.

---

* Chapter 11 – Agriculture and Rural Development – can be found at *http://ec.europa.eu/enlargement/pdf/iceland/key-documents/screening_report_11_is_internet_en.pdf.*

PART II

Chapter 8

Developments in agricultural policies and support in Israel

The Israel country chapter includes a brief evaluation of policy developments and related support to agriculture, contextual information on the framework in which agricultural policies are implemented and the main characteristics of the agricultural sector, an evaluation of support in 2012-13 and in the longer term perspective, and a brief description of the main policy developments in 2013-14.

The statistical data for Israel are supplied by and under the responsibility of the relevant Israeli authorities. The use of such data by the OECD is without prejudice to the status of the Golan Heights, East Jerusalem and Israeli settlements in the West Bank under the terms of international law.

Evaluation of policy developments

- Since the mid-1990s, Israel's level of support to agriculture has been halved as a result of domestic policy reform, slightly lower border protection, and higher prices on world markets. In recent years, reforms were undertaken to lower the cost of food. They included strengthening domestic competition in the agro-food sector and limited liberalisation of agro-food imports.

- While the level of support to agriculture has tended to fall, its composition remains trade and production distortive. This mostly reflects continued high border protection for agricultural commodities that maintain domestic prices above international levels and a relatively high share of support to farm inputs.

- Transfers to farmers from consumers, through market price support, remain a dominant part of the total support and reflect a cost that could further be reduced.

- There is a wide range of policy reforms that could be undertaken to further improve the efficiency of the Israeli agricultural sector and its international competitiveness at lower cost to taxpayers and consumers. In addition to structural reforms, such as diminishing the administrative burden on agricultural land market transactions, Israel could further reduce and simplify import tariffs on agricultural products and could take further steps to loosen the production planning system in the livestock sector.

- Israel has made significant efforts to improve the environmental performance of agriculture, but which can be further improved particularly as regards water use efficiency. The recent increase in the water quota for the farming sector as well as fixing a single price for fresh water must be carefully assessed to ensure that these changes meet the conditions agreed to between the government and farmers in 2006 to increase water prices in order to cover average water production costs by 2015.

Figure 8.1. Israel: PSE level and composition by support categories, 1995-2013

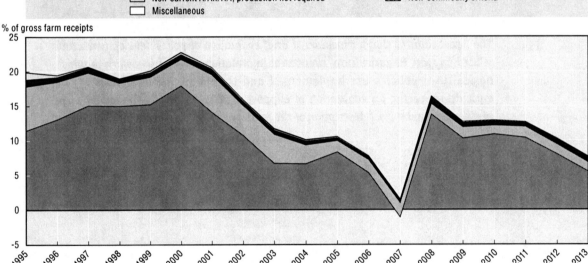

Source: OECD (2014), "Producer and Consumer Support Estimates", OECD Agriculture Statistics Database, http://dx.doi.org/10.1787/agr-pcse-data-en.
StatLink http://dx.doi.org/10.1787/888933109707

Contextual information

Israel's agriculture is a small but dynamic sector accounting for less than 2% of both total employment and of national GDP. It is dominated by co-operative communities, principally the *kibbutz* and *moshav*, accounting for about 80% of agricultural output. Land and water are scarce and nearly all state-owned. Agriculture accounts for 56% of annual water consumption. Almost 60% of water used by agriculture is treated waste and brackish water. An average availability of arable land is at just 0.04 hectare per capita. Fruit and vegetables are the main agro-food exports while cereals, oilseeds, beef and sugar are major agro-food imports. The negative balance of trade in agro-food products tends to increase.

Table 8.1. **Israel: Contextual indicators, 1995, 2012[1]**

	1995	2012[1]
Economic context		
GDP (billion USD)	96	258
Population (million)	5	8
Land area (thousand km^2)	20	20
Population density (inhabitants/km^2)	273	388
GDP per capita, PPP (USD)	18 953	29 349
Trade as % of GDP	24.6	26.4
Agriculture in the economy		
Agriculture in GDP (%)	2.1	1.9
Agriculture share in employment (%)	2.8	1.4
Agro-food exports (% of total exports)	7.0	3.8
Agro-food imports (% of total imports)	6.6	6.9
Characteristics of the agricultural sector		
Agro-food trade balance (million USD)	-526	-2 607
Crop in total agricultural production (%)	61	60
Livestock in total agricultural production (%)	39	40
Agricultural area (AA) (thousand ha)	573	521
Share of arable land in AA (%)	60	58
Share of irrigated land in AA (%)	46.0	38.8
Share of agriculture in water consumption (%)	63	56
Nitrogen balance, kg/ha	..	146

1. Or latest available year.
Note: The statistical data for Israel are supplied by and under the responsibility of the relevant Israeli authorities. The use of such data by the OECD is without prejudice to the status of the Golan Heights, East Jerusalem and Israeli settlements in the West Bank under the terms of international law.
Sources: OECD Statistical Databases, ITCS, *World Development Indicators* and national data.

StatLink ⫘ http://dx.doi.org/10.1787/888933110467

Figure 8.2. **Israel: Main macroeconomic indicators, 1995-2013**

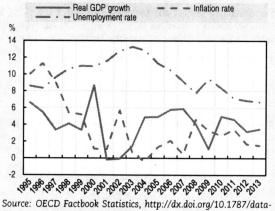

Source: OECD Factbook Statistics, http://dx.doi.org/10.1787/data-00590-en.

StatLink ⫘ http://dx.doi.org/10.1787/888933109726

Figure 8.3. **Israel: Agro-food trade, 1995-2012**

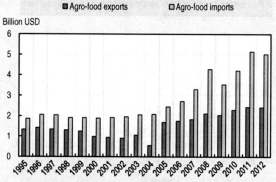

Source: International Trade by Commodity Statistics (ITCS) Database.

StatLink ⫘ http://dx.doi.org/10.1787/888933109745

Note: Detailed definitions of contextual indicators and their sources are provided in Annex II.A1.

Development of support to agriculture

In the long term, although Israel has reduced support to agriculture most production and trade distorting forms of support continue to dominate. The level of price distortions, as measured by the NPC, has declined in the long term, but prices for selected commodities remain regulated by the government and their adjustments are either delayed or delinked from changes of prices on international markets.

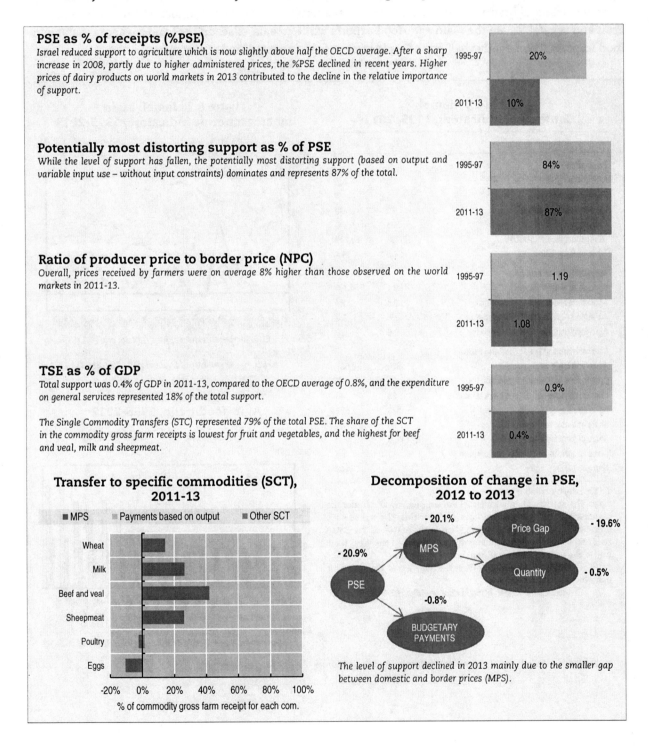

PSE as % of receipts (%PSE)
Israel reduced support to agriculture which is now slightly above half the OECD average. After a sharp increase in 2008, partly due to higher administered prices, the %PSE declined in recent years. Higher prices of dairy products on world markets in 2013 contributed to the decline in the relative importance of support.

1995-97   20%
2011-13   10%

Potentially most distorting support as % of PSE
While the level of support has fallen, the potentially most distorting support (based on output and variable input use – without input constraints) dominates and represents 87% of the total.

1995-97   84%
2011-13   87%

Ratio of producer price to border price (NPC)
Overall, prices received by farmers were on average 8% higher than those observed on the world markets in 2011-13.

1995-97   1.19
2011-13   1.08

TSE as % of GDP
Total support was 0.4% of GDP in 2011-13, compared to the OECD average of 0.8%, and the expenditure on general services represented 18% of the total support.

The Single Commodity Transfers (STC) represented 79% of the total PSE. The share of the SCT in the commodity gross farm receipts is lowest for fruit and vegetables, and the highest for beef and veal, milk and sheepmeat.

1995-97   0.9%
2011-13   0.4%

Transfer to specific commodities (SCT), 2011-13

■ MPS   ■ Payments based on output   ■ Other SCT

Wheat
Milk
Beef and veal
Sheepmeat
Poultry
Eggs

-20% 0% 20% 40% 60% 80% 100%
% of commodity gross farm receipt for each com.

Decomposition of change in PSE, 2012 to 2013

- 20.1%   Price Gap   - 19.6%
- 20.9%   MPS
PSE   Quantity   - 0.5%
-0.8%
BUDGETARY PAYMENTS

The level of support declined in 2013 mainly due to the smaller gap between domestic and border prices (MPS).

Table 8.2. **Israel: Estimates of support to agriculture**

Million ILS

	1995-97	2011-13	2011	2012	2013p
Total value of production (at farm gate)	**11 651**	**29 116**	**28 552**	**29 310**	**29 486**
of which: share of MPS commodities (%)	72.4	80.6	80.5	80.6	80.8
Total value of consumption (at farm gate)	**9 274**	**21 431**	**21 886**	**20 979**	**21 429**
Producer Support Estimate (PSE)	**2 517**	**3 076**	**3 697**	**3 087**	**2 442**
Support based on commodity output	1 669	2 411	3 036	2 409	1 787
Market Price Support[1]	1 604	2 343	2 973	2 338	1 719
Payments based on output	65	67	63	70	68
Payments based on input use	688	429	463	424	399
Based on variable input use	457	265	247	264	282
with input constraints	0	0	0	0	0
Based on fixed capital formation	183	90	129	84	58
with input constraints	0	0	0	0	0
Based on on-farm services	48	74	87	77	59
with input constraints	0	0	0	0	0
Payments based on current A/An/R/I, production required	102	202	163	219	222
Based on Receipts / Income	97	175	136	188	201
Based on Area planted / Animal numbers	5	27	27	31	22
with input constraints	0	0	0	0	0
Payments based on non-current A/An/R/I, production required	0	0	0	0	0
Payments based on non-current A/An/R/I, production not required	56	34	35	35	34
With variable payment rates	0	34	35	35	34
with commodity exceptions	0	0	0	0	0
With fixed payment rates	56	0	0	0	0
with commodity exceptions	0	0	0	0	0
Payments based on non-commodity criteria	0	0	0	0	0
Based on long-term resource retirement	0	0	0	0	0
Based on a specific non-commodity output	0	0	0	0	0
Based on other non-commodity criteria	0	0	0	0	0
Miscellaneous payments	2	0	0	0	0
Percentage PSE (%)	**20.0**	**10.3**	**12.6**	**10.3**	**8.1**
Producer NPC (coeff.)	**1.19**	**1.08**	**1.11**	**1.08**	**1.06**
Producer NAC (coeff.)	**1.25**	**1.12**	**1.14**	**1.11**	**1.09**
General Services Support Estimate (GSSE)[2]	**390**	**640**	**627**	**686**	**607**
Agricultural knowledge and innovation system	155	272	284	266	267
Inspection and control	56	99	94	121	83
Development and maintenance of infrastructure	11	208	202	231	192
Marketing and promotion	59	3	1	3	5
Cost of public stockholding	108	53	45	59	55
Miscellaneous	0	5	1	6	7
Percentage GSSE (% of TSE)	**13.4**	**17.5**	**14.5**	**18.2**	**19.9**
Consumer Support Estimate (CSE)	**-2 127**	**-2 731**	**-3 403**	**-2 627**	**-2 162**
Transfers to producers from consumers	-1 756	-2 094	-2 585	-2 158	-1 538
Other transfers from consumers	-391	-651	-846	-483	-624
Transfers to consumers from taxpayers	0	0	0	0	0
Excess feed cost	20	14	28	14	0
Percentage CSE (%)	**-22.6**	**-12.7**	**-15.6**	**-12.5**	**-10.1**
Consumer NPC (coeff.)	**1.30**	**1.15**	**1.19**	**1.14**	**1.11**
Consumer NAC (coeff.)	**1.29**	**1.15**	**1.18**	**1.14**	**1.11**
Total Support Estimate (TSE)	**2 907**	**3 715**	**4 324**	**3 773**	**3 049**
Transfers from consumers	2 147	2 745	3 432	2 641	2 162
Transfers from taxpayers	1 151	1 622	1 739	1 615	1 511
Budget revenues	-391	-651	-846	-483	-624
Percentage TSE (% of GDP)	**0.9**	**0.4**	**0.5**	**0.4**	**0.3**
GDP deflator (1995-97=100)	**100**	**155**	**149**	**155**	**159**

Note: p: provisional. NPC: Nominal Protection Coefficient. NAC: Nominal Assistance Coefficient. A/An/R/I: Area planted/Animal numbers/Receipts/Income.

The statistical data for Israel are supplied by and under the responsibility of the relevant Israeli authorities. The use of such data by the OECD is without prejudice to the status of the Golan Heights, East Jerusalem and Israeli settlements in the West Bank under the terms of international law.

1. Market Price Support (MPS) is net of producer levies and excess feed cost. MPS commodities for Israel are: wheat, cotton, peanuts, tomatoes, peppers, potatoes, avocados, bananas, oranges, grapefruit, grapes, apples, milk, beef and veal, sheep meat, poultry and eggs.
2. A revised GSSE definition with new categories was introduced in 2014. When possible, the revision was implemented for the whole time series. The GSSE series and the resulting TSE are not comparable with the series published previously (for more details, see Annex 1.A2).

Source: OECD (2014), "Producer and Consumer Support Estimates", OECD *Agriculture Statistics Database*, doi: http://dx.doi.org/10.1787/agr-pcse-data-en.

StatLink ⟹ http://dx.doi.org/10.1787/888933110486

Description of policy developments

Main policy instruments

In 2013, the new government modified the country's **agricultural objectives** to focus on strengthening rural settlements, enhancing agricultural research and development, improving food safety, and developing agriculture and agricultural inputs in a context of global competition and persisting consequences of global economic crisis.

Since the late 1980s, Israel has gradually undertaken reforms in such areas as the provision of subsidies, central planning of agricultural industries, allocation of production quotas, price controls and import protection. But the government continues to be involved in the allocation of key factors of production: land, water and foreign workers. **Land and water resources are nearly all state-owned**. Land is allocated to farmers for a low, nominal fee and is not allowed to be subject to market transactions. In turn, water is allocated to farmers through a quota system. Farmers are given access to water at lower rates compared to other users and benefit from a concession on the water extraction levy. The government also applies a yearly quota of foreign workers with permits to work in agriculture. Both the overall quota and the distribution of workers to individual farmers are strictly regulated.

While some sectors, such as milk and eggs, have been covered by sector specific reforms, they continue to benefit from **guaranteed prices and quotas** aiming at securing profitability for producers. Guaranteed prices for milk and eggs are based on the average cost of production and while they are updated regularly, the level and direction of change diverge quite strongly from the level and evolution of prices on international markets. Minimum prices are also provided for wheat producers. These are based on the Kansas market price, adjusted for quality and transportation costs. During the year there might be changes in price according to developments in international markets, but as these corrections are delayed, the level of prices and the direction of change may diverge. On the other hand, **consumer price controls** are applied to several basic food products, mainly dairy products, eggs and bread.

Egg and broiler producers in peripheral areas benefit from **direct payments**. Income support measures are provided to wheat producers to support rain-fed agriculture and to preserve open space.

Capital grants are provided to develop the agricultural export sector and to encourage the uptake of advanced technologies. Farmers who participate in the investment support scheme are also entitled to income tax exemptions and accelerated depreciation. As from 2009, an investment support programme is being implemented to partly replace foreign workers in agriculture.

Insurance schemes for farmers are subsidised and the government intends to increase state participation in subsidising premiums and to extend it through the inclusion of new crops.

As a result of the implementation of the Uruguay Round Agreement on Agriculture (URAA), Israel now maintains a more transparent and open trade regime. However, **high border tariff protection** on agro-food products remains a key tool supporting agricultural producers. Under the URAA, Israel established Tariff Rate Quotas (TRQs) for wheat, fats and oils, walnuts, prunes, maize, orange and other citrus juices, beef and sheep meat and various dairy products. In addition, all of Israel's preferential trade agreements (apart from the one with the European Free Trade Association [EFTA]) include tariff-quota commitments for agricultural products. In total, Israel administers more than 100 Most Favoured Nation (MFN) and preferential TRQs (WTO, 2012).

Despite some reforms undertaken in 2011-12, Israel's tariff profile for agricultural products remains highly uneven – with very high, sometimes prohibitive, tariffs for such products as dairy, fresh beef, eggs and some fruits and vegetables, and low, sometimes duty-free, tariffs for other commodities such as coarse grains, sugar, oilseeds and frozen beef. The tariff system on agriculture is complicated, involving a large number of non-ad-valorem tariffs (specific, compound or mixed). The **simple average MFN tariff** for agricultural products (WTO definition) was 24.5% in 2012 compared with the average for non-agricultural products at 4.2%. However, around two-thirds of agro-food imports enter Israel duty free, mostly through MFN duty-free access and under preferential agreements (the most important ones are with the EU and the US) (WTO, 2012). With the exception of beef, poultry (including turkeys), and mutton and products thereof, there is no legal requirement that imported food and agricultural products be **kosher**, but non-kosher imported agro-food products are hardly accepted by local marketing channels.

Budgetary allocations for **R&D** have regularly increased and accounted for about 20% of the total agriculture-related budget in recent years. This allowed Israel to become a world leader in agricultural technology, particularly in farming in arid and desert conditions, and to build its comparative advantage in agriculture on knowledge and technological progress (OECD, 2010).

Domestic policy developments in 2013-14

Following the 2011 social protests against high living costs, a number of initiatives were undertaken to address the issue of **high food prices**. Among other measures, some reductions in tariffs on agro-food imports were decided in 2012 (OECD, 2013). In 2013, the government appointed a committee to examine the composition of agricultural support, with a view of transforming support based on prices to less distortive forms based on direct payments to farmers. In early March 2014, the Knesset approved a law to enhance the competition in the food industry and to reduce food prices. The law deals with price transparency and the relationship between retailers and suppliers, including illegal deals. It also limits the shelf space for food giants having a turnover of over ILS 1 billion. Restrictions on major food suppliers will be enforced as from early 2015. In August 2013, the Economic Affairs Committee of the Knesset approved a new bill on the standardization system reform which is intended to lower the cost of living by removing barriers on imports (see section on trade). In early March 2014, the Committee also approved the government proposal to amend the antitrust law to enhance the competition among agro-food wholesalers.

The **guaranteed prices** for raw milk increased on average by 4.2% and for eggs by 6.5% in 2013. However, during the course of the year both prices, particularly for milk, were lowered and in the first two months of 2014 they were lower than in early 2013. As dairy prices on international markets increased sharply in the second half of 2013, the positive price differential for milk declined strongly, which was the main factor for an overall fall in support for the Israeli agriculture in 2013.

In 2013, about ILS 141 million (USD 39 million) were allocated to ease the retirement of small and medium size dairy farmers from the market. As a result, with the consent of the growers, about 100 small and medium dairy farmers retired, about 10% of the total number. Their **milk quotas** were returned to the state and then reallocated to other small dairy farms to improve their efficiency. Following the state audit report on the rise in food prices, a review of the profitability of dairy products was undertaken. As a result, the price committee decided to add white cheese and cream to the list of products with **regulated prices**.

Egg quota holders continued to benefit from direct payments within so called Galilee Law which amounted to ILS 60 million (USD 16 million). At the end of 2013, the upgrading of the egg industry began. This industry, mostly located in the north of the country, is comprised of small units, not well prepared to meet sanitary and animal welfare standards. The reform is intended to ease the adoption of these standards by egg cooperatives and to improve the efficiency of the industry.

In 2013, the approved quota for foreign workers in agriculture was decreased by 2% to 24 000 persons, but an additional 1 000 foreign employees were approved for seasonal work. The government continued to provide **investment support** (grants up to 40% of investment) to encourage farmers to replace foreign labour with machinery. In 2013, this support amounted ILS 26.1 million (USD 7 million).

In line with the 2006 agreement between the government and farmers to further increase water charges paid by farmers so they eventually cover the average cost of water production by 2015 (operation and maintenance and fixed capital costs), farmers are receiving **support to invest in water saving** and in irrigation technologies. Support for this programme amounted to ILS 120 million (USD 33 million) in 2013, 55% above the 2012 level.

In view of the significant progress in seawater desalination, and a certain improvement in the availability of fresh water, the Water Authority Council decided in October 2013 to establish a **three-year quota of fresh water** for agriculture, instead of annual quota applied up to now. For 2014-16, the quota is at 1.8 billion cubic meters, on average 0.6 billion per year, which compares with 0.556 billion allocated to agriculture in 2013. The increase in quota is combined with the unification of the tariff for fresh water, up to 2013 based on the three-tier system in which farmers were charged three different levels of prices depending on the quantity of water used. As from 2014, the new unified price has been fixed at the level slightly higher than the lowest tier price applied in 2013.

Agriculture is also using **marginal water** consisting of recycled effluents, brackish water and surface water. In 2013, the allocation of marginal water for agriculture was at 0.762 billion cubic meters. High levels of effluent purification, past reductions in fresh water quotas and growing prices for fresh water enhanced farmers' demand for marginal water which currently exceeds supply.

Trade policy developments in 2013-14

Following the 2011 recommendations by the Trajtenberg Committee, in August 2013 the Israeli Knesset Economic Committee approved a **standardisation system reform** initiated by the Ministry of Finance (MoF, 2013). The reform promises to have the Israeli Standards Institute recognise international standards such as those of the European Union or the United States. If approved by the Knesset, the new law would permit a broader recognition of certification of conformity by the country of origin. This would allow avoiding further testing and conformity assessment by the Israeli inspection services. The new system is intended to facilitate import clearance and processing, thus to enhance imports and strengthen competition with the expected outcome of lowering domestic prices, including of agricultural and food products (GAIN, 2013).

At the end of February 2014, the Minister of Economy announced that **import tariffs** on a range of dairy products, including butter and yogurt, would be lowered by 80%. Products subject to tariffs reductions would be covered by import quotas.

A **Free Trade Agreement** (FTA) between Israel and **Colombia** was signed in September 2013, but as of March 2014 remains to be ratified by the two Parliaments. According to its terms, tariffs on all industrial goods and on some agricultural and food products traded between the two countries will be eliminated. The agreement is expected to benefit a large part of Colombian agro-food exports to Israel and Israel's exports of agricultural technology to Colombia.

References

GAIN (2013), "Food and Agricultural Import Regulations and Standards – Narrative", *FAIRS Country Report*, USDA FAS, Washington DC, 26 December.

MoF (2013), *Press release*, Ministry of Finance, Israel, 7 August.

OECD (2010), *OECD Review of Agricultural Policies: Israel 2010*, OECD Publishing, Paris, *http://dx.doi.org/10.1787/9789264079397-en*.

OECD (2013), *Agricultural Policy Monitoring and Evaluation 2013: OECD Countries and Emerging Economies*, OECD Publishing, Paris, *http://dx.doi.org/10.1787/agr_pol-2013-en*.

WTO (2012), *Trade Policy Review. Report by the Secretariat: Israel*, WTO, Geneva, 25 September.

PART II

Chapter 9

Developments in agricultural policies and support in Japan

The Japan country chapter includes a brief evaluation of policy developments and related support to agriculture, contextual information on the framework in which agricultural policies are implemented and the main characteristics of the agricultural sector, an evaluation of support in 2012-13 and in the longer term perspective, and a brief description of the main policy developments in 2013-14.

Evaluation of policy developments

- Producer support since 1986-88 has been reduced slightly, but it is still almost three times the OECD average. About 90% of producer support is commodity specific, narrowing farmers' choices of production. A significant share of support continues to be provided through market price support, specifically for rice. Further efforts are needed to shift from market price support to direct payments targeted to key policy objectives, thereby improving the efficiency of agricultural policies and reducing the burden on consumers.

- Japan's agricultural reform plan, announced in 2013, foresees the abolition of income support payments for rice and the phase out of the administrative allocation of rice production. This is an important first step to give farmers more freedom to respond to market signals. However, incentives remain to produce diversion crops, such as rice for feed and manufacturing, which would keep the price of rice high. The next step is to gradually reduce these incentives and narrow the gap between domestic and international prices of rice.

- Another important element of the plan is to limit the eligibility of certain payments to business-oriented farms, and to increase the role of the payments to community organisations engaged in preserving rural resources including infrastructure. This type of payment interferes much less with farmers' production decisions while still contributing to Japan's desire to preserve paddy.

- A set of policies focusing on facilitating the consolidation of farmland and increasing the number of young farmers may have some positive effect. However, these policies alone may not be effective; further efforts are needed to promote farm consolidation.

- A private-public funding scheme was setup in 2013. It offers long-term investments to enterprises composed of farmers and companies from other industries, and may contribute to increasing added value on agricultural products and to improving agriculture innovation systems.

Figure 9.1. **Japan: PSE level and composition by support categories, 1986-2013**

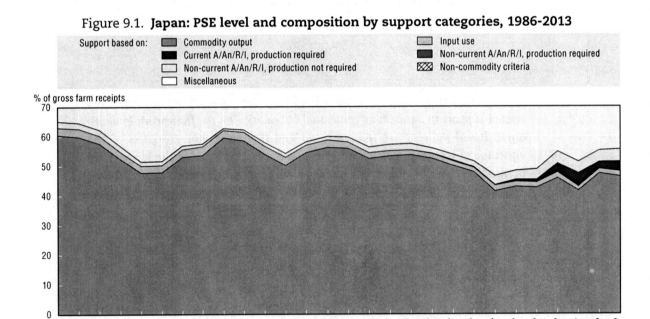

Source: OECD (2014), "Producer and Consumer Support Estimates", *OECD Agriculture Statistics Database, http://dx.doi.org/10.1787/agr-pcse-data-en.*
StatLink ⬛≋ *http://dx.doi.org/10.1787/888933109764*

Contextual information

Japan is a land scarce country, where only 30% of area is suitable for agriculture or urban use. The importance of agriculture in the economy is relatively low at 1.2% in 2012, while its share in employment is 3.5%. Japan is the largest net agro-food importer in the world. Its share of agro-food imports in total imports is 7.5%, while the share of agro-food exports on total exports is less than 1%. Farm structure is based on very small family farms. The majority of farmland is irrigated paddy field. Livestock production largely depends on imported feed and its share in total agricultural production is increasing over time.

Table 9.1. **Japan: Contextual indicators, 1995, 2012**[1]

	1995	2012[1]
Economic context		
GDP (billion USD)	5 334	5 927
Population (million)	126	128
Land area (thousand km^2)	365	365
Population density (inhabitants/km^2)	329	335
GDP per capita, PPP (USD)	22 921	35 622
Trade as % of GDP	7.3	14.2
Agriculture in the economy		
Agriculture in GDP (%)	1.6	1.2
Agriculture share in employment (%)	5.2	3.5
Agro-food exports (% of total exports)	0.4	0.4
Agro-food imports (% of total imports)	12.3	7.5
Characteristics of the agricultural sector		
Agro-food trade balance (million USD)	-39 449	-63 199
Crop in total agricultural production (%)	79	65
Livestock in total agricultural production (%)	21	35
Agricultural area (AA) (thousand ha)	5 443	4 561
Share of arable land in AA (%)	85	93
Share of irrigated land in AA (%)	54.5	54.4
Share of agriculture in water consumption (%)	66	66
Nitrogen balance, kg/ha	175	186

1.   Or latest available year.
Sources: OECD Statistical Databases, ITCS, World Development Indicators and national data.

   StatLink ⬛🔗 http://dx.doi.org/10.1787/888933110505

Figure 9.2. **Japan: Main macroeconomic indicators, 1995-2013**

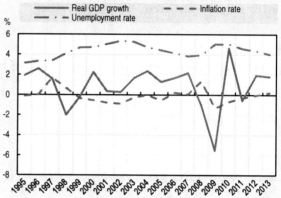

Source: OECD Factbook Statistics, http://dx.doi.org/10.1787/data-00590-en.

   StatLink ⬛🔗 http://dx.doi.org/10.1787/888933109783

Figure 9.3. **Japan: Agro-food trade, 1995-2012**

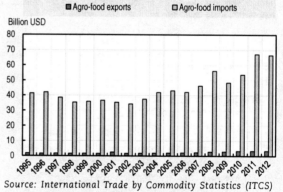

Source: International Trade by Commodity Statistics (ITCS) Database.

   StatLink ⬛🔗 http://dx.doi.org/10.1787/888933109802

Note: Detailed definitions of contextual indicators and their sources are provided in Annex II.A1.

Development of support to agriculture

Japan has progressively reduced its level of support to agriculture and more recently reduced the share of potentially most production and trade distorting forms of support. However, support remains almost three times higher than the OECD average, and is largely delivered in the potentially most production and trade distorting forms. Prices received by farmers are twice the world market prices as estimated by the Nominal Protection Coefficient (NPC). The share of direct payments in the PSE is increasing in recent years particularly in the form of area and income based payments.

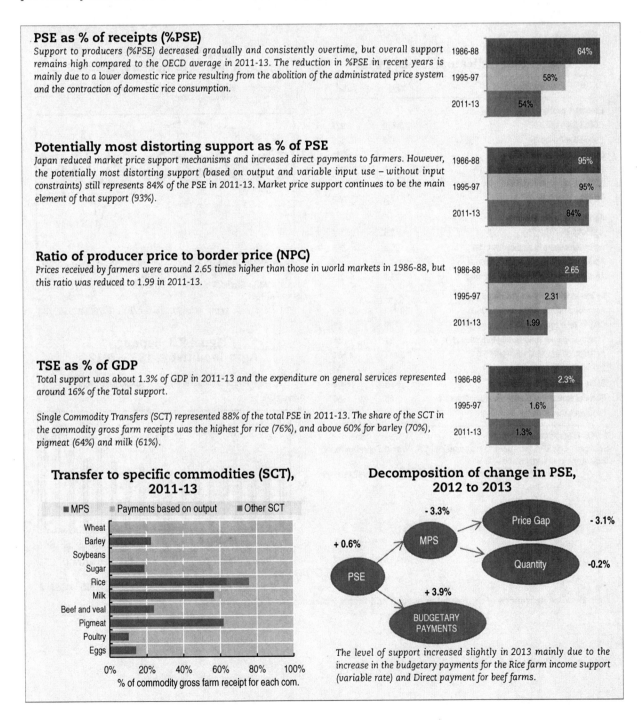

PSE as % of receipts (%PSE)
Support to producers (%PSE) decreased gradually and consistently overtime, but overall support remains high compared to the OECD average in 2011-13. The reduction in %PSE in recent years is mainly due to a lower domestic rice price resulting from the abolition of the administrated price system and the contraction of domestic rice consumption.

1986-88 64%
1995-97 58%
2011-13 54%

Potentially most distorting support as % of PSE
Japan reduced market price support mechanisms and increased direct payments to farmers. However, the potentially most distorting support (based on output and variable input use – without input constraints) still represents 84% of the PSE in 2011-13. Market price support continues to be the main element of that support (93%).

1986-88 95%
1995-97 95%
2011-13 84%

Ratio of producer price to border price (NPC)
Prices received by farmers were around 2.65 times higher than those in world markets in 1986-88, but this ratio was reduced to 1.99 in 2011-13.

1986-88 2.65
1995-97 2.31
2011-13 1.99

TSE as % of GDP
Total support was about 1.3% of GDP in 2011-13 and the expenditure on general services represented around 16% of the Total support.

Single Commodity Transfers (SCT) represented 88% of the total PSE in 2011-13. The share of the SCT in the commodity gross farm receipts was the highest for rice (76%), and above 60% for barley (70%), pigmeat (64%) and milk (61%).

1986-88 2.3%
1995-97 1.6%
2011-13 1.3%

Transfer to specific commodities (SCT), 2011-13

■ MPS   ▨ Payments based on output   ■ Other SCT

Wheat
Barley
Soybeans
Sugar
Rice
Milk
Beef and veal
Pigmeat
Poultry
Eggs

0% 20% 40% 60% 80% 100%
% of commodity gross farm receipt for each com.

Decomposition of change in PSE, 2012 to 2013

- 3.3% MPS
+ 0.6% PSE
Price Gap - 3.1%
Quantity -0.2%
+ 3.9% BUDGETARY PAYMENTS

The level of support increased slightly in 2013 mainly due to the increase in the budgetary payments for the Rice farm income support (variable rate) and Direct payment for beef farms.

Table 9.2. **Japan: Estimates of support to agriculture**

Billion JPY

	1986-88	1995-97	2011-13	2011	2012	2013p
Total value of production (at farm gate)	**10 610**	**10 128**	**8 356**	**8 246**	**8 525**	**8 298**
of which: share of MPS commodities (%)	68.4	67.9	66.4	66.3	67.0	66.0
Total value of consumption (at farm gate)	**14 298**	**15 070**	**11 767**	**11 546**	**11 843**	**11 913**
Producer Support Estimate (PSE)	**7 267**	**6 239**	**5 104**	**4 813**	**5 233**	**5 265**
Support based on commodity output	6 740	5 822	4 263	3 901	4 492	4 397
Market Price Support[1]	6 519	5 651	4 015	3 682	4 268	4 095
Payments based on output	221	171	248	219	224	301
Payments based on input use	299	298	143	126	144	158
Based on variable input use	149	124	51	51	51	51
with input constraints	0	0	0	0	0	0
Based on fixed capital formation	129	153	60	41	62	77
with input constraints	0	0	0	0	0	0
Based on on-farm services	21	21	32	34	31	30
with input constraints	0	0	0	0	0	0
Payments based on current A/An/R/I, production required	0	0	323	419	231	320
Based on Receipts / Income	0	0	76	84	72	72
Based on Area planted / Animal numbers	0	0	247	335	159	248
with input constraints	0	0	2	3	1	2
Payments based on non-current A/An/R/I, production required	0	0	0	0	0	0
Payments based on non-current A/An/R/I, production not required	228	119	374	366	366	390
With variable payment rates	0	0	0	0	0	0
with commodity exceptions	0	0	0	0	0	0
With fixed payment rates	228	119	374	366	366	390
with commodity exceptions	228	119	236	228	228	252
Payments based on non-commodity criteria	0	0	0	0	0	0
Based on long-term resource retirement	0	0	0	0	0	0
Based on a specific non-commodity output	0	0	0	0	0	0
Based on other non-commodity criteria	0	0	0	0	0	0
Miscellaneous payments	0	0	0	0	0	0
Percentage PSE (%)	**64.0**	**58.1**	**54.0**	**51.3**	**55.1**	**55.6**
Producer NPC (coeff.)	**2.65**	**2.31**	**1.99**	**1.86**	**2.06**	**2.05**
Producer NAC (coeff.)	**2.78**	**2.40**	**2.18**	**2.05**	**2.23**	**2.25**
General Services Support Estimate (GSSE)[2]	**1 267**	**2 057**	**948**	**1 004**	**922**	**920**
Agricultural knowledge and innovation system	76	98	121	119	134	110
Inspection and control	8	10	12	14	9	12
Development and maintenance of infrastructure	1 118	1 858	786	840	743	775
Marketing and promotion	22	27	13	14	21	5
Cost of public stockholding	43	63	16	16	15	17
Miscellaneous	0	0	0	0	0	0
Percentage GSSE (% of TSE)	**14.9**	**24.7**	**15.7**	**17.3**	**15.0**	**14.9**
Consumer Support Estimate (CSE)	**-8 910**	**-8 080**	**-5 404**	**-5 111**	**-5 671**	**-5 430**
Transfers to producers from consumers	-6 423	-5 603	-4 016	-3 684	-4 266	-4 099
Other transfers from consumers	-2 483	-2 503	-1 393	-1 432	-1 411	-1 336
Transfers to consumers from taxpayers	-16	26	1	1	1	1
Excess feed cost	11	0	5	4	5	5
Percentage CSE (%)	**-62.3**	**-53.6**	**-45.9**	**-44.3**	**-47.9**	**-45.6**
Consumer NPC (coeff.)	**2.66**	**2.17**	**1.85**	**1.80**	**1.92**	**1.84**
Consumer NAC (coeff.)	**2.65**	**2.16**	**1.85**	**1.79**	**1.92**	**1.84**
Total Support Estimate (TSE)	**8 519**	**8 321**	**6 053**	**5 818**	**6 156**	**6 186**
Transfers from consumers	8 906	8 106	5 409	5 116	5 677	5 435
Transfers from taxpayers	2 096	2 718	2 037	2 134	1 890	2 087
Budget revenues	-2 483	-2 503	-1 393	-1 432	-1 411	-1 336
Percentage TSE (% of GDP)	**2.3**	**1.6**	**1.3**	**1.2**	**1.3**	**1.3**
GDP deflator (1986-88=100)	**100**	**109**	**91**	**91**	**91**	**90**

Note: p: provisional. NPC: Nominal Protection Coefficient. NAC: Nominal Assistance Coefficient. A/An/R/I: Area planted/Animal numbers/Receipts/Income.

1. Market Price Support (MPS) is net of producer levies and excess feed cost. MPS commodities for Japan are: wheat, barley, soybean, rice, sugar, milk, beef and veal, pigmeat, poultry, eggs, apples, chinese cabbage, cucumbers, grapes, mandarins, pears, spinach, strawberries and Welsh onions.

2. A revised GSSE definition with new categories was introduced in 2014. When possible, the revision was implemented for the whole time series. The GSSE series and the resulting TSE are not comparable with the series published previously (for more details, see Annex 1.A2).

Source: OECD (2014), "Producer and Consumer Support Estimates", OECD *Agriculture Statistics Database*, doi: *http://dx.doi.org/10.1787/agr-pcse-data-en.*

StatLink ⊞ᵐᵃ *http://dx.doi.org/10.1787/888933110524*

Description of policy developments

Main policy instruments

Market price support resulting from tariffs and tariff rate quotas, and payments based on output serve as the basis for agricultural policies in Japan. Tariff-rate quota systems are applied to major commodities such as rice, wheat, barley and dairy products. The over-quota tariff-rate of rice is JPY 341 (USD 3.5) per kg, the tariff-quota for rice is 682 200 tonnes (milled rice), and the maximum mark-up for rice imports is set at JPY 292 (USD 3.0) per kg. The Agricultural Production Bureau within the Ministry of Agriculture, Forestry and Fisheries is responsible for importing rice under Japan's WTO URAA minimum-access commitment. In addition to the border measures, the production adjustment scheme for rice, which limits market supply, acts to maintain a higher domestic rice price. Administered prices are applied to pig meat, beef and calves.

The Basic Plan on Food, Agriculture and Rural Areas was previously elaborated in March 2010. It is a national plan for implementing policies on food, agriculture and rural area, and is revised every five years. The Plan sets a self-sufficiency rate targeting 50% on calorie supply basis and 70% on production value basis by FY 2020, compared to 41% and 65% in FY 2008.

The income support payments are implemented for rice and for upland crops. The income support payments for rice are based on the current area of rice production and have two components: predetermined (to be abolished in 2018 crop year) and price contingent payments (to be terminated in 2014 crop year). The predetermined rate was set at JPY 15 000 (USD 154) per 0.1 ha. The price contingent payment is triggered when the average producer price of the current crop year falls below the average of the three consecutive crop years from 2006 to 2008. The price contingent payment was last triggered for the 2010 crop year. Approximately 1 million rice farms signed up for the support payments in FY 2013.

The income support payments for upland crops (wheat, barley, soybean, sugar beet, starch potato, buckwheat and rapeseed) combine non-current area payments and output payments. The non-current area payment aims to maintain the conditions of farmland and the fixed rate of JPY 20 000 (USD 205) per 0.1 ha is paid based on non-current area. The rate of an output payment is set to bridge, on average, the difference between standard costs and sales prices taking quality differences into account together with the non-current area payment. All farms with sales records are eligible for income support payments, while the payments for rice require participating farms to meet the quantitative production target allocated to each farmer. The administrative allocation of rice quota (to be phased out by March 2018) is either reallocated to farmers within the same prefecture or traded across prefectures, in order to maintain the overall production level.

The Setting-up of young farmers' payments provides income support to new young farmers during a training period (maximum two years) and the initial operation period (maximum five years). A fixed rate of JPY 1.5 million (USD 15 369) is paid annually to eligible trainees or farmers. A set of payments is provided to farmers who expand farm size or who lease land to core (potentially viable) farmers. While farmers who expand their farm size will receive additional payments of JPY 20 000 (USD 205) for an additional 0.1 hectare, those who lease their farmland will receive maximum payments of JPY 700 000 (USD 7 172) per household.

Financial support is provided mainly for infrastructure, such as irrigation and drainage facilities as well as the readjustment of agricultural land. The direct payment for environmentally friendly farming supports farmers or groups of farmers who adopt farming practices that address greenhouse gas emissions (e.g. cover-crops), increase biodiversity, and reduce the use of fertiliser and pesticide. The direct payments to farmers in hilly and mountainous areas aim to prevent cultivated areas being abandoned.

Domestic policy developments in 2013-14

In December 2013, Japan announced the Plan to Create Vitality for Agricultural, Forestry and Fishery Industries and Local Communities as a Japan's agricultural policy reform post-2014. According to the plan, a number of changes will be made to current payments for rice and upland crops. A main element of the change is to terminate income support payments for rice and to phase out the administrative allocation of rice production quota, which has been in place for 40 years.

Box 9.1. **Japan's agricultural policy reform post-2014**

On the 10th of December 2013, Japan announced the Plan to Create Vitality for Agricultural, Forestry and Fishery Industries and Local Communities. The reform is the first major agricultural policy change since the introduction of income support payments in 2011. The Plan aims at doubling the incomes of agricultural industries and communities within a decade, doubling food exports up to JPY 1 trillion (USD 10.2 billion) by 2020, doubling the number of new entrants to agriculture (young farmers), concentrating 80% of farmland use to core (potentially viable) farmers and lowering the cost of rice production of core farmers by 40%. To achieve these goals, the Plan is based on four pillars: i) strengthening farms and production; ii) reforming agricultural subsidies with careful attention to the multifunctionality of agriculture; iii) establishing food value chains; and iv) increasing demand for food and other agricultural products. This plan was developed against the backdrop of an increased need for supply-side structural reform in Japan. Over the past two decades, the agricultural sector experienced a decrease of nearly 30% of agricultural production (JPY 11.2 to 8.2 trillion), a drop in agricultural income of more than 40% (JPY 4.9 to 2.8 trillion), an increase in the average age of farmers by seven years (from 59 to 66 years) and a doubling of the size of abandoned farmland.

According to the Plan, the allocation of the rice production quota will be phased out by March 2018. The programme limits the supply of rice by allocating a production quota to rice farmers, and it keeps the price above the market equilibrium level. In spite of the production limits, the rice farming sector has experienced a price decrease of over 30% over the last two decades (1992-2011), driven by a decrease in consumption at an average rate of 80 000 tonnes annually. The government, agricultural organisations and farmers will work together in the next few years to create a situation where farmers plan rice production and shipment according to actual rice demand, without depending on the allocation of the rice production quota. In order to realise the situation, the government will provide more information on the forecast for supply and demand for rice and monthly data on selling and price situation by growing area to farmers. A number of changes have been planned for the payments for rice and upland crops. Starting in 2014, the direct payment for rice production, (under the income support payments), offered to rice farmers who met the quantitative target set by the government, will be reduced by half, from the current JPY 15 000 (USD 154) per 0.1 ha to JPY 7 500 (USD 77) per 0.1 ha. This payment will be abolished in 2018. The price-contingent payment for rice will be eliminated in 2014 crop year. This payment, for which all farms with sales records are eligible, triggers when the average producer price of current crop year fell below the average price of the three crop years from 2006 to 2008.

The direct payment under the income support payments for upland crops (wheat, barley, soybean, sugar beet, starch potato, buckwheat and rapeseed), for which all farms with sales records are eligible, will remain unchanged in 2014, but it will be made to core farmers regardless of their farm size from 2015 onwards. Also starting in 2015, the eligibility for the income-based payment (which is available to producers of rice, wheat, barley, soybean, sugar beet and starch potato) will be limited to

---

Box 9.1. **Japan's agricultural policy reform post-2014** (*cont.*)

core farmers, independent of their farm size. The income-based payment compensates 90% of the loss of income compared with the average income of the preceding three crop years (an average of three out of the previous five, leaving out the highest and lowest). If a farm is eligible for both the price contingent payment and the income-based payment, the income-based payment is made after subtracting the amount of the price contingent payment so as to avoid duplication of payment. A policy option to introduce income insurance will be considered in the medium-term. Incentives to diversify crops (e.g. rice for feed) will be reinforced by increasing the amount of payments as well as introducing a quantity based payment to support rice farmers who want to shift from table rice production into other crops. In addition, a new multi-functional payment to local community activities to conserve and improve the quality of rural resources will be introduced in 2014 through reorganising the current financial support for infrastructure, such as irrigation and drainage facilities. Discussions on related issues are also taking place in other fora. The Council for Regulatory Reform is responsible for the reform of the agricultural sector, including agricultural cooperatives and requirements for land ownership of private companies. The Industrial Competitiveness Council deals with deliberating measures to increase added values of agricultural products and to double food exports. Based on these reforms, Japan will launch discussions to revise the Basic Plan on Food, Agriculture and Rural Areas in 2014. The Basic Plan is a national plan for implementing policies on food, agriculture and rural areas, which is revised every five years. The Basic Plan was previously revised in 2010. One of the key issues in the next revision will be to discuss whether the current food self-sufficiency target of 50% on a calorie supply basis and 70% on production value basis by 2020 is sufficient. This is in comparison to the former Basic Plan (revised in 2005), which targeted 45% on a calorie supply basis and 76% on a production value basis by 2015. The actual rates were reported at 39% and 68% in 2012 for calorie supply and production value, respectively.

Sources: Based on information available on the websites of the Prime Minister of Japan and His Cabinet *www.kantei.go.jp*; and of the Ministry of Agriculture, Forestry and Fisheries of Japan *www.maff.go.jp.*

A government-supported institution is to be established in each prefecture in 2014 to accelerate the consolidation of farmland. The institution leases agricultural farmlands from various owners who wish to rent their farmlands. After the institution consolidates and upgrades farmlands as needed, such as improving irrigation and drainage facilities of the farmlands, it lends farmlands to farmers who wish to expand their lands. Another government-supported institution, "Agriculture, Forestry and Fisheries Fund Corporation for Innovation, Value-chain and Expansion Japan (A-FIVE)" was set up in February 2013 for a limited period of 20 years with a total funding of JPY 32 billion (USD 328 million). It provides long-term investments to joint enterprises composed of farmers and companies from other industries to add value to agricultural products in an innovative way, making new combinations, and creating value chains. Half of the investments are co-financed by the private sector. In 2013, A-FIVE along with private banks invested a total of JPY 66.6 billion (USD 682 million).

The quantitative target of rice production was marginally reduced from 7 910 thousand tonnes in 2013 to 7 650 thousand tonnes in 2014, based on demand projection. On the other hand, the administered prices for livestock have increased in 2014 in response to the surge in imported feed costs. The floor level of the price stabilisation bands for pig meat and beef were JPY 425 000 (USD 4 150) and JPY 850 000 (USD 8 709) per tonne in 2014. Similarly, all guaranteed prices per head of calves have increased in 2014: JPY 329 000 (USD 3 371) for Japanese Black; JPY 300 000 (USD 3 074) for Japanese Brown; JPY 215 000 (USD 2 203) for other beef breeds; JPY 195 000 (USD 1 998) for cross breeds; JPY 128 000 (USD 1 312) for dairy breeds. The government-set ceiling of manufacturing milk to be covered by direct payments in 2014, decreased by 10 000 tonnes from the previous year to 1.8 million tonnes, but the payment rate was increased to JPY 12 800 (USD 131) per tonne.

Trade policy developments in 2013-14

Japan's tariff-rate-quotas continued to be under-filled in 2012 for some products, including butter and butter oil, prepared whey for infant formula, skimmed milk powder for school lunches and other purposes, and ground nuts. Japan used special safeguard measures in 2012 for some products, including milk and cream, buttermilk, butter, rice flour, certain starches, and inulin. In May 2013, Japan was classified by the OIE as a country having a negligible risk status for BSE, following the classification of a controlled risk status for BSE in 2009.

Following the launch of the negotiations on the Economic Partnership Agreements (EPAs) with **Canada**, **Colombia** and **Mongolia** in 2012, Japan began negotiations on the **China-Japan-Korea** FTA, the **EU-Japan** EPA, and the Regional Comprehensive Economic Partnership in 2013. In July 2013, Japan participated in the **Trans-Pacific Partnership** (TPP) negotiations, after a long debate over its participation. According to the estimate released by the Cabinet Secretariat in March 2013, the overall economic impact of the TPP due to tariff elimination is projected to be positive, with real GDP increasing by 3.2 trillion yen (around 0.7% of GDP) in the mid to long term, including a decrease in the value of domestic agriculture produces by JPY 3 trillion (USD 30.7 billion) from the current JPY 8.3 trillion. The TPP currently comprises 12 countries – **Australia**, **Brunei Darussalam**, **Canada**, **Chile**, **Japan**, **Malaysia**, **Mexico**, **New Zealand**, **Peru**, **Singapore**, **the United States**, and **Viet Nam** – together accounting for nearly 40% of global GDP and about one-third of all world trade.

PART II

Chapter 10

Developments in agricultural policies and support in Korea

The Korea country chapter includes a brief evaluation of policy developments and related support to agriculture, contextual information on the framework in which agricultural policies are implemented and the main characteristics of the agricultural sector, an evaluation of support in 2012-13 and in the longer term perspective, and a brief description of the main policy developments in 2013-14.

Evaluation of policy developments

- Overall, very modest progress has been made towards more market oriented policies. Although reduced from its level in 1986-88, producer support, as measured by the %PSE, is still 2.5 times higher than the OECD average. It is overwhelmingly dominated by the potentially most distorting support.

- After a reduction in 2010, the level of support in 2011-13 increased back to the 2009 level, due to a rebound in domestic rice prices and decreasing world rice prices. Market price support still dominates in producer support, although the share of support through budgetary payment schemes has gradually increased in most recent years. More than 90% of producer support is commodity specific, and concentrates on a small number of products.

- The Development Plan for Agriculture, Rural Area and Food Industry for the period of 2013-17 set a quantity-based self-sufficiency ratio of grains at 30%. The next Development Plan will include the target self-sufficiency rate for total food calorie supply. Achieving these targets will put a heavy burden on Korea as, for example, the grains self-sufficiency rate in 2012 was of 23.6%.

- The action plan has not yet taken its definite form and the discussions stalled in 2012. If approved, efforts to integrate various direct payment systems and to enhance farm registration should improve the efficiency of support delivery.

- Defining food self-sufficiency targets often results in higher market price support. Re-orientation of policies towards increased market orientation, enhancing productivity, innovation and improving environmental performance are more promising in the long run.

Figure 10.1. **Korea: PSE level and composition by support categories, 1986-2013**

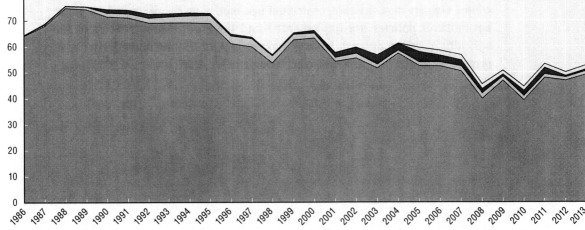

Source: OECD (2014), "Producer and Consumer Support Estimates", OECD Agriculture Statistics Database, http://dx.doi.org/10.1787/agr-pcse-data-en.
StatLink 🔗 http://dx.doi.org/10.1787/888933109821

Contextual information

Korea is a country with relatively high GDP per capita, dynamic growth and low levels of unemployment. Korea is a land-scarce country with high population density, where only 17% of the area is being used for farming. The importance of agriculture in the economy has been decreasing with its share in domestic GDP declining to 2.6% in 2012, while its share of employment is 6%. Korea is one of the largest net agro-food importers in the world. The share of agro-food imports in total imports is around 4.5%, while that of exports is less than 1%. Most farms are small family farms with less than 2 hectares of agricultural land.

Table 10.1. **Korea: Contextual indicators, 1995, 2012**[1]

	1995	2012[1]
Economic context		
GDP (billion USD)	531	1 130
Population (million)	45	50
Land area (thousand km^2)	99	97
Population density (inhabitants/km^2)	449	488
GDP per capita, PPP (USD)	12 832	30 011
Trade as % of GDP	24.5	47.2
Agriculture in the economy		
Agriculture in GDP (%)	6.2	2.6
Agriculture share in employment (%)	11.2	6.0
Agro-food exports (% of total exports)	1.3	0.9
Agro-food imports (% of total imports)	7.0	4.7
Characteristics of the agricultural sector		
Agro-food trade balance (million USD)	-7 837	-19 094
Crop in total agricultural production (%)	77	64
Livestock in total agricultural production (%)	23	36
Agricultural area (AA) (thousand ha)	2 048	1 756
Share of arable land in AA (%)	87	85
Share of irrigated land in AA (%)	44.2	44.8
Share of agriculture in water consumption (%)	48	48
Nitrogen balance, kg/ha	258	215

1. Or latest available year.
Sources: OECD Statistical Databases, ITCS, World Development Indicators and national data.

StatLink ⸺ http://dx.doi.org/10.1787/888933110543

Figure 10.2. **Korea: Main macroeconomic indicators, 1995-2013**

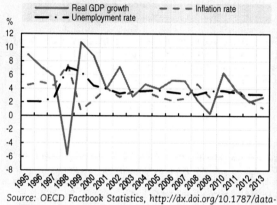

Source: OECD Factbook Statistics, http://dx.doi.org/10.1787/data-00590-en.

StatLink ⸺ http://dx.doi.org/10.1787/888933109840

Figure 10.3. **Korea: Agro-food trade, 1995-2012**

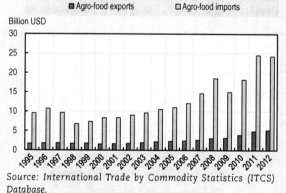

Source: International Trade by Commodity Statistics (ITCS) Database.

StatLink ⸺ http://dx.doi.org/10.1787/888933109859

Note: Detailed definitions of contextual indicators and their sources are provided in Annex II.A1.

Development of support to agriculture

Since 1986-88, Korea has gradually reduced its support to agriculture especially in the last decade. However, support still remains high and the potentially most production and trade distorting forms of support are still around 90% of the support. Moreover, the level and developments of market price support reflect the border protection on a number of commodities, of which rice.

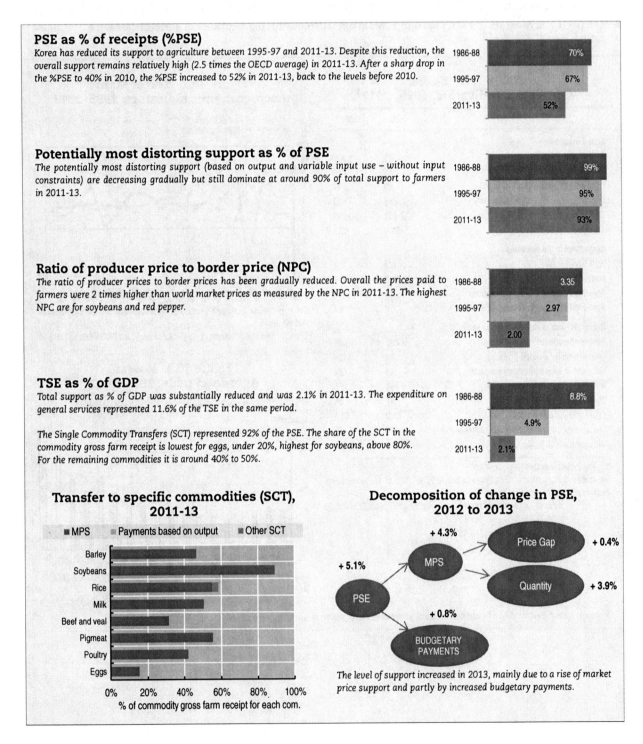

PSE as % of receipts (%PSE)
Korea has reduced its support to agriculture between 1995-97 and 2011-13. Despite this reduction, the overall support remains relatively high (2.5 times the OECD average) in 2011-13. After a sharp drop in the %PSE to 40% in 2010, the %PSE increased to 52% in 2011-13, back to the levels before 2010.

1986-88 70%
1995-97 67%
2011-13 52%

Potentially most distorting support as % of PSE
The potentially most distorting support (based on output and variable input use – without input constraints) are decreasing gradually but still dominate at around 90% of total support to farmers in 2011-13.

1986-88 99%
1995-97 95%
2011-13 93%

Ratio of producer price to border price (NPC)
The ratio of producer prices to border prices has been gradually reduced. Overall the prices paid to farmers were 2 times higher than world market prices as measured by the NPC in 2011-13. The highest NPC are for soybeans and red pepper.

1986-88 3.35
1995-97 2.97
2011-13 2.00

TSE as % of GDP
Total support as % of GDP was substantially reduced and was 2.1% in 2011-13. The expenditure on general services represented 11.6% of the TSE in the same period.

The Single Commodity Transfers (SCT) represented 92% of the PSE. The share of the SCT in the commodity gross farm receipt is lowest for eggs, under 20%, highest for soybeans, above 80%. For the remaining commodities it is around 40% to 50%.

1986-88 8.8%
1995-97 4.9%
2011-13 2.1%

Transfer to specific commodities (SCT), 2011-13

■ MPS ■ Payments based on output ■ Other SCT

Barley
Soybeans
Rice
Milk
Beef and veal
Pigmeat
Poultry
Eggs

0%   20%   40%   60%   80%   100%
% of commodity gross farm receipt for each com.

Decomposition of change in PSE, 2012 to 2013

+ 4.3%
+ 5.1%
PSE
MPS
Price Gap + 0.4%
Quantity + 3.9%
+ 0.8%
BUDGETARY PAYMENTS

The level of support increased in 2013, mainly due to a rise of market price support and partly by increased budgetary payments.

Table 10.2. **Korea: Estimates of support to agriculture**

Billion KRW

	1986-88	1995-97	2011-13	2011	2012	2013p
Total value of production (at farm gate)	**13 624**	**27 747**	**43 438**	**41 308**	**44 480**	**44 527**
of which: share of MPS commodities (%)	72.0	64.3	59.3	58.8	57.3	61.9
Total value of consumption (at farm gate)	**14 367**	**30 693**	**57 180**	**59 332**	**57 958**	**54 250**
Producer Support Estimate (PSE)	**9 605**	**19 277**	**23 514**	**23 243**	**23 063**	**24 236**
Support based on commodity output	9 511	18 199	21 708	20 922	21 605	22 598
Market Price Support[1]	9 511	18 199	21 708	20 922	21 605	22 598
Payments based on output	0	0	0	0	0	0
Payments based on input use	70	871	580	589	552	599
Based on variable input use	23	136	270	271	255	283
with input constraints	3	11	76	76	76	76
Based on fixed capital formation	44	725	223	234	210	224
with input constraints	0	70	43	42	43	45
Based on on-farm services	3	10	87	83	87	92
with input constraints	0	0	0	0	0	0
Payments based on current A/An/R/I, production required	24	206	549	1 080	254	312
Based on Receipts / Income	24	196	238	233	210	271
Based on Area planted / Animal numbers	0	11	311	847	44	41
with input constraints	0	0	44	47	44	41
Payments based on non-current A/An/R/I, production required	0	0	0	0	0	0
Payments based on non-current A/An/R/I, production not required	0	0	677	653	652	726
With variable payment rates	0	0	0	0	0	0
with commodity exceptions	0	0	0	0	0	0
With fixed payment rates	0	0	677	653	652	726
with commodity exceptions	0	0	0	0	0	0
Payments based on non-commodity criteria	0	0	0	0	0	0
Based on long-term resource retirement	0	0	0	0	0	0
Based on a specific non-commodity output	0	0	0	0	0	0
Based on other non-commodity criteria	0	0	0	0	0	0
Miscellaneous payments	0	0	0	0	0	0
Percentage PSE (%)	**69.7**	**67.1**	**52.0**	**53.3**	**50.2**	**52.5**
Producer NPC (coeff.)	**3.35**	**2.97**	**2.00**	**2.03**	**1.94**	**2.03**
Producer NAC (coeff.)	**3.38**	**3.09**	**2.08**	**2.14**	**2.01**	**2.11**
General Services Support Estimate (GSSE)[2]	**842**	**2 852**	**3 104**	**2 761**	**3 229**	**3 324**
Agricultural knowledge and innovation system	54	315	786	722	756	880
Inspection and control	21	63	189	170	195	202
Development and maintenance of infrastructure	374	2 121	1 516	1 433	1 617	1 499
Marketing and promotion	0	12	71	69	72	70
Cost of public stockholding	394	341	543	366	589	672
Miscellaneous	0	0	0	0	0	0
Percentage GSSE (% of TSE)	**7.9**	**12.7**	**11.6**	**10.6**	**12.3**	**12.0**
Consumer Support Estimate (CSE)	**-9 425**	**-19 748**	**-28 012**	**-29 622**	**-27 812**	**-26 600**
Transfers to producers from consumers	-9 304	-17 861	-21 467	-20 920	-21 605	-21 877
Other transfers from consumers	-181	-2 148	-6 592	-8 749	-6 256	-4 771
Transfers to consumers from taxpayers	59	260	48	47	49	48
Excess feed cost	0	0	0	0	0	0
Percentage CSE (%)	**-65.7**	**-64.8**	**-49.0**	**-50.0**	**-48.0**	**-49.1**
Consumer NPC (coeff.)	**2.94**	**2.91**	**1.96**	**2.00**	**1.93**	**1.97**
Consumer NAC (coeff.)	**2.93**	**2.89**	**1.96**	**2.00**	**1.92**	**1.96**
Total Support Estimate (TSE)	**10 507**	**22 390**	**26 666**	**26 050**	**26 340**	**27 608**
Transfers from consumers	9 484	20 009	28 060	29 669	27 861	26 648
Transfers from taxpayers	1 203	4 529	5 199	5 130	4 735	5 731
Budget revenues	-181	-2 148	-6 592	-8 749	-6 256	-4 771
Percentage TSE (% of GDP)	**8.8**	**4.9**	**2.1**	**2.1**	**2.1**	**2.1**
GDP deflator (1986-88=100)	100	190	275	272	275	278

Note: p: provisional. NPC: Nominal Protection Coefficient. NAC: Nominal Assistance Coefficient. A/An/R/I: Area planted/Animal numbers/ Receipts/Income.

1. Market Price Support (MPS) is net of producer levies and excess feed cost. MPS commodities for Korea are: barley, garlic, red pepper, chinese cabbage, rice, soybean, milk, beef and veal, pigmeat, poultry and eggs.
2. A revised GSSE definition with new categories was introduced in 2014. When possible, the revision was implemented for the whole time series. The GSSE series and the resulting TSE are not comparable with the series published previously (for more details, see Annex 1.A2).

Source: OECD (2014), "Producer and Consumer Support Estimates", OECD *Agriculture Statistics Database, doi: http://dx.doi.org/10.1787/agr-pcse-data-en.*

StatLink ⬛⬛⬛ *http://dx.doi.org/10.1787/888933110562*

Description of policy developments

Main policy instruments

Tariffs and a wide range of tariff rate quotas (TRQs) are applied based on multilateral and bilateral trade agreements. Under the WTO Agreement on Agriculture, rice is the last remaining sensitive product designated by Korea. Recently, direct payment schemes have been introduced, while maintaining a public stockholding scheme for rice, which is a purchase and release mechanism based on current market price. In 2009, five kinds of direct payment programmes have been implemented with different objectives; including rice income compensation, promotion of environmentally-friendly agriculture, maintain agriculture in less-favoured areas, and rural landscape conservation.

The **Basic Law for Agriculture, Rural Area and Food Industry** was established in 2007 and lays out the basic policy principles in agriculture. Korea's rural development policies consist of two categories: improving living conditions of rural residents and enhancing economic vitality of the rural regions. In 2009, the **Empowerment Support Project**, the **Local Industry Promotion Project**, and the **Specialised Product Promotion Project** were merged into the **Rural Vitalisation Promotion Project**. Korea gives high priority to enhancing the competitiveness of the food supply chain. A comprehensive plan to develop the food industry was established in December 2008, which aimed to reduce entry barriers to agriculture for non-agricultural companies.

Domestic policy developments in 2013-14

The **direct payment scheme for paddy fields** is moving forward to decoupled income support.[1] The government increased the target price for the crop year 2013-17 from KRW 170 083 (USD 155) to KRW 188 000 (USD 172) per 80 kilos of rice, which has remained at the same level since the scheme was introduced in 2005. The fixed payment, started at KRW 600 000 (USD 548) in 2005 and increased to KRW 700 000 (USD 639) in 2006 and to KRW 800 000 (USD 731) in 2013, also increased to KRW 900 000 (USD 822) per hectare. The variable payment was paid in the first three years while the domestic price was quite low, but it was not triggered in 2008 due to the increase of the post-harvest price. With sharp rice price falls, it was triggered again in 2009 and 2010. The variable payment per hectare was KRW 733 708 (USD 670) in 2009 and rose to KRW 950 868 (USD 868) in 2010. As the price recovered from 2011 and the fixed payment was raised in 2012, the variable payment was not triggered since 2011.

The **Farm Registration Programme**, which was implemented nation-wide in 2009 with a view to customise services for farmers and to improve the effectiveness of agricultural policies, began to serve as a management system of the various direct payments. Registration has been done on a voluntary basis, but related policy measures have been linked with the farm registration scheme. Farmers who want to benefit from the direct payments programmes should register to the system. The Ministry can monitor the status and performance of farmers through the integrated database in order to avoid direct payments fraud cases like the rice paddy field fraud in 2008 where ineligible landowners received direct payments.

The government added wheat and soybean to the **public stockholding programme**, which has had only one product, rice, until 2013. The amount of purchase was set to 10 000 tonnes of wheat and 5 000 tonnes of soybean in 2014, and will gradually increase until 2017. The targets of public stockholding of the two products were set up as five percent of the consumption level of each product in 2017. The amount of public stockholding of rice was fixed at 720 000 tonnes until 2013. To this end, the government purchased 370 000 tonnes of rice in 2013.

In October 2013, based on the **Basic Law for Agriculture, Rural Area and Food Industry**, the Ministry established the **Development Plan for Agriculture, Rural Area and Food Industry**, which provided policy guidelines for the period of 2013-17. In the plan, the Ministry set out a target for food self-sufficiency. The target for the amount-based self-sufficiency ratio of grains (including animal feed) is 30% in 2017, and the actual level in 2012 was 23.6%. On the other hand, Korea amended the **Basic Law** in August and made it effective from November 2013 in order to make the **Development Plan** a regular plan to be carried out over a five-year period. By this amendment, the Ministry should include the target for total food self-sufficiency ratio calculated by calorie base, which was 40% in 2011, in the next development plan.

Trade policy developments in 2013-14

As a result of the WTO rice negotiations in 2004, the TRQ for rice increased by 20 347 tonnes annually, and reached 388 353 tonnes in 2013.[2]

The Free Trade Agreement (FTA) with **Turkey** became effective on 1 May 2013. Korea currently has eight other bilateral and regional FTAs with **Chile, Singapore, EFTA (European Free Trade Association), ASEAN (Association of South East Asian Nations), India, the European Union, Peru** and **the United States**. The FTA with **Colombia**, which was concluded in June 2012, is not effective yet pending the domestic approval process by **Colombia**.

There has been a significant advance in the FTA negotiations with other countries which had been delayed for years. Korea concluded FTA negotiations with **Australia** in December 2013 and with **Canada** in March 2014. The negotiations with **New Zealand** reopened in December 2013. Negotiations started in 2012 with **China, Indonesia, Viet Nam** and the negotiations of the **Korea-China-Japan FTA** and the Regional Comprehensive Economic Partnership in East Asia are proceeding actively.

In December 2013, Korea expressed interest in participating in the **Trans-Pacific Partnership** negotiations, which currently comprise 12 countries; **Australia, Brunei Darussalam, Canada, Chile, Japan, Malaysia, Mexico, New Zealand, Peru, Singapore, the United States,** and **Viet Nam**. As a second mover of the negotiations, Korea is examining the possibility of participating through bilateral talks with each country. However, Korea is exploring ways to resume the FTA negotiations with **Japan, Mexico** and the **Gulf Co-operation Council** (Saudi Arabia, UAE, Oman, Qatar, Bahrain, and Kuwait).

Notes

1. This scheme was introduced in 2005, superseding the previous rice price support policy. It is composed of a fixed payment and a variable payment mechanism. The fixed payment was designed for the registered paddy fields in production during 1998-2000. The variable payment is given only to farmers currently producing rice on registered farmland. The amount of this payment is determined according to the difference between a target price and each year's post-harvest price. If the post-harvest price is lower than the target price, farmers receive 85% of the difference.

2. The WTO Agreement on Agriculture (AA) provided Korea's minimum market access for rice, known as "special treatment" for the first ten implementing years from 1995 to 2004. The WTO AA allowed that the special treatment could be extended for an additional length of time, but only after individual WTO member countries had the opportunity to negotiate concessions for the extension. In January 2004, the Korean government notified the WTO and began negotiating with nine trading countries that officially expressed interest. When the negotiations ended in December 2004, Korea had been granted one more ten-year grace period for *tariffication*, while its TRQ had been doubled from 205 228 tonnes in 2004 to 408 700 tonnes in 2014.

PART II

Chapter 11

Developments in agricultural policies and support in Mexico

The Mexico country chapter includes a brief evaluation of policy developments and related support to agriculture, contextual information on the framework in which agricultural policies are implemented and the main characteristics of the agricultural sector, an evaluation of support in 2012-13 and in the longer term perspective, and a brief description of the main policy developments in 2013-14.

Evaluation of policy developments

- Agricultural support in Mexico should shift towards strategic investments for the long term productivity, sustainability and profitability of the sector. Public spending on agriculture innovation, food inspection systems and related infrastructure is low while relatively ineffective subsidies linked to production and input use remain high. The rationale for Productive-PROAGRO as a revision of PROCAMPO that re-links support to production and the use of inputs should be re-considered.
- Eliminating subsidies to electricity for pumping water and fuel would contribute to more sustainable use of water resources. Agriculture currently represents over 75% of water consumption in Mexico. Direct support to help farmers adopt practices that would improve the sustainable use of water and land could also be considered.
- The dual structure of Mexican agriculture requires a targeted policy approach to respond to the different needs of commercial producers and very small farms producing largely for own consumption. Agricultural risk management measures should be introduced to enable commercial farmers to manage normal business risks while also offering predictable government support in response to unavoidable catastrophic events. High subsidies for specific instruments such as price hedging should be avoided.
- As Mexico grows and develops its overall economy, poverty reduction should be pursued through place-based development policies and social measures rather than through ineffective agriculture subsidies and land tenure restrictions.
- Mexico should begin to move towards removing limits to private ownership of land in the *ejidos*. This could foster investment in agriculture and structural adjustment.

Figure 11.1. **Mexico: PSE level and composition by support categories, 1991-2013**

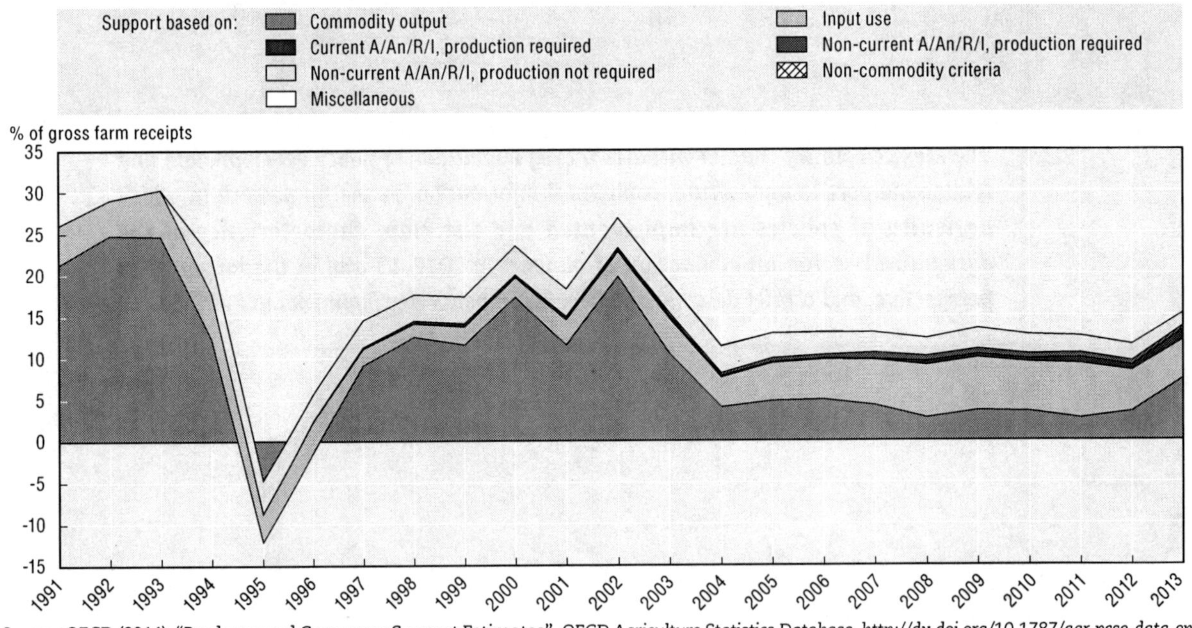

Source: OECD (2014), "Producer and Consumer Support Estimates", *OECD Agriculture Statistics Database*, *http://dx.doi.org/10.1787/agr-pcse-data-en*.

StatLink http://dx.doi.org/10.1787/888933109878

Contextual information

Mexico is a large country in terms of population (113 million) and land area. Since the mid-1990s, the Mexican economy had been characterised by relatively low inflation and stable exchange rates. The economy shrunk in 2009, has been growing at a rate of around 4% in 2010-12 and slowed to a pace of 1.2% in 2013. The agricultural sector produces 3.4% of GDP but employs 13.1% of the labour force. Mexico is a net agro-food importer, and agro-food accounts for 7% of total imports. Half of the territory of Mexico is subject to communal land ownership (*ejidos*) which, despite reforms, constrains the sale of agricultural land.

Table 11.1. **Mexico: Contextual indicators, 1995, 2012[1]**

	1995	2012[1]
Economic context		
GDP (billion USD)	314	1 171
Population (million)	90	110
Land area (thousand km^2)	1 944	1 944
Population density (inhabitants/km^2)	47	59
GDP per capita, PPP (USD)	7 549	17 952
Trade as % of GDP	24.2	31.7
Agriculture in the economy		
Agriculture in GDP (%)	5.4	3.4
Agriculture share in employment (%)	22.2	13.1
Agro-food exports (% of total exports)	7.3	5.7
Agro-food imports (% of total imports)	7.2	6.7
Characteristics of the agricultural sector		
Agro-food trade balance (million USD)	593	-3 417
Crop in total agricultural production (%)	56	51
Livestock in total agricultural production (%)	44	49
Agricultural area (AA) (thousand ha)	107 200	103 166
Share of arable land in AA (%)	23	25
Share of irrigated land in AA (%)	4.8	5.5
Share of agriculture in water consumption (%)	85	77
Nitrogen balance, kg/ha	24	21

1. Or latest available year.
Sources: OECD Statistical Databases, ITCS, World Development Indicators and national data.

StatLink ⟐⟐ *http://dx.doi.org/10.1787/888933110581*

Figure 11.2. **Mexico: Main macroeconomic indicators, 1995-2013**

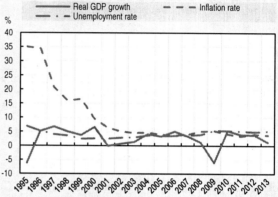

Source: OECD Factbook Statistics, http://dx.doi.org/10.1787/data-00590-en.

StatLink ⟐⟐ *http://dx.doi.org/10.1787/888933109897*

Figure 11.3. **Mexico: Agro-food trade, 1995-2012**

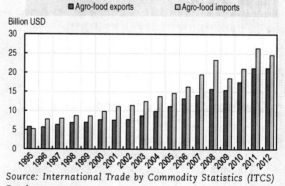

Source: International Trade by Commodity Statistics (ITCS) Database.

StatLink ⟐⟐ *http://dx.doi.org/10.1787/888933109916*

Note: Detailed definitions of contextual indicators and their sources are provided in Annex II.A1.

Development of support to agriculture

Mexico has undertaken significant agricultural policy reform in the last two decades. The amount of support in gross farm receipts has been reduced by more than half since 1991-93, and the remaining support has been reallocated to less distorting forms. Consequently, the level of price distortions has fallen to only 4% in 2011-13 as documented by the Nominal Protection Coefficient. However, since 2000 Mexico has increased payments based on variable input use, in particular subsidies to electricity and to price hedging contracts. The new programme Productive PROAGRO, which replaces PROCAMPO, links the payments to the production purposes.

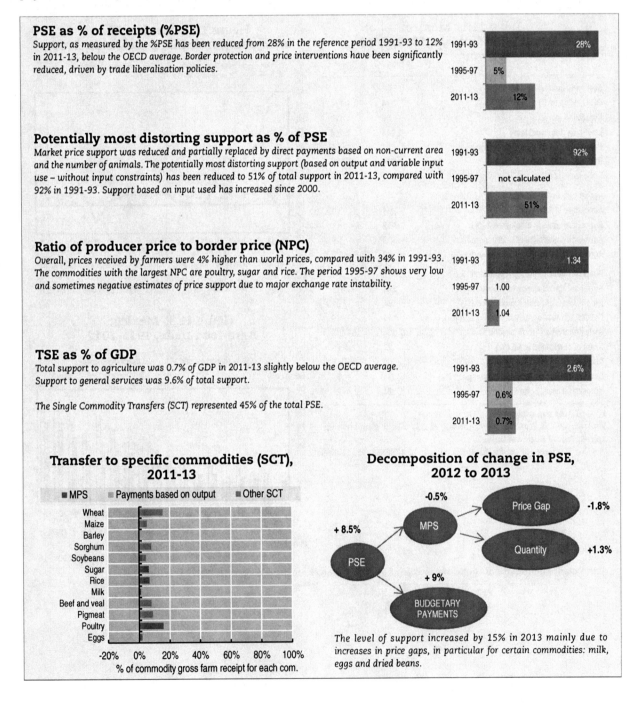

PSE as % of receipts (%PSE)

Support, as measured by the %PSE has been reduced from 28% in the reference period 1991-93 to 12% in 2011-13, below the OECD average. Border protection and price interventions have been significantly reduced, driven by trade liberalisation policies.

1991-93   28%
1995-97   5%
2011-13   12%

Potentially most distorting support as % of PSE

Market price support was reduced and partially replaced by direct payments based on non-current area and the number of animals. The potentially most distorting support (based on output and variable input use – without input constraints) has been reduced to 51% of total support in 2011-13, compared with 92% in 1991-93. Support based on input used has increased since 2000.

1991-93   92%
1995-97   not calculated
2011-13   51%

Ratio of producer price to border price (NPC)

Overall, prices received by farmers were 4% higher than world prices, compared with 34% in 1991-93. The commodities with the largest NPC are poultry, sugar and rice. The period 1995-97 shows very low and sometimes negative estimates of price support due to major exchange rate instability.

1991-93   1.34
1995-97   1.00
2011-13   1.04

TSE as % of GDP

Total support to agriculture was 0.7% of GDP in 2011-13 slightly below the OECD average. Support to general services was 9.6% of total support.

The Single Commodity Transfers (SCT) represented 45% of the total PSE.

1991-93   2.6%
1995-97   0.6%
2011-13   0.7%

Transfer to specific commodities (SCT), 2011-13

■ MPS ■ Payments based on output ■ Other SCT

Wheat, Maize, Barley, Sorghum, Soybeans, Sugar, Rice, Milk, Beef and veal, Pigmeat, Poultry, Eggs

-20% 0% 20% 40% 60% 80% 100%
% of commodity gross farm receipt for each com.

Decomposition of change in PSE, 2012 to 2013

-0.5% Price Gap -1.8%
+8.5% MPS
PSE Quantity +1.3%
+9%
BUDGETARY PAYMENTS

The level of support increased by 15% in 2013 mainly due to increases in price gaps, in particular for certain commodities: milk, eggs and dried beans.

Table 11.2. **Mexico: Estimates of support to agriculture**

Million MXN

	1991-93	1995-97	2011-13	2011	2012	2013p
Total value of production (at farm gate)	**86 539**	**182 276**	**685 397**	**618 901**	**696 731**	**740 559**
of which: share of MPS commodities (%)	68.7	70.1	67.5	67.8	67.9	66.8
Total value of consumption (at farm gate)	**82 475**	**181 410**	**756 437**	**681 343**	**817 916**	**770 052**
Producer Support Estimate (PSE)	**25 995**	**12 953**	**92 778**	**86 593**	**91 962**	**99 779**
Support based on commodity output	21 540	289	26 488	18 896	31 060	29 508
Market Price Support[1]	21 380	211	25 595	18 059	29 609	29 116
Payments based on output	160	79	893	837	1 451	392
Payments based on input use	4 445	5 729	42 098	44 961	37 207	44 127
Based on variable input use	2 296	2 373	20 478	23 161	17 132	21 142
with input constraints	0	0	0	0	0	0
Based on fixed capital formation	1 680	2 340	17 203	17 229	16 414	17 965
with input constraints	0	0	0	0	0	0
Based on on-farm services	469	1 016	4 417	4 571	3 661	5 020
with input constraints	0	0	0	0	0	0
Payments based on current A/An/R/I, production required	10	234	6 586	4 903	4 698	10 159
Based on Receipts / Income	0	100	0	0	0	0
Based on Area planted / Animal numbers	10	134	6 586	4 903	4 698	10 159
with input constraints	0	0	0	0	0	0
Payments based on non-current A/An/R/I, production required	0	0	3 832	3 956	4 041	3 497
Payments based on non-current A/An/R/I, production not required	0	6 701	13 774	13 878	14 956	12 488
With variable payment rates	0	0	0	0	0	0
with commodity exceptions	0	0	0	0	0	0
With fixed payment rates	0	6 701	13 774	13 878	14 956	12 488
with commodity exceptions	0	9	0	0	0	0
Payments based on non-commodity criteria	0	0	0	0	0	0
Based on long-term resource retirement	0	0	0	0	0	0
Based on a specific non-commodity output	0	0	0	0	0	0
Based on other non-commodity criteria	0	0	0	0	0	0
Miscellaneous payments	0	0	0	0	0	0
Percentage PSE (%)	**28.4**	**5.2**	**12.3**	**12.6**	**12.1**	**12.3**
Producer NPC (coeff.)	**1.34**	**1.00**	**1.04**	**1.03**	**1.05**	**1.04**
Producer NAC (coeff.)	**1.40**	**1.06**	**1.14**	**1.14**	**1.14**	**1.14**
General Services Support Estimate (GSSE)[2]	**3 229**	**2 743**	**10 267**	**9 958**	**12 554**	**8 287**
Agricultural knowledge and innovation system	889	1 486	5 575	5 304	5 540	5 883
Inspection and control	0	156	1 324	771	1 714	1 487
Development and maintenance of infrastructure	875	453	3 075	3 707	4 860	657
Marketing and promotion	255	161	290	176	439	256
Cost of public stockholding	1 210	487	2	1	2	3
Miscellaneous	0	0	0	0	0	1
Percentage GSSE (% of TSE)	**10.1**	**9.6**	**9.7**	**9.9**	**11.7**	**7.5**
Consumer Support Estimate (CSE)	**-19 400**	**-760**	**-24 272**	**-15 591**	**-31 053**	**-26 171**
Transfers to producers from consumers	-21 871	-1 829	-25 273	-18 697	-28 006	-29 116
Other transfers from consumers	-770	-3 513	-2 264	-884	-5 907	0
Transfers to consumers from taxpayers	2 629	4 515	3 237	3 904	2 861	2 946
Excess feed cost	612	67	29	86	0	0
Percentage CSE (%)	**-24.3**	**1.3**	**-3.2**	**-2.3**	**-3.8**	**-3.4**
Consumer NPC (coeff.)	**1.38**	**1.02**	**1.04**	**1.03**	**1.04**	**1.04**
Consumer NAC (coeff.)	**1.32**	**0.99**	**1.03**	**1.02**	**1.04**	**1.04**
Total Support Estimate (TSE)	**31 854**	**20 211**	**106 281**	**100 455**	**107 377**	**111 012**
Transfers from consumers	22 642	5 342	27 537	19 581	33 913	29 116
Transfers from taxpayers	9 983	18 382	81 008	81 758	79 370	81 895
Budget revenues	-770	-3 513	-2 264	-884	-5 907	0
Percentage TSE (% of GDP)	**2.6**	**0.6**	**0.7**	**0.7**	**0.7**	**0.7**
GDP deflator (1991-93=100)	100	201	673	654	677	689

Note: p: provisional. NPC: Nominal Protection Coefficient. NAC: Nominal Assistance Coefficient. A/An/R/I: Area planted/Animal numbers/ Receipts/Income.

1. Market Price Support (MPS) is net of producer levies and excess feed cost. MPS commodities for Mexico are: wheat, maize, barley, sorghum, coffee, beans, tomatoes, rice, soybean, sugar, milk, beef and veal, pigmeat, poultry and eggs.

2. A revised GSSE definition with new categories was introduced in 2014. When possible, the revision was implemented for the whole time series. The GSSE series and the resulting TSE are not comparable with the series published previously (for more details, see Annex 1.A2).

Source: OECD (2014), "Producer and Consumer Support Estimates", OECD *Agriculture Statistics Database*, doi: *http://dx.doi.org/10.1787/agr-pcse-data-en*.

StatLink ᴍᴋᴸ *http://dx.doi.org/10.1787/888933110600*

Description of policy developments

Main policy instruments

Mexico has significantly reformed its agricultural policies in the last two decades, reducing border protection through WTO, NAFTA and other trade agreements and implementing direct payment programmes. However, Mexico provides market price support to some commodities and implements a programme of payments based on output (*Ingreso Objetivo*), whose budgetary allocations had been reduced as commodity prices increased. Mexico has two large payment programmes based on historical parameters: **PROCAMPO** that is based on historical area and was established in 1994 and **PROGAN** that is based on historical livestock numbers and imposes environmental conditions since 2003.

Following the approval of the **National Development Plan** (NDP) 2013-18, a new programming framework or NDP 2013-18 for the food and agriculture sector was approved in December 2013. The plan will cover the six-year period of the new government. The plan contains a large set of diverse objectives: productivity, competitiveness, sustainability, equity and guaranteeing Mexican food security.

PROCAMPO will be substituted by **Productive PROAGRO** in 2014. The Productive PROAGRO requires that the payment is used for on-farm investment or expenditures on on-farm inputs. Subsidies to **price hedging** contracts and **energy** consumption (electricity and fuel) have recently increased and become significant agricultural programmes. Mexico also provides payments based on **on-farm investment** and subsidies to **crop insurance** through AGROASEMEX. Consumption subsidies for basic staples which target poor families are provided through the DICONSA rural shops and through LICONSA (for milk). Overall, Mexico has significantly reduced market price support in favour of direct payments based on historical levels and has more recently increased expenditure on payments based on input use.

Over half of Mexican territory operates under some type of social land ownership – *ejidos* or agrarian communities – in which special management regimes govern both collective land and land plots granted to individuals. This communal land system was intended to serve certain societal needs given the absence of the broader social safety nets that exist in most OECD countries. Reforms of the community land system in 1990 had limited practical impact. Although considered socially important, some of the provisions of the community land undermine investment in the agriculture sector, as well as its efficiency and adjustment capacity.

Domestic policy developments in 2013-14

The new **Food and Agriculture National Development Plan 2013-18** fixes quantitative objectives in terms of increasing the share of domestic production in the supply of main grains and oilseeds from 58% in 2011 to 75% in 2018, doubling the agricultural GDP growth to an annual rate of 3% and bringing the agro-food trade balance from deficit to zero. The ten pillars of the proposed strategy are: increasing the productivity of small farms, optimal use of water, enhancing the production of national inputs such as fertilisers and seeds, enhancing innovation through new extension, risk prevention and management, promoting the production of healthy food, enhancing competitive financing, supply and demand planning with information systems, and modernisation of the agriculture Ministry.

The main change in specific programmes is the transformation of PROCAMPO into a new programme called Productive PROAGRO. The beneficiaries are those farmers having received

PROCAMPO in the previous year and therefore, are still based on the historical entitlements defined in the register of PROCAMPO. Recipients of PROAGRO payments are divided into three groups: subsistence farmers (up to 5 hectares of rain-fed land or 0.2 hectares of irrigated land); transition farmers (from 5 to 20 ha, or 0.2 to 5 ha for irrigated land); and commercial farmers (more than 20 ha of rain fed or 5 ha of irrigated land). The amount of payment differs for each type of farm. Self-consumption farmers will receive MEX 1 300 (USD 102) per hectare, with a minimum payment equivalent to one hectare. If they have less than three hectares and are located in municipalities under the **National Program Mexico Without Hunger** (PNMSH), they will receive a higher payment of MEX 1 500 (USD 117). Other farmers will receive MEX 963 (USD 75) per hectare. The payment per person is subject to an area limitation of 100 ha.

Productive PROAGRO payments require farmers to plant. Unlike PROCAMPO, the new payments are linked to specific actions to improve land productivity ("vinculación productiva"). Farmers will have to give proof that the payment has been used for technical, productive, organisational or investment improvements, that is, technical assistance, machinery, certified seeds, fertilisers, restructuring, insurance or price hedging.

The 2014 budget includes MEX 7 738 million (USD 606 million) for the market development programme. This will be mainly spent on price hedging subsidies and *Ingreso Objetivo* payments based on output. No particular changes are foreseen for these policy programmes.

Trade policy developments in 2013-14

In December 2013, a new import tariff law was published. Amongst the changes there is an increase in the MFN tariff of white maize from zero to 20%.

In December 2008, Mexico and Canada requested consultations on the **United States** mandatory country of origin labelling (COOL) provisions in the Food, Conservation, and Energy Act 2008 (2008 Farm Bill). The Appellate Body report of June 2012 upheld the purpose of the COOL measure but found that the manner in which it fulfilled that purpose was inconsistent with the United States' WTO obligations. The United States informed the Dispute Settlement Body (DSB) that it intended to come to comply with the Appellate Body findings. At the DSB meeting on 24 May 2013, the United States informed the DSB that on 23 May 2013, the United States Department of Agriculture (USDA) issued a final ruling that made certain changes to the COOL labelling requirements that were inconsistent with Article 2.1 of the TBT Agreement. On 19 August 2013, Mexico requested the establishment of a compliance panel. On 27 September 2013, a compliance panel was formed to determine whether the new regulation brings COOL into conformity with the WTO obligations. The Compliance Panel is expected to issue its findings in July 2014.

PART II

Chapter 12

Developments in agricultural policies and support in New Zealand

The New Zealand country chapter includes a brief evaluation of policy developments and related support to agriculture, contextual information on the framework in which agricultural policies are implemented and the main characteristics of the agricultural sector, an evaluation of support in 2012-13 and in the longer term perspective, and a brief description of the main policy developments in 2013-14.

Evaluation of policy developments

- Following the agricultural policy reforms in the mid-1980s, production and trade distorting policies supporting the sector have virtually disappeared, and the level of support has been the lowest across the OECD for the last two decades. Almost all domestic prices are aligned with world market prices, and support is only provided in the context of animal disease control and relief in the event of climatic disasters.

- Following reforms of the statutory producer organisation and the marketing board, almost all sectors have been deregulated. Restrictions on who could export dairy products have been eliminated since the end of 2010. The kiwifruit sector is an exception, as Zespri, a New Zealand company, is the only company that has automatic rights to export New Zealand produced kiwifruit to markets other than Australia. Other groups can export in collaboration with Zespri or independently to Australia.

- New Zealand has established national frameworks for land and water quality and allocation to enhance the sustainable management of biological and natural resources. Agriculture has started mandatory reporting to the Emissions Trading Scheme in 2012. A review of the scheme is scheduled for 2015. The price-based mechanism will be extended to encourage the reduction of agriculture green-house gas emissions. Efforts to develop additional market-based approaches to environmental issues offer opportunities to enhance environmentally sustainable development.

- New Zealand's Import Health Standards effectively prevent fresh poultry, eggs and some bee products from being imported under current economic conditions. In light of past OECD work on non-tariff measures, New Zealand should investigate alternatives to the current system for achieving its sanitary objectives.

Figure 12.1. **New Zealand: PSE level and composition by support categories, 1986-2013**

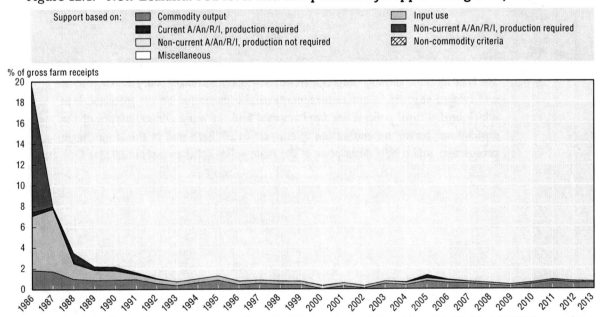

Source: OECD (2014), "Producer and Consumer Support Estimates", OECD Agriculture Statistics Database, http://dx.doi.org/10.1787/agr-pcse-data-en.

StatLink ⟶ http://dx.doi.org/10.1787/888933109935

Contextual information

New Zealand is a small open economy with a relatively high dependency on international trade. New Zealand is a consistent net exporter of agro-food products, with more than half of its total exports coming from the agro-food sector. In turn, agro-food imports represent some 11% of the country's total imports. New Zealand is the world's largest exporter of dairy products and sheep meat. The importance of agriculture in the total economy is high compared to most other OECD countries, with agriculture accounting for some 7% in both GDP and employment. New Zealand's farming system is primarily based on year-round grass-fed livestock.

Table 12.1. New Zealand: Contextual indicators, 1995, 2012[1]

	1995	2012[1]
Economic context		
GDP (billion USD)	62	171
Population (million)	3.7	4.4
Land area (thousand km^2)	263	263
Population density (inhabitants/km^2)	14	16
GDP per capita, PPP (USD)	17 639	32 847
Trade as % of GDP	22.3	22.1
Agriculture in the economy		
Agriculture in GDP (%)	7.1	6.6
Agriculture share in employment (%)	9.4	6.9
Agro-food exports (% of total exports)	49.1	57.0
Agro-food imports (% of total imports)	7.8	10.7
Characteristics of the agricultural sector		
Agro-food trade balance (million USD)	5 657	17 200
Crop in total agricultural production (%)	25	22
Livestock in total agricultural production (%)	75	78
Agricultural area (AA) (thousand ha)	14 975	11 371
Share of arable land in AA (%)	11	4
Share of irrigated land in AA (%)	..	6
Share of agriculture in water consumption (%)	24	57
Nitrogen balance, kg/ha	34	48

1. Or latest available year.
Sources: OECD Statistical Databases, ITCS, World Development Indicators and national data.

StatLink ⬛ http://dx.doi.org/10.1787/888933110619

Figure 12.2. New Zealand: Main macroeconomic indicators, 1995-2013

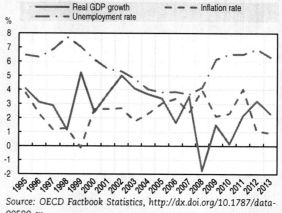

Source: OECD Factbook Statistics, http://dx.doi.org/10.1787/data-00590-en.

StatLink ⬛ http://dx.doi.org/10.1787/888933109954

Figure 12.3. New Zealand: Agro-food trade, 1995-2012

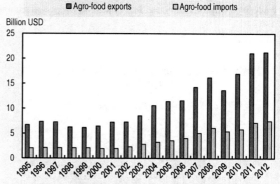

Source: International Trade by Commodity Statistics (ITCS) Database.

StatLink ⬛ http://dx.doi.org/10.1787/888933109973

Note: Detailed definitions of contextual indicators and their sources are provided in Annex II.A1.

Development of support to agriculture

New Zealand's agriculture is an export oriented sector, representing more than half of the country's total exports. With the exception of a few products subject to import restrictions related to sanitary measures, domestic prices are aligned with world markets, and the level of support is consistently the lowest among OECD countries. Policy measures focus on sector-wide general services, particularly research, animal disease control and water management.

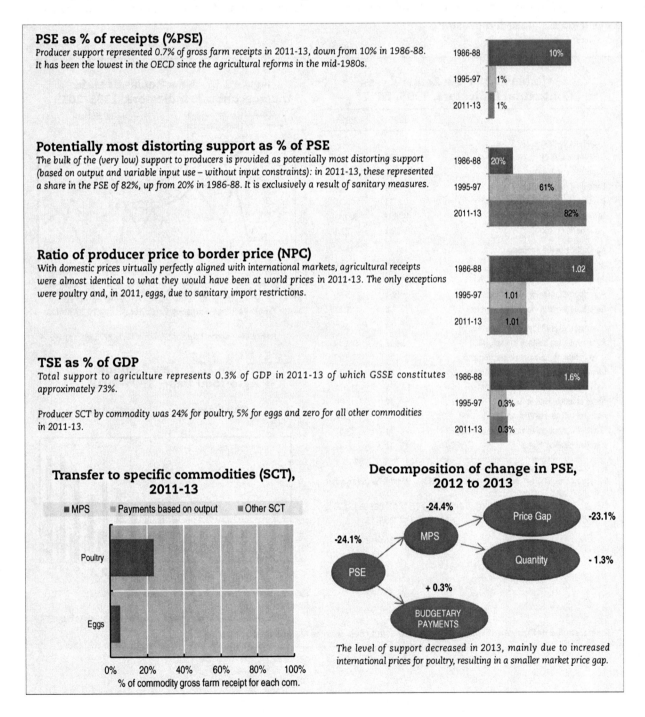

PSE as % of receipts (%PSE)
Producer support represented 0.7% of gross farm receipts in 2011-13, down from 10% in 1986-88. It has been the lowest in the OECD since the agricultural reforms in the mid-1980s.

1986-88 — 10%
1995-97 — 1%
2011-13 — 1%

Potentially most distorting support as % of PSE
The bulk of the (very low) support to producers is provided as potentially most distorting support (based on output and variable input use – without input constraints): in 2011-13, these represented a share in the PSE of 82%, up from 20% in 1986-88. It is exclusively a result of sanitary measures.

1986-88 — 20%
1995-97 — 61%
2011-13 — 82%

Ratio of producer price to border price (NPC)
With domestic prices virtually perfectly aligned with international markets, agricultural receipts were almost identical to what they would have been at world prices in 2011-13. The only exceptions were poultry and, in 2011, eggs, due to sanitary import restrictions.

1986-88 — 1.02
1995-97 — 1.01
2011-13 — 1.01

TSE as % of GDP
Total support to agriculture represents 0.3% of GDP in 2011-13 of which GSSE constitutes approximately 73%.

Producer SCT by commodity was 24% for poultry, 5% for eggs and zero for all other commodities in 2011-13.

1986-88 — 1.6%
1995-97 — 0.3%
2011-13 — 0.3%

Transfer to specific commodities (SCT), 2011-13

■ MPS   ■ Payments based on output   ■ Other SCT

Poultry

Eggs

0%   20%   40%   60%   80%   100%
% of commodity gross farm receipt for each com.

Decomposition of change in PSE, 2012 to 2013

-24.4%   Price Gap   -23.1%
-24.1%   MPS
PSE   Quantity   - 1.3%
+ 0.3%
BUDGETARY PAYMENTS

The level of support decreased in 2013, mainly due to increased international prices for poultry, resulting in a smaller market price gap.

Table 12.2. **New Zealand: Estimates of support to agriculture**

Million NZD

	1986-88	1995-97	2011-13	2011	2012	2013p
Total value of production (at farm gate)	**6 860**	**9 669**	**23 174**	**22 556**	**21 583**	**25 384**
of which: share of MPS commodities (%)	72.1	72.1	78.3	77.9	77.6	79.5
Total value of consumption (at farm gate)	**1 683**	**2 333**	**3 875**	**4 019**	**3 693**	**3 913**
Producer Support Estimate (PSE)	**786**	**94**	**172**	**202**	**179**	**136**
Support based on commodity output	114	58	141	172	148	104
Market Price Support[1]	112	58	141	172	148	104
Payments based on output	3	0	0	0	0	0
Payments based on input use	314	35	30	29	31	31
Based on variable input use	3	0	0	0	0	0
with input constraints	0	0	0	0	0	0
Based on fixed capital formation	271	0	0	0	0	0
with input constraints	0	0	0	0	0	0
Based on on-farm services	40	35	30	29	31	31
with input constraints	0	0	0	0	0	0
Payments based on current A/An/R/I, production required	42	1	1	1	0	1
Based on Receipts / Income	42	1	1	1	0	1
Based on Area planted / Animal numbers	0	0	0	0	0	0
with input constraints	0	0	0	0	0	0
Payments based on non-current A/An/R/I, production required	315	0	0	0	0	0
Payments based on non-current A/An/R/I, production not required	0	0	0	0	0	0
With variable payment rates	0	0	0	0	0	0
with commodity exceptions	0	0	0	0	0	0
With fixed payment rates	0	0	0	0	0	0
with commodity exceptions	0	0	0	0	0	0
Payments based on non-commodity criteria	0	0	0	0	0	0
Based on long-term resource retirement	0	0	0	0	0	0
Based on a specific non-commodity output	0	0	0	0	0	0
Based on other non-commodity criteria	0	0	0	0	0	0
Miscellaneous payments	0	0	0	0	0	0
Percentage PSE (%)	**10.4**	**1.0**	**0.8**	**0.9**	**0.8**	**0.5**
Producer NPC (coeff.)	**1.02**	**1.01**	**1.01**	**1.01**	**1.01**	**1.00**
Producer NAC (coeff.)	**1.12**	**1.01**	**1.01**	**1.01**	**1.01**	**1.01**
General Services Support Estimate (GSSE)[2]	**203**	**180**	**455**	**457**	**475**	**433**
Agricultural knowledge and innovation system	102	116	174	156	197	171
Inspection and control	54	43	180	208	169	164
Development and maintenance of infrastructure	47	20	100	93	110	97
Marketing and promotion	0	0	0	0	0	0
Cost of public stockholding	0	0	0	0	0	0
Miscellaneous	0	0	0	0	0	0
Percentage GSSE (% of TSE)	**26.4**	**65.8**	**72.7**	**69.3**	**72.7**	**76.1**
Consumer Support Estimate (CSE)	**-110**	**-51**	**-135**	**-158**	**-143**	**-105**
Transfers to producers from consumers	-106	-51	-135	-158	-143	-104
Other transfers from consumers	-3	0	0	0	0	0
Transfers to consumers from taxpayers	0	0	0	0	0	0
Excess feed cost	0	0	0	0	0	0
Percentage CSE (%)	**-6.6**	**-2.2**	**-3.5**	**-3.9**	**-3.9**	**-2.7**
Consumer NPC (coeff.)	**1.07**	**1.02**	**1.04**	**1.04**	**1.04**	**1.03**
Consumer NAC (coeff.)	**1.07**	**1.02**	**1.04**	**1.04**	**1.04**	**1.03**
Total Support Estimate (TSE)	**989**	**274**	**627**	**659**	**654**	**568**
Transfers from consumers	110	51	135	158	143	105
Transfers from taxpayers	882	223	492	501	512	464
Budget revenues	-3	0	0	0	0	0
Percentage TSE (% of GDP)	**1.6**	**0.3**	**0.3**	**0.3**	**0.3**	**0.3**
GDP deflator (1986-88=100)	**100**	**129**	**182**	**181**	**180**	**185**

Note: p: provisional. NPC: Nominal Protection Coefficient. NAC: Nominal Assistance Coefficient. A/An/R/I: Area planted/Animal numbers/ Receipts/Income.

1. Market Price Support (MPS) is net of producer levies and excess feed cost. MPS commodities for New Zealand are: wheat, maize, oats, barley, milk, beef and veal, sheep meat, wool, pigmeat, poultry and eggs.

2. A revised GSSE definition with new categories was introduced in 2014. When possible, the revision was implemented for the whole time series. The GSSE series and the resulting TSE are not comparable with the series published previously (for more details, see Annex 1.A2).

Source: OECD (2014), "Producer and Consumer Support Estimates", OECD *Agriculture Statistics Database, doi: http://dx.doi.org/10.1787/agr-pcse-data-en.*

StatLink ⟐⟐⟐ *http://dx.doi.org/10.1787/888933110638*

Description of policy developments

Main policy instruments

New Zealand largely limits its agriculture support to expenditures on general services, such as agricultural research and bio security controls for pests and diseases. A significant share of the costs of regulatory and operational functions, including border control, is charged to beneficiaries.

In the event of natural disasters that are beyond the response capacity of private insurance, local farmer organisations or territorial local authorities, farmers may receive restricted assistance to help replace production capacity. In the event of a medium or large scale natural disaster farmers whose income falls below a threshold level may, for a limited period and if the farmers cannot support themselves with cash assets or with other sources of income, be eligible for the equivalent of the unemployment benefit.

New Zealand requires **Import Health Standards (IHS)** for all risk goods before they can be imported into New Zealand. Some products (representing a small share of New Zealand's agricultural output: eggs, uncooked poultry and some bee products) cannot be imported as they fail to meet the relevant IHS. These measures lead to some market price support for the mentioned products.

Statutory marketing boards, which historically controlled most agricultural production, were disestablished during the 1980s and 1990s. Remaining restrictions on rights to export dairy products into specific tariff quota markets had been removed by the end of 2010. Regulations are maintained on exports of kiwifruit: the New Zealand company *Zespri* has the default but not sole right to export kiwifruit to all markets other than Australia, while other groups willing to export can do so independently to Australia or in collaboration with *Zespri* to other countries. In case of objection by *Zespri* to collaborative marketing applications, Kiwifruit New Zealand (the regulator) can still approve collaborative marketing applications if it expects overall wealth of New Zealand kiwifruit suppliers to increase.

"Industry good" activities[1] (such as research and development, forming and developing marketing strategies, and providing technical advice) previously undertaken by statutory marketing boards are now managed through producer levy-funded industry organisations under the Commodity Levies Act 1990. Under this legislation, levies can only be imposed if they are supported by producers, and producers themselves decide how levies are spent. With a very limited number of exceptions, levy funds may not be spent on commercial or trading activities. The levying organisations must seek a new mandate to collect levies every six years through a referendum of levy payers.

Two key policy measures that address agri-environmental issues are the **Resource Management Act 1991 (RMA)** and the **Sustainable Farming Fund (SFF)**. The objective of the RMA is to promote the sustainable management of natural and physical resources, including soil, water, air, biodiversity and the coastal environment. RMA responsibilities are generally assigned to regional and district councils. They include environmental regulation, soil conservation, flood control and drainage works, and plant and animal pest control. In early 2013, the Government initiated proposals to reform the RMA. The proposals include increased national direction on planning matters, aiming at greater consistency and improved planning certainty.

The SFF, which was set up in 2000, supports community and industry driven projects aimed at improving the productive and environmental performance of the primary sectors. In 2011, the SFF was expanded to include aquaculture reflecting the Ministry for Primary Industries' new responsibility for fisheries as well as agriculture, forestry and food safety. In late 2012, a smaller and additional funding round was held, which focused specifically on Maori agribusiness projects. Overall, the Fund has backed around 900 projects over 13 years, supporting sustainability and resilience in the primary sector.

The **Primary Growth Partnership (PGP)** programme was introduced in 2009 and is administered by the Ministry for Primary Industries. The PGP is a Public-Private-Partnership initiative (industry contributions must be at least equal to Crown funding) that invests in significant programmes of research and innovation to boost agricultural productivity, economic growth and the sustainability of New Zealand's primary, forestry and food sectors. The total PGP funding commitment from government and industry in these programmes is NZD 701 million (USD 574 million),[2] with NZD 85 million (USD 70 million) paid to programmes underway to 30 September 2013.

Domestic policy developments in 2013-14

The main policy developments that may impact on agricultural production include changes to dairy industry regulations; encouraging innovation and sustainable growth; managing water and land resources; greenhouse gas initiatives; and biosecurity. The detailed policy changes are as follows:

A number of changes were made to the **Dairy Industry Restructuring Act of 2001 (DIRA)** and its associated Raw Milk Regulations in 2012-13. These changes were to improve transparency of the milk price setting process by Fonterra (New Zealand's largest farmer owned dairy cooperative), enabling Fonterra to proceed with tradability of its shares (which it chose to do in November 2012), and to ensure that the regulations remained appropriate. The Government continues to monitor and evaluate the implementation of these changes. Since the DIRA regime was put in place, the share of milk collected by the Fonterra Co-operative has declined from about 96% of the New Zealand total in 2002-03 to approximately 89% in the 2012-13 season.

The **Irrigation Acceleration Fund (IAF)** was announced in the 2011-12 budget. The IAF superseded the Community Irrigation Fund established in 2007 and additionally builds on the grant funding support previously provided to irrigation-related projects through the Sustainable Farming Fund. The IAF has a budget of NZD 35 million (USD 29 million), spread over five years, and will support development of proposals to an investment-ready stage as well as strategic water management studies. To be eligible for funding, the projects will need to promote efficient use of water, environmental management, and demonstrate a commitment to good industry practice.

The **Crown Water Irrigation Investments Limited (CWI)** was announced as part of the 2013-14 budget and then established on 1 July 2013. The company has been established to act as a minority investor for regional off-farm water infrastructure projects, including potentially projects that were supported to the investment-ready phase by the IAF. The company will only provide bridging investment through the critical uptake risk period. Projects must be demonstrably viable in the medium term with clear exit strategies required before any investment proceeds. The Government has indicated a total investment of up to NZD 400 million (USD 328 million); an initial tranche of NZD 80 million (USD 66 million) has been provided to the company.

Agriculture began mandatory reporting at processor level in the **New Zealand Emissions Trading Scheme** (NZ ETS) from 1 January 2012. This affects meat processors, dairy processors, nitrogen fertiliser manufacturers and importers, and live animal exporters, although some exemptions apply. The NZ ETS also imposes an emissions cost on the transport fuels, electricity production, synthetic gases, waste and industrial processes sectors. This provides an incentive to reduce emissions from farm inputs including petrol, diesel and electricity, as well as the transport and processing of farm products. The New Zealand Government continues to look at ways to develop mitigation technologies to reduce agricultural greenhouse gas emissions. This includes through funding the New Zealand Agricultural Greenhouse Gas Research Centre and by committing NZD 45 million (USD 37 million) until June 2016 to fund New Zealand's participation in the Global Research Alliance. The Alliance brings countries together to focus on research, development and extension of technologies and practices that will help deliver ways to grow more food (and more climate-resilient food systems) without increasing greenhouse gas emissions. New Zealand currently holds the Secretariat of the Global Research Alliance.

The Ministry for Primary Industries is supporting the industry-led programme for **managing the kiwifruit disease Psa** (*Pseudomonas syringae pv. actinidiae*). Since its first identification in New Zealand in 2010, Psa has spread to the majority of kiwifruit growing areas. In December 2012, the Government declared Psa to be a biosecurity event under New Zealand's Primary Sector Recovery Policy (which covers adverse climatic and biosecurity events). This declaration means that kiwifruit growers who have been severely impacted by Psa may be eligible for Rural Assistance Payments. Farm households must apply to receive the Rural Assistance Payment and are only eligible when they have no other significant income from the farm business as a result of the biosecurity event, or other sources of income and realisable cash assets. The level of the payment provides for essential living expenses only and at the same rate as unemployment benefits. Payments are for a maximum of 12 months and do not cover losses of income, livestock, land or other production factors. In the event that a climatic or biosecurity event occurs on a scale that will seriously impact the regional or national economy, central government may provide additional support to local community and regional organisations under the **Primary Sector Recovery Policy**.

New Zealand's mandatory **National Animal Identification and Tracing (NAIT)** scheme, which is compulsory for cattle since July 2012, has been expanded to become compulsory for deer from 1 March 2013. Along with other benefits, the NAIT scheme will ensure that New Zealand keeps pace with individual animal traceability systems adopted by other countries. By 30 November 2013, over 74 000 people in day-to-day charge of cattle or deer were registered as "persons in charge of animals" (PICAs) under the NAIT scheme. The NAIT Act 2012 sets out the legal framework for collecting information on livestock location, movement and other history. To support the development of NAIT, the Ministry for Primary Industries developed FarmsOnLine, a web-based system that supplies the contact and location detail of rural properties in New Zealand. This system, which became operational in March 2011, also improves the ability to respond to biosecurity alerts or natural disasters.

Progress has been made on developing a Maori agribusiness programme. The focus of the programme is to provide Maori landowners with access to information, skills and networks to assist them with improving productivity on their collectively owned lands. A stocktake of initiatives that deliver skills, training and capacity development opportunities relevant to Maori was undertaken in 2012/13. Prototype projects, such as supporting the development of a Memorandum of Understanding (MoU) between iwi (tribal groups) for the joint management of a property, have also been launched. To date, over NZD 200 000 (USD 164 000) has been spent on activities including advisory services and feasibility studies.

Trade policy developments in 2013-14

New Zealand currently has nine **Free Trade Agreements** (FTAs) in force, which account for some 50% of its primary industry exports. In the past six years, New Zealand has entered into three new FTAs with individual countries: **China** (2008); **Malaysia** (2009); and **Hong Kong (China)** (2011). New Zealand has also entered into a regional trade agreement with the **Association of South East Asian Nations (ASEAN)** and **Australia**. The **ASEAN Australia and New Zealand** Free Trade

Agreement (AANZFTA) entered into force for all signatories on 10 January 2012. In 2013, an Economic Co-operation Agreement between New Zealand and the **Separate Customs Territory of Taiwan, Penghu, Kinmen,** and **Matsu (Chinese Taipei)** was also concluded, which entered into force in December 2013.

During the 2012/13 period, New Zealand was heavily involved in FTA negotiations with: countries under the **Trans-Pacific Partnership** (TPP); the Regional Comprehensive Economic Partnership (RCEP); the **customs union of Russia, Belarus and Kazakhstan**; **Korea**, and **India**. Finally, New Zealand began discussions with **Colombia** with a view to a future FTA.

Notes

1. Activities "beneficial to the industry, but whose benefits cannot be captured by those who fund or provide the activity", or "long-term investments in the industry made with the expectation of accelerating delivery of better technology and products for the industry" (NZIER, 2007).

2. All values in this policy description use the 2013 exchange rate for monetary conversion.

Reference

NZIER (2007), "Productivity, Profitability and Industry Good Activities", *Report to Dairy Insight*, February 2007, accessed on 28 March 2014 from *http://nzier.org.nz/sites/nzier.org.nz/files/Productivity%20profitability%20 and%20industry%20good%20activities%20Feb%202007.pdf.*

PART II

Chapter 13

Developments in agricultural policies and support in Norway

The Norway country chapter includes a brief evaluation of policy developments and related support to agriculture, contextual information on the framework in which agricultural policies are implemented and the main characteristics of the agricultural sector, an evaluation of support in 2012-13 and in the longer term perspective, and a brief description of the main policy developments in 2013-14.

Evaluation of policy developments

● In the past decades, the move towards less support was rather modest. The level of support has been reduced but it is still three times higher than the OECD average. Despite much lower price distortions, agriculture in Norway remains among the most highly protected. Greater efforts can be made to further reduce the share of production-linked support and increase market access. Policy reforms such as the removal of the administered price for beef, sheep meat and eggs, and increased flexibility in milk quota leasing would improve market orientation and allow better allocation of resources. Further reduction of border protection is another step to be considered in that direction.

● There has been some move away from payments based on output, but market price support remains the main component of support to farms. Payments based on current production factors have increased. While the share of potentially most production and trade distorting support has declined, it still represents around half of the support in the most recent years.

● Measures to improve environmental performance of agriculture, such as the action plan to reduce risk related to the use of pesticides with a stronger focus on integrated plant management, provide important opportunities to further improve sustainability in production.

● To reach its objectives of rural development particularly in remote areas, Norway should consider the use of more space-based rural development policies and social policies, rather than agriculture specific policies to reach its objectives.

● Overall, Norway should continue its effort to reach its various policy objectives (food security, maintain agriculture across the whole country, landscape amenities) at lower costs to consumers and taxpayers. More market orientation of the sector and better targeted direct payments, and a switch to more general policy instruments are avenues to be further explored.

Figure 13.1. Norway: PSE level and composition by support categories, 1986-2013

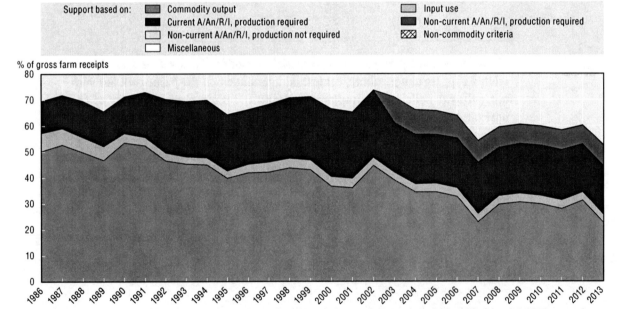

Source: OECD (2014), "Producer and Consumer Support Estimates", OECD Agriculture Statistics Database, doi: http://dx.doi.org/10.1787/agr-pcse-data-en.
StatLink ⧉ http://dx.doi.org/10.1787/888933109992

Contextual information

Norway is a developed, high-income country. It has the second highest GDP per capita in the OECD area, and a relatively low unemployment and modest inflation rate. Agriculture constitutes a relatively small share of GDP (1.5%) and employment (1.9%). Given the cold climate and the widespread incidence of thin soils and mountainous areas, only a small fraction of the land is suitable for cultivation. The farm structure is dominated by relatively small family farms, many of which are in remote locations operating under difficult conditions. Norway is a net agro-food importing country. Agro-food imports represent around 8% of total imports while agro-food exports represented 0.6% of total exports.

Table 13.1. **Norway: Contextual indicators, 1995, 2012[1]**

	1995	2012[1]
Economic context		
GDP (billion USD)	149	500
Population (million)	4	5
Land area (thousand km^2)	304	305
Population density (inhabitants/km^2)	11	13
GDP per capita, PPP (USD)	23 571	66 135
Trade as % of GDP	25.0	24.8
Agriculture in the economy		
Agriculture in GDP (%)	3.1	1.2
Agriculture share in employment (%)	4.3	1.8
Agro-food exports (% of total exports)	1.3	0.6
Agro-food imports (% of total imports)	6.2	8.6
Characteristics of the agricultural sector		
Agro-food trade balance (million USD)	-1 497	-6 570
Crop in total agricultural production (%)	25	24
Livestock in total agricultural production (%)	75	76
Agricultural area (AA) (thousand ha)	1 127	998
Share of arable land in AA (%)	88	82
Share of irrigated land in AA (%)	..	4
Share of agriculture in water consumption (%)	9	28
Nitrogen balance, kg/ha	108	95

1. Or latest available year.
Sources: OECD Statistical Databases, ITCS, World Development Indicators and national data.

StatLink ⏩ http://dx.doi.org/10.1787/888933110657

Figure 13.2. **Norway: Main macroeconomic indicators, 1995-2013**

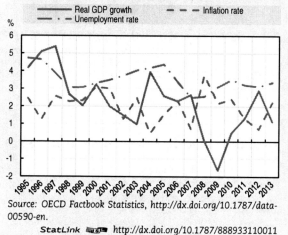

Source: OECD Factbook Statistics, http://dx.doi.org/10.1787/data-00590-en.

StatLink ⏩ http://dx.doi.org/10.1787/888933110011

Figure 13.3. **Norway: Agro-food trade, 1995-2012**

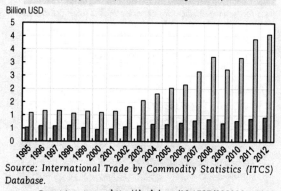

Source: International Trade by Commodity Statistics (ITCS) Database.

StatLink ⏩ http://dx.doi.org/10.1787/888933110030

Note: Detailed definitions of contextual indicators and their sources are provided in Annex II.A1.

Development of support to agriculture

While Norway has made continuous but rather modest progress in reducing the level of support, a more pronounced shift in the composition of support has taken place. Commodity based support (mainly market price support) now represents around half of total support. Despite the reduction in price distortions, prices received by producers are on average 70% above world market prices. There is a rather even distribution of support among commodities.

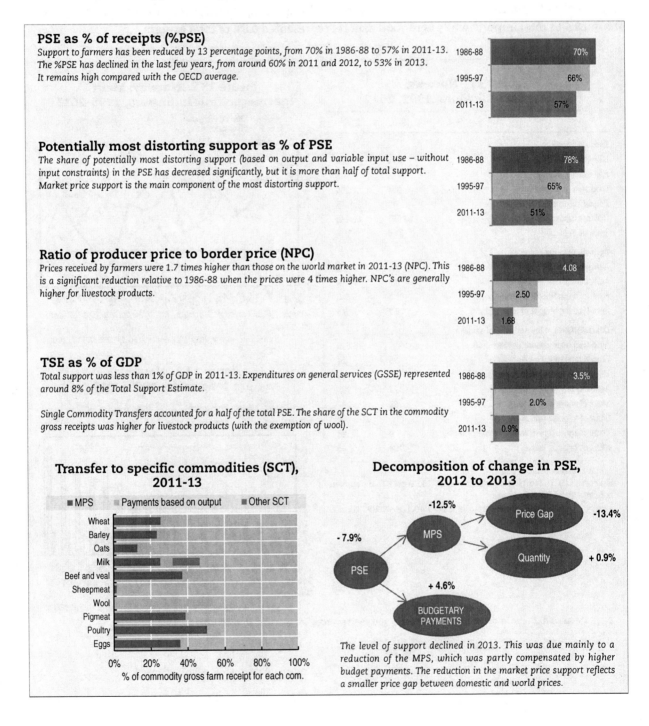

PSE as % of receipts (%PSE)
Support to farmers has been reduced by 13 percentage points, from 70% in 1986-88 to 57% in 2011-13. The %PSE has declined in the last few years, from around 60% in 2011 and 2012, to 53% in 2013. It remains high compared with the OECD average.

1986-88 — 70%
1995-97 — 66%
2011-13 — 57%

Potentially most distorting support as % of PSE
The share of potentially most distorting support (based on output and variable input use – without input constraints) in the PSE has decreased significantly, but it is more than half of total support. Market price support is the main component of the most distorting support.

1986-88 — 78%
1995-97 — 65%
2011-13 — 51%

Ratio of producer price to border price (NPC)
Prices received by farmers were 1.7 times higher than those on the world market in 2011-13 (NPC). This is a significant reduction relative to 1986-88 when the prices were 4 times higher. NPC's are generally higher for livestock products.

1986-88 — 4.08
1995-97 — 2.50
2011-13 — 1.68

TSE as % of GDP
Total support was less than 1% of GDP in 2011-13. Expenditures on general services (GSSE) represented around 8% of the Total Support Estimate.

Single Commodity Transfers accounted for a half of the total PSE. The share of the SCT in the commodity gross receipts was higher for livestock products (with the exemption of wool).

1986-88 — 3.5%
1995-97 — 2.0%
2011-13 — 0.9%

Transfer to specific commodities (SCT), 2011-13

■ MPS   Payments based on output   ■ Other SCT

Wheat, Barley, Oats, Milk, Beef and veal, Sheepmeat, Wool, Pigmeat, Poultry, Eggs

0%   20%   40%   60%   80%   100%
% of commodity gross farm receipt for each com.

Decomposition of change in PSE, 2012 to 2013

PSE -7.9%
MPS -12.5%
Price Gap -13.4%
Quantity +0.9%
BUDGETARY PAYMENTS +4.6%

The level of support declined in 2013. This was due mainly to a reduction of the MPS, which was partly compensated by higher budget payments. The reduction in the market price support reflects a smaller price gap between domestic and world prices.

Table 13.2. **Norway: Estimates of support to agriculture**

Million NOK

	1986-88	1995-97	2011-13	2011	2012	2013p
Total value of production (at farm gate)	**17 354**	**18 232**	**25 669**	**24 230**	**25 974**	**26 803**
of which: share of MPS commodities (%)	73.3	77.5	74.7	76.6	71.5	75.9
Total value of consumption (at farm gate)	**17 899**	**18 129**	**28 022**	**25 816**	**29 396**	**28 854**
Producer Support Estimate (PSE)	**19 175**	**19 246**	**22 173**	**21 623**	**23 371**	**21 527**
Support based on commodity output	13 877	11 997	10 593	10 360	12 107	9 312
Market Price Support[1]	9 274	8 444	8 971	8 779	10 526	7 607
Payments based on output	4 603	3 554	1 622	1 581	1 581	1 705
Payments based on input use	1 721	960	1 261	1 253	1 253	1 279
Based on variable input use	1 020	551	707	689	689	741
with input constraints	0	1	0	0	0	0
Based on fixed capital formation	628	339	466	476	476	447
with input constraints	0	0	0	0	0	0
Based on on-farm services	73	70	88	87	87	91
with input constraints	2	0	0	0	0	0
Payments based on current A/An/R/I, production required	3 577	6 254	7 314	7 167	7 167	7 609
Based on Receipts / Income	0	0	863	789	789	1 012
Based on Area planted / Animal numbers	3 577	6 254	6 451	6 378	6 378	6 597
with input constraints	0	104	587	583	583	594
Payments based on non-current A/An/R/I, production required	0	0	2 950	2 791	2 791	3 268
Payments based on non-current A/An/R/I, production not required	0	0	0	0	0	0
With variable payment rates	0	0	0	0	0	0
with commodity exceptions	0	0	0	0	0	0
With fixed payment rates	0	0	0	0	0	0
with commodity exceptions	0	0	0	0	0	0
Payments based on non-commodity criteria	0	34	55	53	53	59
Based on long-term resource retirement	0	0	0	0	0	0
Based on a specific non-commodity output	0	34	55	53	53	59
Based on other non-commodity criteria	0	0	0	0	0	0
Miscellaneous payments	0	0	0	0	0	0
Percentage PSE (%)	**70.3**	**66.3**	**57.1**	**58.3**	**60.2**	**52.9**
Producer NPC (coeff.)	**4.08**	**2.50**	**1.68**	**1.74**	**1.75**	**1.54**
Producer NAC (coeff.)	**3.38**	**2.97**	**2.34**	**2.40**	**2.51**	**2.12**
General Services Support Estimate (GSSE)[2]	**848**	**1 046**	**1 996**	**1 911**	**1 953**	**2 123**
Agricultural knowledge and innovation system	472	623	1 045	1 003	1 036	1 096
Inspection and control	33	173	671	644	644	726
Development and maintenance of infrastructure	202	108	217	211	220	222
Marketing and promotion	141	120	62	54	54	79
Cost of public stockholding	0	22	0	0	0	0
Miscellaneous	0	0	0	0	0	0
Percentage GSSE (% of TSE)	**3.9**	**5.0**	**8.1**	**8.0**	**7.6**	**8.8**
Consumer Support Estimate (CSE)	**-9 141**	**-8 343**	**-9 597**	**-9 738**	**-10 484**	**-8 569**
Transfers to producers from consumers	-11 381	-9 038	-9 550	-9 710	-10 409	-8 530
Other transfers from consumers	-959	-548	-679	-647	-693	-698
Transfers to consumers from taxpayers	1 522	542	436	437	437	433
Excess feed cost	1 677	700	196	181	181	225
Percentage CSE (%)	**-55.8**	**-47.5**	**-34.9**	**-38.4**	**-36.2**	**-30.2**
Consumer NPC (coeff.)	**3.24**	**2.13**	**1.58**	**1.67**	**1.61**	**1.47**
Consumer NAC (coeff.)	**2.27**	**1.91**	**1.54**	**1.62**	**1.57**	**1.43**
Total Support Estimate (TSE)	**21 545**	**20 834**	**24 605**	**23 971**	**25 761**	**24 083**
Transfers from consumers	12 340	9 585	10 229	10 357	11 102	9 228
Transfers from taxpayers	10 164	11 796	15 056	14 262	15 352	15 553
Budget revenues	-959	-548	-679	-647	-693	-698
Percentage TSE (% of GDP)	**3.5**	**2.0**	**0.9**	**0.9**	**0.9**	**0.8**
GDP deflator (1986-88=100)	**100**	**128**	**263**	**256**	**263**	**268**

Note: p: provisional. NPC: Nominal Protection Coefficient. NAC: Nominal Assistance Coefficient. A/An/R/I: Area planted/Animal numbers/Receipts/Income.

1. Market Price Support (MPS) is net of producer levies and excess feed cost. MPS commodities for Norway are: wheat, barley, oats, milk, beef and veal, sheep meat, wool, pigmeat, poultry and eggs.

2. A revised GSSE definition with new categories was introduced in 2014. When possible, the revision was implemented for the whole time series. The GSSE series and the resulting TSE are not comparable with the series published previously (for more details, see Annex 1.A2).

Source: OECD (2014), "Producer and Consumer Support Estimates", OECD *Agriculture Statistics Database, doi: http://dx.doi.org/10.1787/agr-pcse-data-en.*

StatLink ᨡᨡᨏ *http://dx.doi.org/10.1787/888933110676*

Description of policy developments

Main policy instruments

The **White Paper** No. 9 (2011-12) **on Norwegian Agriculture and Food Production,** approved in April 2012, represents the basis for agricultural policy and defines its four main objectives: food security; agriculture throughout all of Norway; creating more added-value; and sustainable agriculture.

Border measures and **budgetary payments** are the main policy instruments supporting agriculture in Norway. Market price support, in the form of wholesale target prices, is provided for milk, pork, grains, some fruits and some vegetables. These target prices and the budgetary framework for payments to farmers, are negotiated annually between the government and farmers' organisations. Marketing fees are collected from producers to finance marketing activities dealing with surpluses, including export subsidies for livestock products. Export subsidies of processed products to the European Union and marketing activities for horticultural products are financed directly by the government. Norway has gradually reformed its target price system. For beef, lamb, eggs and poultry there are no longer target prices.

Milk **production quotas** were introduced in 1983 and a system of buying and selling quotas was introduced in 1997. Most of Norway's tariff-rate-quotas were eliminated in 2000 when the WTO bound tariff rates became equal to the in-tariff quota rates. Tariffs for most products are set between 100-400% although there is a system of "open periods" for imports at reduced tariff rates when domestic prices rise above threshold levels.

A variety of **direct payments** to farmers, including area, headage, and payments based on output (meat production) continue to be implemented. Many of these payments are differentiated by region and farm size in order to provide adequate income support across all type of farms and regions. Environmental levies on agricultural pesticides are applied. These levies are differentiated according to the health and environmental risk characteristics of the product and the degree of exposure.

In October 2013, a new minority coalition government formed by the Conservative Party and the Progress Party took office. According to the new government declaration Norwegian agriculture is strongly committed to values such as the respect for private property, freedom to engage in business and protection of the cultural and natural heritage. One of the Government priorities is the promotion of efficient agro-food production associated in a longer term with a reduction of import barriers and reduction of subsidies. Efforts should be devoted to encouraging alternative business development that can provide the basis for a more robust and future-oriented agricultural production across the entire country. Limits on quotas and licences that prevent full usage of capacity in individual and cooperative farms must be as far as possible be abolished. The Government also wants a clearer distinction between agricultural and regional policies.

Domestic policy developments in 2013-14

In May 2013, an agreement was reached between the government and the farmers' organisations on the agriculture policy settings to be implemented in 2013/14 (this is a contrast to the situation in 2012 when such an agreement was not reached and the Parliament applied the Government proposal).

The main changes relative to the previous period (2012/13) are the following:

● An increase in **target prices** with a total budgetary effect of NOK 580 million (USD 99 million) from 1 July 2013.

- An increase in budgetary expenditures of NOK 500 million (USD 85 million) from 2013 to 2014.

- An extraordinary increase of budgetary support to strengthen the Agricultural Development Fund.

- A strengthening of the investment support and of the reimbursement for hiring replacement labour for periods of vacation or illness.

- Increased payments to environmental programmes including incentives to promote better agronomy practices.

From 2014, the start of the milk quota year was moved from 1 March to 1 January, in order to simplify the overall management of the quota system. For the quota year starting 1 January 2014 and ending 31 December 2014, both the basic quotas and the actual production possibilities are set to be the same as the year before.

Most **agri-environmental measures** are included in the National Environmental Programme (NEP). This programme was revised in 2012 and includes the following key measures: Acreage Cultural Landscape Support, payments for extensive grazing and for grazing animals, organic agriculture, Regional Environmental programmes, and special environmental measures in agriculture. The role of the Regional Environmental Programmes (REP) is increasing as they have a stronger environmental focus with more measures directed towards specific (site specific) environmental challenges. In 2014, the total payments in REP increased to NOK 448 million (USD 76 million) and is equivalent to around 10% of the NEP budget.

The Regional Environmental Programmes were revised in 2012-13. A new system with a set menu of measures was put in place from 2013. Among others, it provides for easier aggregation of data, and therefore makes it easier to follow the environmental performance. Under the REP, payments could be provided for measures to reduce water pollution from agricultural fields, mowing small (abandoned) fields with high or special biodiversity in the forest and mountains areas, grazing on islands, maintenance around heritage sites, maintenance of walking paths in the agricultural landscape, etc.

The **rural development** aspects of Norwegian agricultural policy include several programmes designed to stimulate innovation and establishment of alternative businesses on farms and alternative employment in rural areas. Most of the funding is financed through the Agricultural Development Fund (ADF). For 2013, the total allocation of ADF was NOK 1 447 million (USD 246 million) and for 2014 the budgeted sum is of NOK 1 197 million (USD 204 million). From 2013, regional programmes, containing regional plans and means to promote agricultural business development, have been established. The programme of each region also contains a regional environmental plan and a regional forest and climate plan. However, the political platform of the new Government signals a more distinct separation between agricultural policies and rural policies.

There was some follow up to the report "The powerful and the powerless in the food supply chain" published in 2011 by the *Commission to investigate the effects of recent and possible future developments in the food supply chain*. The report by the Law Committee in April 2013 suggests an "Act on Good Trading Practices in the grocery chain" and the establishment of a "Trade Surveillance Authority" vested with the power to apply and enforce the Act. The proposal seeks to merge "good trading practices" with a "consumer welfare standard" by drafting the good practices standard in order to cater to consumer interests in the form of lower prices, extended choice, enhanced availability and quality.

Trade policy developments in 2013-14

Article 19 of the **European Economic Area** (EEA) agreement provides that contracting parties will periodically carry reviews of the conditions of trade in agricultural products. A new agreement was reached in January 2010, and was implemented from 1 January 2012. Further negotiations were agreed in 2013, and such talks are scheduled to start in 2014.

Within the European Free Trade Association (EFTA), Norway has negotiated 25 Free Trade Agreements with 36 partner countries. Three of these agreements (**Colombia, Gulf Cooperation Council**, and **Bosnia and Herzegovina**) have not yet entered into force for Norway. There are ongoing free trade negotiations between EFTA and **India**, **Indonesia**, **Viet Nam**, **Malaysia** and the **customs union of Russia, Belarus and Kazakhstan**. These Free Trade Agreements and negotiations include processed agricultural products and a range of primary agricultural products.

On 1 January 2013, Norway implemented a revised Generalised System of Preferences (GSP) regime. The most extensive change under the revision was to establish a new category of countries: lower middle income countries with a population of less than 75 million people. This group of countries, named the "GSP plus", was granted better market access than the ordinary GSP countries. On the other hand, "GSP plus" countries are not granted duty free and market free access along the same lines as the Least Developed and Low Income countries, which are granted duty-free and quota-free market access for all products. One of the reasons behind establishing of the "GSP plus" group was to soften the transition for countries graduating ("moving up") from the Low Income Country group, where they had free access to the Norwegian market, to the middle income country group where ordinary GSP preferences apply.

PART II

Chapter 14

Developments in agricultural policies and support in Switzerland

The Switzerland country chapter includes a brief evaluation of policy developments and related support to agriculture, contextual information on the framework in which agricultural policies are implemented and the main characteristics of the agricultural sector, an evaluation of support in 2012-13 and in the longer term perspective, and a brief description of the main policy developments in 2013-14.

Evaluation of policy developments

● With the reforms started in the 1990s, gradual progress has been achieved in improving market orientation. The share of market price support and the potentially most production and trade distorting forms of support have declined. These policies represented 41% of total support in 2011-13, compared with 69% in the mid-1990s. However, due to an increase in direct payments over the same period, the total level of support to agriculture fell at a slower pace and remains almost three times higher than the OECD average.

● The removal of milk price controls and milk quota, together with the elimination of export subsidies on primary agricultural products and the reduction of some tariff barriers has a potential to improve economic efficiency of the sector and to contribute to the food security objective. The elimination of the remaining export subsidies to processed products should be considered to further reduce interference with domestic and world markets.

● The move away from market price support and the simultaneous increase in direct payments implemented by the Agricultural Policy reform 2011 (2008-13), has resulted in an increasing share of support being decoupled from production. However, most of these payments are general direct payments which are rather poorly targeted to the declared policy objectives such as rural development, environmental and animal welfare issues.

● The steps outlined in the Agricultural Policy 2014, to eliminate the general area payment and to replace the headage payments by area payments for pasture are steps in the right direction. Focus should be put on developing a set of better targeted direct payments to meet the various societal concerns and to further reduce border protection in order to meet the declared (and sometimes conflicting) objectives at the lowest costs to consumers and taxpayers.

Figure 14.1. **Switzerland: PSE level and composition by support categories, 1986-2013**

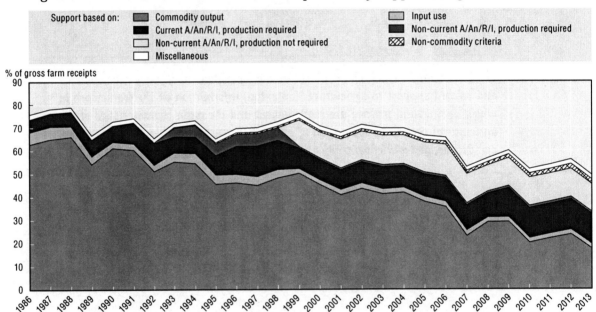

Source: OECD (2014), "Producer and Consumer Support Estimates", OECD Agriculture Statistics Database, http://dx.doi.org/10.1787/agr-pcse-data-en.
StatLink ⟨⟨⟨ http://dx.doi.org/10.1787/888933110049

Contextual information

Switzerland is a small, highly-developed, industry and services driven, open-economy with a high GDP per capita and relatively low inflation and unemployment. The share of agriculture in the Swiss economy is below 1%, while its share in employment is much higher at around 4%. The farm structure is dominated by relatively small family farms. Hills and mountain farming areas are used for extensive milk and meat production. Arable land and irrigated land represents respectively 27% and 2% of total agricultural area. Switzerland has consistently been a net agro-food importer; its share of agro-food imports in total imports is around 6%, while the share of agro-food exports in total exports is around 4%.

Table 14.1. **Switzerland: Contextual indicators, 1995, 2012[1]**

	1995	2012[1]
Economic context		
GDP (billion USD)	324	631
Population (million)	7	8
Land area (thousand km^2)	40	40
Population density (inhabitants/km^2)	170	187
GDP per capita, PPP (USD)	27 269	53 641
Trade as % of GDP	25.0	33.6
Agriculture in the economy		
Agriculture in GDP (%)	1.7	0.7
Agriculture share in employment (%)	4.4	4.1
Agro-food exports (% of total exports)	3.3	3.9
Agro-food imports (% of total imports)	7.0	5.9
Characteristics of the agricultural sector		
Agro-food trade balance (million USD)	-2 937	-2 915
Crop in total agricultural production (%)	30	31
Livestock in total agricultural production (%)	70	69
Agricultural area (AA) (thousand ha)	1 581	1 523
Share of arable land in AA (%)	27	27
Share of irrigated land in AA (%)	2	3
Share of agriculture in water consumption (%)	..	..
Nitrogen balance, kg/ha	73	68

1. Or latest available year.
Sources: OECD Statistical Databases, ITCS, World Development Indicators and national data.

StatLink ⫘ http://dx.doi.org/10.1787/888933110695

Figure 14.2. **Switzerland: Main macroeconomic indicators, 1995-2013**

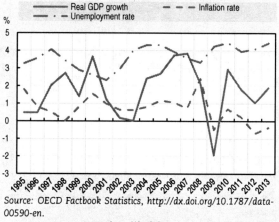

Source: OECD Factbook Statistics, http://dx.doi.org/10.1787/data-00590-en.

StatLink ⫘ http://dx.doi.org/10.1787/888933110068

Figure 14.3. **Switzerland: Agro-food trade, 1995-2012**

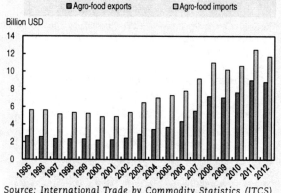

Source: International Trade by Commodity Statistics (ITCS) Database.

StatLink ⫘ http://dx.doi.org/10.1787/888933110087

Note: Detailed definitions of contextual indicators and their sources are provided in Annex II.A1.

Development of support to agriculture

Switzerland has progressively reduced its support to agriculture and especially the most trade and production distorting forms of support since 1986-88. However, support remains high relative to the OECD average. The level of price distortions has been significantly reduced, although domestic prices remain on average 40% above world prices. Budgetary payments are mostly provided in the form of general area payments and headage payments, but the share of payments targeted towards environment and animal welfare is steadily increasing.

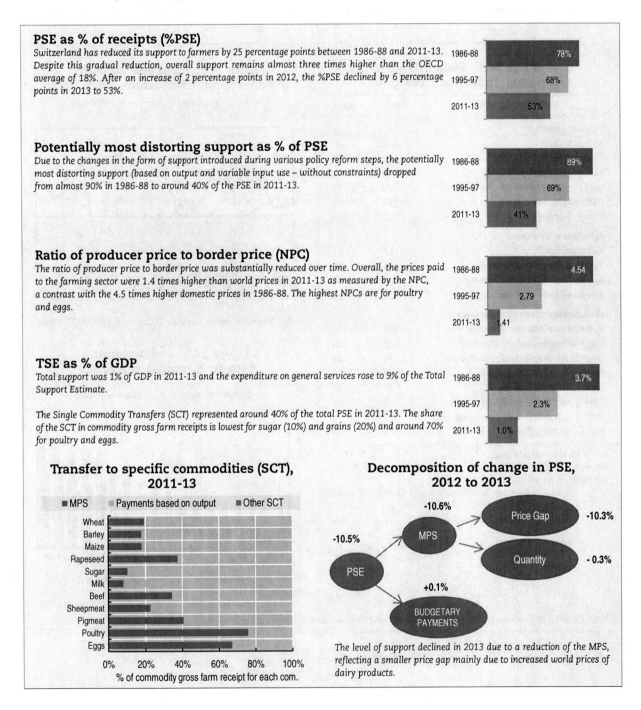

PSE as % of receipts (%PSE)
Switzerland has reduced its support to farmers by 25 percentage points between 1986-88 and 2011-13. Despite this gradual reduction, overall support remains almost three times higher than the OECD average of 18%. After an increase of 2 percentage points in 2012, the %PSE declined by 6 percentage points in 2013 to 53%.

1986-88	78%
1995-97	68%
2011-13	53%

Potentially most distorting support as % of PSE
Due to the changes in the form of support introduced during various policy reform steps, the potentially most distorting support (based on output and variable input use – without constraints) dropped from almost 90% in 1986-88 to around 40% of the PSE in 2011-13.

1986-88	89%
1995-97	69%
2011-13	41%

Ratio of producer price to border price (NPC)
The ratio of producer price to border price was substantially reduced over time. Overall, the prices paid to the farming sector were 1.4 times higher than world prices in 2011-13 as measured by the NPC, a contrast with the 4.5 times higher domestic prices in 1986-88. The highest NPCs are for poultry and eggs.

1986-88	4.54
1995-97	2.79
2011-13	1.41

TSE as % of GDP
Total support was 1% of GDP in 2011-13 and the expenditure on general services rose to 9% of the Total Support Estimate.

The Single Commodity Transfers (SCT) represented around 40% of the total PSE in 2011-13. The share of the SCT in commodity gross farm receipts is lowest for sugar (10%) and grains (20%) and around 70% for poultry and eggs.

1986-88	3.7%
1995-97	2.3%
2011-13	1.0%

Transfer to specific commodities (SCT), 2011-13

■ MPS   ▨ Payments based on output   ■ Other SCT

Wheat, Barley, Maize, Rapeseed, Sugar, Milk, Beef, Sheepmeat, Pigmeat, Poultry, Eggs

0%   20%   40%   60%   80%   100%
% of commodity gross farm receipt for each com.

Decomposition of change in PSE, 2012 to 2013

-10.6% → Price Gap → -10.3%

-10.5% → MPS

PSE → Quantity → - 0.3%

+0.1% → BUDGETARY PAYMENTS

The level of support declined in 2013 due to a reduction of the MPS, reflecting a smaller price gap mainly due to increased world prices of dairy products.

Table 14.2. **Switzerland: Estimates of support to agriculture**

Million CHF

	1986-88	1995-97	2011-13	2011	2012	2013p
Total value of production (at farm gate)	**9 482**	**8 236**	**6 521**	**6 586**	**6 404**	**6 574**
of which: share of MPS commodities (%)	81.5	82.3	69.9	71.2	71.4	67.1
Total value of consumption (at farm gate)	**11 394**	**9 557**	**7 899**	**7 902**	**7 746**	**8 048**
Producer Support Estimate (PSE)	**8 509**	**7 362**	**5 330**	**5 442**	**5 566**	**4 983**
Support based on commodity output	7 091	4 918	2 118	2 230	2 356	1 769
Market Price Support[1]	7 049	4 835	1 822	1 938	2 058	1 470
Payments based on output	42	83	296	292	298	299
Payments based on input use	563	411	201	198	201	203
Based on variable input use	454	309	81	81	81	81
with input constraints	0	180	14	14	13	14
Based on fixed capital formation	72	78	119	116	119	121
with input constraints	0	0	0	0	0	0
Based on on-farm services	36	25	1	1	1	1
with input constraints	0	0	0	0	0	0
Payments based on current A/An/R/I, production required	612	1 203	1 310	1 309	1 310	1 311
Based on Receipts / Income	15	0	0	0	0	0
Based on Area planted / Animal numbers	597	1 203	1 310	1 309	1 310	1 311
with input constraints	340	1 050	1 299	1 297	1 299	1 299
Payments based on non-current A/An/R/I, production required	28	569	102	102	102	102
Payments based on non-current A/An/R/I, production not required	0	0	1 203	1 218	1 195	1 195
With variable payment rates	0	0	0	0	0	0
with commodity exceptions	0	0	0	0	0	0
With fixed payment rates	0	0	1 203	1 218	1 195	1 195
with commodity exceptions	0	0	0	0	0	0
Payments based on non-commodity criteria	0	61	200	190	205	206
Based on long-term resource retirement	0	0	0	0	0	0
Based on a specific non-commodity output	0	61	200	190	205	206
Based on other non-commodity criteria	0	0	0	0	0	0
Miscellaneous payments	216	200	197	196	198	198
Percentage PSE (%)	**77.7**	**68.4**	**53.2**	**53.9**	**56.2**	**49.4**
Producer NPC (coeff.)	**4.54**	**2.79**	**1.41**	**1.44**	**1.49**	**1.30**
Producer NAC (coeff.)	**4.51**	**3.18**	**2.14**	**2.17**	**2.28**	**1.98**
General Services Support Estimate (GSSE)[2]	**677**	**590**	**499**	**483**	**515**	**500**
Agricultural knowledge and innovation system	173	164	123	114	133	123
Inspection and control	14	15	11	11	11	11
Development and maintenance of infrastructure	126	83	87	83	87	90
Marketing and promotion	45	45	59	55	65	57
Cost of public stockholding	103	83	39	40	38	39
Miscellaneous	216	200	180	180	180	180
Percentage GSSE (% of TSE)	**6.6**	**6.5**	**8.6**	**8.1**	**8.5**	**9.1**
Consumer Support Estimate (CSE)	**-7 535**	**-4 994**	**-2 133**	**-2 260**	**-2 345**	**-1 792**
Transfers to producers from consumers	-7 088	-5 053	-1 660	-1 784	-1 895	-1 301
Other transfers from consumers	-1 767	-1 221	-497	-499	-478	-514
Transfers to consumers from taxpayers	1 099	1 053	7	5	4	11
Excess feed cost	221	227	17	18	23	11
Percentage CSE (%)	**-73.1**	**-58.7**	**-27.1**	**-28.6**	**-30.3**	**-22.3**
Consumer NPC (coeff.)	**4.50**	**2.91**	**1.38**	**1.41**	**1.44**	**1.29**
Consumer NAC (coeff.)	**3.74**	**2.42**	**1.37**	**1.40**	**1.43**	**1.29**
Total Support Estimate (TSE)	**10 285**	**9 005**	**5 836**	**5 930**	**6 085**	**5 494**
Transfers from consumers	8 855	6 274	2 157	2 283	2 373	1 815
Transfers from taxpayers	3 197	3 952	4 177	4 146	4 190	4 194
Budget revenues	-1 767	-1 221	-497	-499	-478	-514
Percentage TSE (% of GDP)	**3.7**	**2.3**	**1.0**	**1.0**	**1.0**	**0.9**
GDP deflator (1986-88=100)	**100**	**125**	**143**	**142**	**143**	**143**

Note: p: provisional. NPC: Nominal Protection Coefficient. NAC: Nominal Assistance Coefficient. A/An/R/I: Area planted/Animal numbers/Receipts/Income.

1. Market Price Support (MPS) is net of producer levies and excess feed cost. MPS commodities for Switzerland are: wheat, maize, barley, rapeseed, sugar, milk, beef and veal, sheep meat, pigmeat, poultry and eggs.

2. A revised GSSE definition with new categories was introduced in 2014. When possible, the revision was implemented for the whole time series. The GSSE series and the resulting TSE are not comparable with the series published previously (for more details, see Annex 1.A2).

Source: OECD (2014), "Producer and Consumer Support Estimates", OECD *Agriculture Statistics Database, doi: http://dx.doi.org/10.1787/agr-pcse-data-en.*

StatLink 🔗 *http://dx.doi.org/10.1787/888933110714*

Description of policy developments

Main policy instruments

The year 2013 is the last year for implementation of the policy package decided under the **Agricultural policy reform 2011** (AP 2011) which started in 2008. The key feature of AP 2011 was a further reduction of 30% in budgetary expenditures for market price support. The outlays were transferred to direct payments for roughage-consuming cattle, to compensate for difficult production conditions, to enhance sustainable use of natural resources and animal welfare practices. All export subsidies for primary agricultural products were eliminated by 1 January 2010, while those for some processed agricultural products were maintained. All state guarantees for prices and sales had already been abolished in 1999. For feed grains and animal feed, imports remain subject to variable custom duties based on threshold prices. Despite some gradual reductions, import measures consist of a combination of low in quota tariffs and high out-of quota tariffs within a system of tariff rate quotas (TRQs) for most products. The resulting Market Price Support corresponded to 18% of gross farm receipts and represented 34% of the total estimated support to agriculture in 2011-13.

There are two main categories of direct payments. **General direct payments** are mainly granted in the form of payments per hectare of farmland and payments per head of cattle. They also include payments to farmers operating in difficult conditions mainly in the form of headage and area payments. **Ecological direct payments** are mainly granted in the form of area and headage payments to farmers who voluntarily apply stricter farming practices than those required by public regulations and the ecological proof of performance (*Prestations écologiques requises* – PER) which is compulsory to both general and ecological direct payments (cross-compliance). A relatively important share of the ecological direct payments is provided in the form of contributions to stimulate voluntary adoption of practices to improve animal welfare (*ethological contributions*). There are also payments based on output related to milk production (milk used for cheese processing and milk produced without silage) and since 2008 an area payment for sugarbeet. Overall, the share of direct payments in total PSE is gradually increasing and represented 66% of the support in 2011-13.

In 2013, Switzerland adopted a new policy framework for the period 2014-17 (*Politique Agricole 2014-17*). The main change refers to the direct payment system. All general area payments have been eliminated. The direct payments to farmers are more closely related to specific objectives and to specific agricultural practices. Also, the general headage payments to livestock (ruminants) will be replaced by area payments to pastures while maintaining a minimal level of livestock husbandry. The total budgeted annual amount of these payments remains on the current level rather stable for the whole period at CHF 2.8 billion (USD 2.6 billion).*

Domestic policy developments in 2013-14

Since the abolition of the **milk quotas** in May 2009, all dairy farmers are obliged to conclude milk delivery contracts with their milk purchasers. For 2014, inter-branch organisations for milk are responsible for standard milk delivery contracts that may be made compulsory by the Federal Council. Exempted are those farmers who sell their milk directly to final consumers and farmers who produce cheeses and other dairy products on farm. Due to border measures the price paid to milk producers remains on average 30% above the world market prices (producer NPC) in 2011-13.

---

* A more detailed description of the *Politique Agricole* 2014-17 is provided in Part I of the report.

Since 2010, **output payments** consist of the allowance for milk transformed into cheese and the additional allowance when milk is produced without silage feed. These payments reached CHF 298 million (USD 279 million) in 2012 and CHF 299 million (USD 277 million) in 2013. The payments are maintained under the PA 2014-17, and the yearly sum budgeted for 2014-17 is CHF 293 million (USD 272 million).

The structure of the programmes and the eligibility conditions applied within the **General direct payments** and the **Ecological direct payments** have remained largely unchanged under the AP 2011 (implemented from 2008 to 2013). The yearly changes in the amount of the total payments are not significant, but the trends are different among general and ecological payments. Around three-quarters of the total payments are granted under **General direct payments**, which are declining over time. On the other hand, the **Ecological Direct Payments** continued their upward trend and increased by 3.7% in 2012, but only by 0.6% in 2013 (Table 14.3).

Table 14.3. **Switzerland: Outlays for direct payments**[1]

CHF million

Type of payment	2011	2012	2013p	Percentage change	
				2011 to 2012	2012 to 2013p
General direct payments	**2 192**	**2 163**	**2 147**	**-1.3**	**-0.7**
of which:					
Area payments	1 218	1 195	1 195	-1.8	0.0
Holding of roughage-consuming animals	508	504	504	-0.8	0.0
Payments for farming in difficult production locations	466	464	464	-0.5	-0.1
Holding of livestock under difficult conditions	352	350	350	-0.6	-0.1
Farming on steep slopes	103	102	102.3	-0.3	0.0
Wine cultivation on steep slopes	11	11	11.3	0.0	0.0
Ecological payments	**618**	**641**	**645**	**3.7**	**0.6**
of which:					
Ecological compensation	134	137	145	2.6	5.5
Contributions for environmental quality	72	83	84	16.4	1.0
Extensive cereal and rapeseed farming	30	30	30	-1.0	1.0
Organic farming	30	33	33	11.4	-0.3
Regularly keeping animals outdoors	165	166	166	0.4	0.2
Animal welfare through housing systems	64	66	66	3.6	-0.3
Summer pasturing	102	102	101.5	0.0	0.0
Water protection, sustainable use of natural ressources	22	25	25	9.4	2.0
Total	**2 810**	**2 804**	**2 792**	**-0.2**	**-0.4**

p: provisional.
1. Direct payments are subject to restrictions of environmental and farm management practices.
Source: Federal Office of Agriculture, *Rapport Agricole 2013*, Bern, 2013.

StatLink ⟶ *http://dx.doi.org/10.1787/888933110733*

Trade policy developments in 2013-14

Agro-food imports to Switzerland are regulated either by single tariffs or, for a number of products, by a combination of relatively low in-quota tariffs and high out-of-quota **import tariffs** within a system of **Tariff Rate Quotas** (TRQ). These cover a number of basic agricultural and food products, in particular, meat, milk products, potatoes, fruits, vegetables, bread cereals and wine. Since 1999, allocated TRQ volumes have been transferable from one importer to another. An auctioning system has been used to allocate some of the TRQs to traders.

In November 2008, Switzerland and the European Union launched negotiations on full trade liberalisation in the agro-food sector. So far, three comprehensive rounds of negotiations have taken place. The negotiations have however slowed down due among other things to institutional issues. As a member of the European Free Trade Association (EFTA), Switzerland participates in ongoing free trade negotiations between the EFTA and, respectively, *India, Indonesia, Viet Nam,* the *customs union of Russia, Belarus and Kazakhstan*, as well as Central American States (free trade agreements with *Costa Rica and Panama* are signed; negotiations with *Guatemala* and *Honduras* are on hold). Negotiations started with *Algeria* and *Thailand* are on hold for the moment. Negotiations with *Bosnia and Herzegovina* have been completed and the agreement signed in June 2013. On a bilateral basis, Switzerland signed on 6th July 2013 a free trade agreement with *China*. These Free Trade Agreements and the ongoing negotiations cover also processed agricultural products and a range of basic agricultural products.

Preferential tariff rates are applied to imports from developing countries under a system of preferences scheme. In the context of the initiative of the Swiss government to grant zero tariffs on all products imported from Least Developed Countries (LDC), since September 2009 all agricultural imports from LDC countries are duty and quota free.

PART II

Chapter 15

Developments in agricultural policies and support in Turkey

The Turkey country chapter includes a brief evaluation of policy developments and related support to agriculture, contextual information on the framework in which agricultural policies are implemented and the main characteristics of the agricultural sector, an evaluation of support in 2012-13 and in the longer term perspective, and a brief description of the main policy developments in 2013-14.

Evaluation of policy developments

- Since 1986-88, policy reforms aimed at improving market orientation have been variable. Frequent ad hoc changes to policy settings have been made, within a macroeconomic context of high inflation and volatile exchange rates. The share of producer support in gross farm receipts (%PSE) in 2011-13 remained almost unchanged from 1986-88, at around 20%, which is higher than the OECD average.

- Turkey ranks as the 7th largest agricultural producer in the world, but notwithstanding the impressive progress that has been achieved in recent years towards strengthening the agricultural sector's legal and institutional framework, ample scope remains to improve its efficiency and productivity, and to increase the market orientation of the sector by further decreasing its reliance on the potentially most distorting types of support. Such policies accounted for 87% of total support to farmers in 2011-13.

- Greater efforts need to be made to transform the remaining agriculture-related State Economic Enterprises (SEEs) and Agricultural Sales Co-operatives and Agricultural Sales Co-operative Unions (ASCUs) into truly commercial and economically viable entities, operating under more competitive market conditions.

Figure 15.1. **Turkey: PSE level and composition by support categories, 1986-2013**

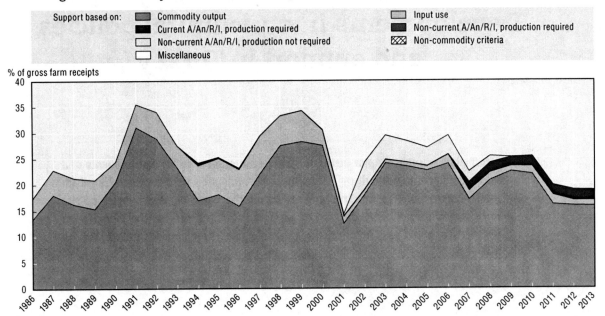

Source: OECD (2014), "Producer and Consumer Support Estimates", OECD Agriculture Statistics Database, http://dx.doi.org/10.1787/agr-pcse-data-en.

StatLink ⟶ http://dx.doi.org/10.1787/888933110106

Contextual information

Growth has picked up in 2013, driven by a surge in public infrastructure spending and robust private consumption. Inflation and the current account deficit remain excessively high (7.5% and 7.1% of GDP, respectively). Agricultural production, particularly crop production, has grown rapidly over the past two decades. Notwithstanding various structural bottlenecks, such as low labour productivity, Turkey ranks globally as a significant agricultural producer and is the world's 7th largest agricultural producer.

The share of agriculture in employment decreased from 44.1% in 1995 to 24.6% in 2012, but still remains one of the most important sectors in terms of employment. The share of agriculture in GDP (at current prices) declined from 11.9% in 1995 to 8.9 % in 2012. Agriculture supplied 9.9% of exports, and accounts for 5.3% of imports in 2012. Turkey's main trading partners are the European Union, the United States and the Middle East.

Table 15.1. **Turkey: Contextual indicators, 1995, 2012**[1]

	1995	2012[1]
Economic context		
GDP (billion USD)	228	790
Population (million)	62	75
Land area (thousand km^2)	770	770
Population density (inhabitants/km^2)	75	95
GDP per capita, PPP (USD)	7 119	18 315
Trade as % of GDP	12.6	24.6
Agriculture in the economy		
Agriculture in GDP (%)	11.9	8.9
Agriculture share in employment (%)	44.1	24.6
Agro-food exports (% of total exports)	19.9	9.9
Agro-food imports (% of total imports)	9.9	5.3
Characteristics of the agricultural sector		
Agro-food trade balance (million USD)	778	2 522
Crop in total agricultural production (%)	68	74
Livestock in total agricultural production (%)	32	26
Agricultural area (AA) (thousand ha)	39 493	38 247
Share of arable land in AA (%)	62	54
Share of irrigated land in AA (%)	8	9
Share of agriculture in water consumption (%)	87	87
Nitrogen balance, kg/ha	33	31

1. Or latest available year.
Sources: OECD Statistical Databases, ITCS, World Development Indicators and national data.
StatLink ⫶ http://dx.doi.org/10.1787/888933110752

Figure 15.2. **Turkey: Main macroeconomic indicators, 1995-2013**

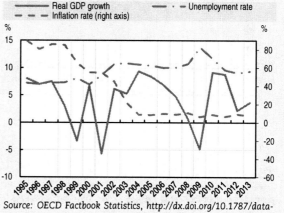

Source: OECD Factbook Statistics, http://dx.doi.org/10.1787/data-00590-en.
StatLink ⫶ http://dx.doi.org/10.1787/888933110125

Figure 15.3. **Turkey: Agro-food trade, 1995-2012**

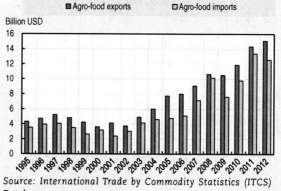

Source: International Trade by Commodity Statistics (ITCS) Database.
StatLink ⫶ http://dx.doi.org/10.1787/888933110144

Note: Detailed definitions of contextual indicators and their sources are provided in Annex II.A1.

Development of support to agriculture

Turkey has implemented a series of ambitious reforms since the late 1990s. However, the level of support varies from year to year and remains higher than the average for the OECD area, and the most distorting forms of support prevail. Decoupled direct payments were abolished in 2009, while payments based on commodity output have increased since then.

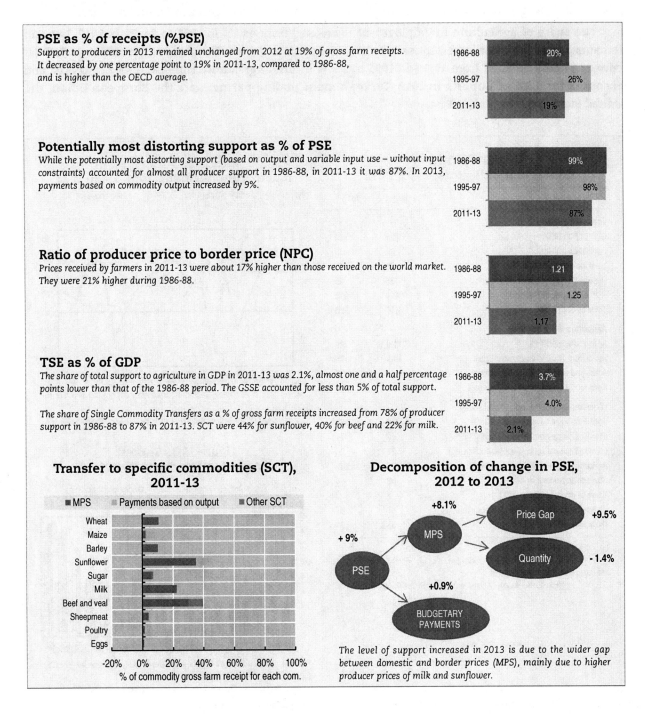

PSE as % of receipts (%PSE)
Support to producers in 2013 remained unchanged from 2012 at 19% of gross farm receipts. It decreased by one percentage point to 19% in 2011-13, compared to 1986-88, and is higher than the OECD average.

1986-88   20%
1995-97   26%
2011-13   19%

Potentially most distorting support as % of PSE
While the potentially most distorting support (based on output and variable input use – without input constraints) accounted for almost all producer support in 1986-88, in 2011-13 it was 87%. In 2013, payments based on commodity output increased by 9%.

1986-88   99%
1995-97   98%
2011-13   87%

Ratio of producer price to border price (NPC)
Prices received by farmers in 2011-13 were about 17% higher than those received on the world market. They were 21% higher during 1986-88.

1986-88   1.21
1995-97   1.25
2011-13   1.17

TSE as % of GDP
The share of total support to agriculture in GDP in 2011-13 was 2.1%, almost one and a half percentage points lower than that of the 1986-88 period. The GSSE accounted for less than 5% of total support.

The share of Single Commodity Transfers as a % of gross farm receipts increased from 78% of producer support in 1986-88 to 87% in 2011-13. SCT were 44% for sunflower, 40% for beef and 22% for milk.

1986-88   3.7%
1995-97   4.0%
2011-13   2.1%

Transfer to specific commodities (SCT), 2011-13

■ MPS ■ Payments based on output ■ Other SCT

Wheat, Maize, Barley, Sunflower, Sugar, Milk, Beef and veal, Sheepmeat, Poultry, Eggs

-20% 0% 20% 40% 60% 80% 100%
% of commodity gross farm receipt for each com.

Decomposition of change in PSE, 2012 to 2013

+9% PSE → +8.1% MPS → Price Gap +9.5%
MPS → Quantity -1.4%
+0.9% → BUDGETARY PAYMENTS

The level of support increased in 2013 is due to the wider gap between domestic and border prices (MPS), mainly due to higher producer prices of milk and sunflower.

Table 15.2. **Turkey: Estimates of support to agriculture**

Million TRY

	1986-88	1995-97	2011-13	2011	2012	2013p
Total value of production (at farm gate)	**18**	**2 440**	**139 614**	**132 413**	**138 038**	**148 391**
of which: share of MPS commodities (%)	56.5	74.9	60.1	60.3	60.7	59.4
Total value of consumption (at farm gate)	**15**	**2 227**	**108 744**	**106 755**	**106 323**	**113 153**
Producer Support Estimate (PSE)	**4**	**707**	**28 326**	**27 689**	**27 414**	**29 876**
Support based on commodity output	3	514	23 566	22 543	23 014	25 141
Market Price Support[1]	3	505	20 964	20 108	20 278	22 508
Payments based on output	0	10	2 601	2 434	2 737	2 633
Payments based on input use	1	189	1 859	2 499	1 447	1 630
Based on variable input use	1	182	985	568	1 114	1 274
with input constraints	0	0	0	0	0	0
Based on fixed capital formation	0	6	851	1 909	311	333
with input constraints	0	0	0	0	0	0
Based on on-farm services	0	1	22	22	22	22
with input constraints	0	0	0	0	0	0
Payments based on current A/An/R/I, production required	0	4	2 901	2 646	2 952	3 105
Based on Receipts / Income	0	0	268	249	263	290
Based on Area planted / Animal numbers	0	4	2 633	2 397	2 689	2 815
with input constraints	0	0	21	16	23	23
Payments based on non-current A/An/R/I, production required	0	0	0	0	0	0
Payments based on non-current A/An/R/I, production not required	0	0	1	1	1	1
With variable payment rates	0	0	0	0	0	0
with commodity exceptions	0	0	0	0	0	0
With fixed payment rates	0	0	1	1	1	1
with commodity exceptions	0	0	0	0	0	0
Payments based on non-commodity criteria	0	0	0	0	0	0
Based on long-term resource retirement	0	0	0	0	0	0
Based on a specific non-commodity output	0	0	0	0	0	0
Based on other non-commodity criteria	0	0	0	0	0	0
Miscellaneous payments	0	0	0	0	0	0
Percentage PSE (%)	**20.5**	**25.9**	**19.3**	**19.8**	**18.9**	**19.2**
Producer NPC (coeff.)	**1.21**	**1.25**	**1.17**	**1.19**	**1.15**	**1.16**
Producer NAC (coeff.)	**1.26**	**1.35**	**1.24**	**1.25**	**1.23**	**1.24**
General Services Support Estimate (GSSE)[2]	**0**	**221**	**1 372**	**2 390**	**163**	**1 563**
Agricultural knowledge and innovation system	0	4	62	34	71	82
Inspection and control	0	7	91	76	92	105
Development and maintenance of infrastructure	0	1	0	0	0	0
Marketing and promotion	0	202	1 219	2 280	0	1 376
Cost of public stockholding	0	0	0	0	0	0
Miscellaneous	0	6	0	0	0	0
Percentage GSSE (% of TSE)	**7.0**	**23.6**	**4.5**	**7.9**	**0.6**	**5.0**
Consumer Support Estimate (CSE)	**-3**	**-492**	**-15 642**	**-18 239**	**-13 810**	**-14 877**
Transfers to producers from consumers	-3	-493	-15 513	-17 550	-13 770	-15 218
Other transfers from consumers	0	-28	-568	-1 039	-440	-225
Transfers to consumers from taxpayers	0	0	0	0	0	0
Excess feed cost	0	29	438	350	399	566
Percentage CSE (%)	**-19.2**	**-21.3**	**-14.4**	**-17.1**	**-13.0**	**-13.1**
Consumer NPC (coeff.)	**1.26**	**1.29**	**1.17**	**1.21**	**1.15**	**1.16**
Consumer NAC (coeff.)	**1.24**	**1.27**	**1.17**	**1.21**	**1.15**	**1.15**
Total Support Estimate (TSE)	**4**	**928**	**29 698**	**30 079**	**27 577**	**31 440**
Transfers from consumers	3	521	16 080	18 589	14 210	15 443
Transfers from taxpayers	1	435	14 186	12 529	13 807	16 222
Budget revenues	0	-28	-568	-1 039	-440	-225
Percentage TSE (% of GDP)	**3.7**	**4.0**	**2.1**	**2.3**	**1.9**	**2.0**
GDP deflator (1986-88=100)	**100**	**13 840**	**471 190**	**441 710**	**471 661**	**500 198**

Note: p: provisional. NPC: Nominal Protection Coefficient. NAC: Nominal Assistance Coefficient. A/An/R/I: Area planted/Animal numbers/ Receipts/Income.

1. Market Price Support (MPS) is net of producer levies and excess feed cost. MPS commodities for Turkey are: wheat, maize, barley, sunflower, sugar, potatoes, tomatoes, grapes, apples, cotton, tobacco, milk, beef and veal, sheep meat, poultry and eggs.
2. A revised GSSE definition with new categories was introduced in 2014. When possible, the revision was implemented for the whole time series. The GSSE series and the resulting TSE are not comparable with the series published previously (for more details, see Annex 1.A2).

Source: OECD (2014), "Producer and Consumer Support Estimates", OECD *Agriculture Statistics Database, doi: http://dx.doi.org/10.1787/agr-pcse-data-en.*

StatLink ᵐˢᵖ *http://dx.doi.org/10.1787/888933110771*

Description of policy developments

Main policy instruments[*]

The strategic objectives of Turkey's agricultural policy are given in the **9th Development Plan** as: to ensure sustainable food security and safety and to form an agricultural structure that is harmonised with that of the EU. The **2013-17 Strategic Plan** of the Ministry of Food, Agriculture and Livestock defines five strategic areas in the agricultural sector: i) agricultural production and supply security; ii) food safety; iii) phytosanitary and animal health; iv) agricultural infrastructure and rural development; and v) institutional capacity building.

The tools of agricultural support to be used for achieving the strategic objectives include deficiency payments, compensatory payments, livestock support (for fodder crops, artificial insemination, milk premiums, risk-free livestock regions, bee-keeping, fisheries), support for crop insurance, rural development support and environmental set-aside.

Import tariffs – complemented by fixed purchasing prices for cereals, sugar and tobacco – provide support for domestic production. **Export subsidies** are applied to a number of products, including fresh and processed fruits and vegetables, derived food products, poultry meat and eggs. **Production quotas** at processing plant level are applied for sugar beet.

Deficiency payments ("premium payments") are provided for the products that are in short domestic supply. Producers of oilseeds, olive oil, cotton, cereals and tea (since 2005) benefit from such payments. Hazelnut producers receive payments based on area. Payments are also provided for fodder crops, organic farming, certified seeds, gasoline and fertiliser use implemented on the basis of area. Most farmers are exempt from income tax since the average farm size is small, and average farm income is rather low.

Input subsidies are provided mainly in the form of interest concessions and payments to improve animal breeds and farm production capacity (e.g. field levelling, drainage, soil improvement and protection, land consolidation and research and development). A number of regulations control water and soil pollution, and provide protection to wetlands. The government plays a major role in providing **infrastructure investment**, especially for irrigation. A feature of Turkish agriculture is its widespread co-operative organisation, from production co-operatives (e.g. irrigation and sugar beet cooperatives) to credit and marketing co-operatives.

To diminish the instability in milk and meat markets, a grant programme to support establishment of large-scale dairy enterprises has being implemented in the South-eastern Region since 2009 and another one to support establishment of large-scale beef cattle enterprises in the eastern region has being continued since 2011. Grants are provided to enterprises for a certain percentage of construction, equipment and livestock costs.

The **10th Development Plan** (2014-18) was enacted by Parliament in June 2013. The main objective in the agriculture and food sectors identified in the Plan is to develop a globally competitive and environmentally-friendly agricultural sector, whose fundamental aim is to provide sufficient and balanced nutrition to population. Particular emphasis is given to innovations, productivity improvement and the more efficient use of water in agriculture. The plan aims to achieve a growth of 3.1% in the agricultural sector annually, while the share of agricultural employment in total employment is projected to decline from the current 24.6% to 21.9% and the share of the sector in GDP is projected to be 6.8% by 2018.

* For a detailed analysis of Turkey's policy instruments, see OECD (2011), *Evaluation of Policy Reforms in Turkey.*

Domestic policy developments in 2013-14

A "basin-based support programme," which differentiates the crops that will be eligible for **deficiency payments** across agricultural basins, was presented to Council of Ministers by the Minister of Food, Agriculture and Livestock in April 2013. By differentiating budgetary crop-specific supports across regions, the government aims to: i) to increase productivity, with crops to be produced based on the most suitable ecological conditions; and ii) change the crop pattern by increasing the production of imported crops, while decreasing excess supply in some other crops. Thirty basic agricultural basins were established in 2009, based on a model developed by the Ministry of Food, Agriculture and Livestock, which takes into account ecological and production conditions.

Each farmer registered under the National Farmer Registration System (NFRS) received a so-called "diesel payment" of TRY 43 (USD 23) per hectare and a "fertiliser payment" of TRY 55 (USD 29) per hectare, on average, in 2013. Region specific programmes and infrastructural support to improve cattle breeds remained unchanged.

The **insurance support scheme**, which is in operation since 2006, continued in 2013. The scheme is open to all producers and covers crops, orchards on fields, greenhouses, cattle, poultry, apiculture and aquaculture. The government reimburses 50% of the premium costs. As of end of 2013, 892 000 insurance policies were issued and TRY 290.4 million (USD 152 million) has been paid.

Farmers benefit from **loans** offered at concessional rates by the agricultural bank *Ziraat Bank* (TCZB) and *Agricultural Credit Co-operatives* (ACC), with a subsidy rate that varies between 25% and 100% of the TCZB's current agricultural credit rate. The difference between the current rates and the rates applied to farmers ("income loss") is paid by the Treasury to the TCZB and ACC. Treasury's payments reached a total of TRY 1 500 million (USD 788 million) in 2013. Agricultural enterprises and farmers are entitled to benefit from interest concessions applied for various loan purposes, including organic farming, good farming practices, irrigation, livestock breeding and R&D.

With regard to **agricultural state economic enterprises**, privatisation of public enterprises continues. By the end of 2013, the tobacco and salt public enterprise was privatised. The privatisation of the sugar enterprise is still in process. In 2013, TRY 0.560 million (USD 0.294 million) was paid as duty loss by the Treasury to the Privatisation Administration portfolio. At the same time, in 2013, TRY 927.3 million (USD 487 million) was paid as duty loss and TRY 443.3 million (USD 233 million) equity was injected by the Treasury to agricultural enterprises in the Treasury portfolio.

On **rural development**, a new national Rural Development Strategy is due to be issued in 2014. The ongoing support on rural development projects involves co-financing beneficiaries to mobilise private-sector resources. Implementation of the second phase of the Pre-Accession Assistance Rural Development Programme (IPARD) for 2007-13 continues. The Programme sets up measures for Turkey to achieve consistency with the EU's rural development policy and the EU's Common Agricultural Policy. The total budget for the support of rural development programmes has been increased from TRY 240 million (USD 126 million) in 2012 to nearly TRY 480 million (USD 252 million) in 2013. Within the scope of IPARD programme in 2013, studies regarding "investments for restructuring agricultural enterprises and achieving the European Union's standards", "restructuring the processing and marketing of agricultural and fishery products and achieving the European Union's standards" and "diversification and enhancing rural economic activities" are continuing.

Several projects are underway to harmonise national legislation with those of the European Union, within the scope of the negotiation chapters for EU accession related to rural development, food safety, veterinary, phytosanitary and fisheries.

Trade policy developments in 2013-14

The average rate of *customs duties* for agricultural products was 58.9% in 2013 (58.4% in 2012). Customs duties on wheat starch, pectic substances, pectinates and pectates, malt extract, food preparations containing cacao and chocolate for medical purposes, and salted chips and biscuits for medical purposes were decreased; customs duties on coconut oil and its fractions and some seeds increased.

Export subsidies for agricultural products were announced in the Official Gazette in 2013 and were applied on exports during the 2013 calendar year. In 2013, 16 commodity groups, out of the 44 groups eligible under Turkey's WTO commitments, received export subsidies. The subsidies are provided to exporters in the form of deductions to their payments to public corporations such as taxes, or the costs of social insurance premiums, telecommunications or energy.

PART II

Chapter 16

Developments in agricultural policies and support in the United States

The United States country chapter includes a brief evaluation of policy developments and related support to agriculture, contextual information on the framework in which agricultural policies are implemented and the main characteristics of the agricultural sector, an evaluation of support in 2012-13 and in the longer term perspective, and a brief description of the main policy developments in 2013-14.

Evaluation of policy developments

● Levels of producer support and border protection have decreased substantially since 1986-88. However, since 2002 the decline has been primarily due to higher world commodity prices, as several of the support policies in place are linked to changes in prices.

● While actions taken by the Commodity Credit Corporation in 2013 to address the sugar surplus in the US market have been successful in avoiding forfeitures, they accentuate economic distortions and shelter domestic sugar producers from international competition.

● The mandate of the 2014 Farm Act to end the practice of paying out farm support on an automatic basis each year, regardless of farm prices or income. But the ultimate economic impacts of the new programmes will depend on price and revenue developments.

● The increasing emphasis on risk management warrants a rigorous evaluation of the cost-effectiveness of crop insurance measures in reducing risks.

● Reforms to the cotton support regime, stipulated by the 2014 Farm Act, are steps in the right direction as they enhance compliance with multilateral trade obligations and are less production and trade-distorting than the previous policy regime.

Figure 16.1. **United States: PSE level and composition by support categories, 1986-2013**

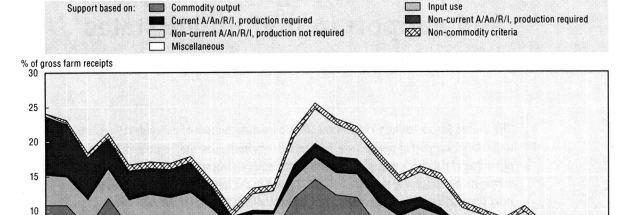

Support based on:
- Commodity output
- Current A/An/R/I, production required
- Non-current A/An/R/I, production not required
- Miscellaneous
- Input use
- Non-current A/An/R/I, production required
- Non-commodity criteria

Source: OECD (2014), "Producer and Consumer Support Estimates", *OECD Agriculture Statistics Database, http://dx.doi.org/10.1787/agr-pcse-data-en.*
StatLink ᴍ᱑᱕ᴺ *http://dx.doi.org/10.1787/888933110163*

Contextual information

The United States is the world's biggest economy, with a high GDP per capita and low levels of inflation and unemployment (although the latter has been high in recent years). In 2013, economic growth has been modest. The United States is one of the most important producers of agricultural commodities in the world, and, in addition to having a very large domestic market, it is the world's largest exporter of agricultural products. US agricultural policies therefore exert a strong influence on world agricultural markets. Agriculture is dominated by grains, oilseeds, cattle, dairy, poultry, and fruits and vegetables.

Table 16.1. United States: Contextual indicators, 1995, 2012[1]

	1995	2012[1]
Economic context		
GDP (billion USD)	7 338	16 245
Population (million)	263	314
Land area (thousand km^2)	9 159	9 147
Population density (inhabitants/km^2)	28	33
GDP per capita, PPP (USD)	28 748	51 689
Trade as % of GDP	9.2	11.9
Agriculture in the economy		
Agriculture in GDP (%)	1.6	1.2
Agriculture share in employment (%)	2.9	2.4
Agro-food exports (% of total exports)	10.9	9.7
Agro-food imports (% of total imports)	4.4	4.9
Characteristics of the agricultural sector		
Agro-food trade balance (million USD)	29 671	35 967
Crop in total agricultural production (%)	53	59
Livestock in total agricultural production (%)	47	41
Agricultural area (AA) (thousand ha)	420 139	411 263
Share of arable land in AA (%)	43	39
Share of irrigated land in AA (%)	5	5
Share of agriculture in water consumption (%)	41	40
Nitrogen balance, kg/ha	37	28

1. Or latest available year.
Sources: OECD Statistical Databases, ITCS, World Development Indicators and national data.

StatLink ⟶ http://dx.doi.org/10.1787/888933110790

Figure 16.2. United States: Main macroeconomic indicators, 1995-2013

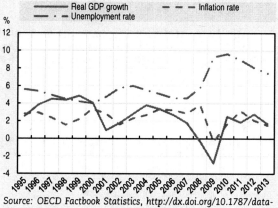

Source: OECD Factbook Statistics, http://dx.doi.org/10.1787/data-00590-en.

StatLink ⟶ http://dx.doi.org/10.1787/888933110182

Figure 16.3. United States: Agro-food trade, 1995-2012

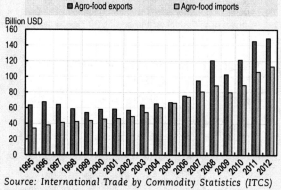

Source: International Trade by Commodity Statistics (ITCS) Database.

StatLink ⟶ http://dx.doi.org/10.1787/888933110201

Note: Detailed definitions of contextual indicators and their sources are provided in Annex II.A1.

Development of support to agriculture

Support to farmers in the United States is low, in comparison with other OECD countries. Over the 2011-13 period, producer support in the United States was the fourth-lowest in the OECD area, and less than half the OECD average. Box 16.1 provides a description of the main changes in the United States' GSSE and TSE estimates resulting from the change in the definition of the General Services Support Estimate.

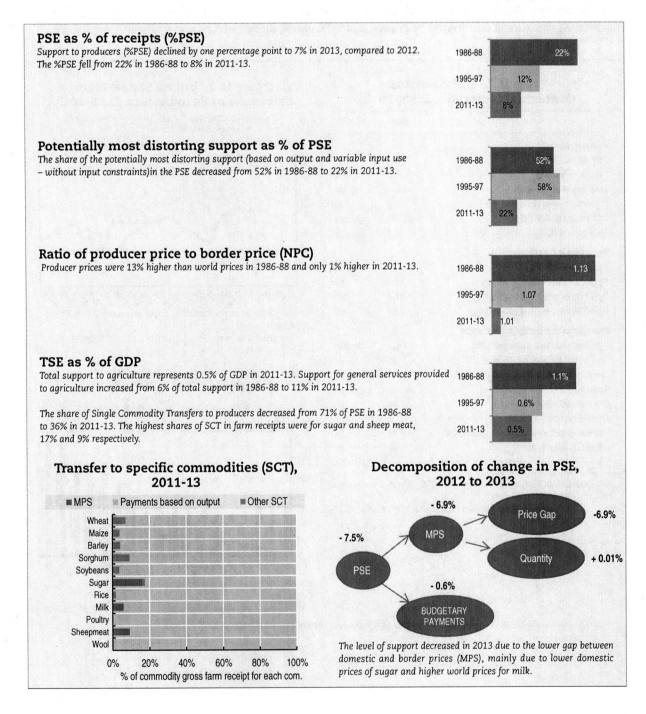

PSE as % of receipts (%PSE)
Support to producers (%PSE) declined by one percentage point to 7% in 2013, compared to 2012. The %PSE fell from 22% in 1986-88 to 8% in 2011-13.

1986-88   22%
1995-97   12%
2011-13   8%

Potentially most distorting support as % of PSE
The share of the potentially most distorting support (based on output and variable input use – without input constraints)in the PSE decreased from 52% in 1986-88 to 22% in 2011-13.

1986-88   52%
1995-97   58%
2011-13   22%

Ratio of producer price to border price (NPC)
Producer prices were 13% higher than world prices in 1986-88 and only 1% higher in 2011-13.

1986-88   1.13
1995-97   1.07
2011-13   1.01

TSE as % of GDP
Total support to agriculture represents 0.5% of GDP in 2011-13. Support for general services provided to agriculture increased from 6% of total support in 1986-88 to 11% in 2011-13.

The share of Single Commodity Transfers to producers decreased from 71% of PSE in 1986-88 to 36% in 2011-13. The highest shares of SCT in farm receipts were for sugar and sheep meat, 17% and 9% respectively.

1986-88   1.1%
1995-97   0.6%
2011-13   0.5%

Transfer to specific commodities (SCT), 2011-13

■ MPS   ▨ Payments based on output   ■ Other SCT

Wheat
Maize
Barley
Sorghum
Soybeans
Sugar
Rice
Milk
Poultry
Sheepmeat
Wool

0%   20%   40%   60%   80%   100%
% of commodity gross farm receipt for each com.

Decomposition of change in PSE, 2012 to 2013

- 7.5%   PSE
- 6.9%   MPS
- 0.6%   BUDGETARY PAYMENTS
Price Gap   -6.9%
Quantity   + 0.01%

The level of support decreased in 2013 due to the lower gap between domestic and border prices (MPS), mainly due to lower domestic prices of sugar and higher world prices for milk.

Table 16.2. **United States: Estimates of support to agriculture**

Million USD

	1986-88	1995-97	2011-13	2011	2012	2013p
Total value of production (at farm gate)	**143 469**	**200 325**	**388 665**	**379 486**	**396 606**	**389 904**
of which: share of MPS commodities (%)	71.8	70.4	75.3	75.8	75.4	74.6
Total value of consumption (at farm gate)	**132 032**	**176 428**	**329 168**	**322 030**	**340 426**	**325 047**
Producer Support Estimate (PSE)	**36 411**	**26 614**	**31 869**	**31 038**	**33 548**	**31 022**
Support based on commodity output	16 188	12 488	4 272	2 076	6 638	4 103
Market Price Support[1]	13 077	12 337	3 999	2 000	6 162	3 837
Payments based on output	3 111	151	273	77	476	266
Payments based on input use	7 061	6 638	10 157	10 172	10 019	10 279
Based on variable input use	3 697	3 088	3 192	3 321	3 132	3 123
with input constraints	739	264	527	480	556	546
Based on fixed capital formation	1 233	553	1 891	1 849	1 889	1 936
with input constraints	1 233	536	1 873	1 795	1 889	1 936
Based on on-farm services	2 131	2 997	5 074	5 002	4 999	5 220
with input constraints	349	543	1 224	1 226	1 188	1 258
Payments based on current A/An/R/I, production required	12 231	1 825	9 135	10 323	8 512	8 570
Based on Receipts / Income	912	721	1 109	912	1 203	1 213
Based on Area planted / Animal numbers	11 319	1 104	8 026	9 410	7 309	7 358
with input constraints	2 565	557	7 799	9 142	6 971	7 284
Payments based on non-current A/An/R/I, production required	0	0	0	0	0	0
Payments based on non-current A/An/R/I, production not required	338	3 824	5 665	5 799	5 776	5 420
With variable payment rates	0	0	24	0	0	73
with commodity exceptions	0	0	24	0	0	73
With fixed payment rates	338	3 824	5 641	5 799	5 776	5 347
with commodity exceptions	0	3 824	4 685	4 846	4 822	4 387
Payments based on non-commodity criteria	592	1 839	2 640	2 668	2 603	2 650
Based on long-term resource retirement	592	1 839	2 574	2 567	2 556	2 600
Based on a specific non-commodity output	0	0	0	0	0	0
Based on other non-commodity criteria	0	0	66	101	47	50
Miscellaneous payments	0	0	0	0	0	0
Percentage PSE (%)	**21.9**	**12.3**	**7.6**	**7.6**	**7.9**	**7.4**
Producer NPC (coeff.)	**1.13**	**1.07**	**1.01**	**1.01**	**1.02**	**1.01**
Producer NAC (coeff.)	**1.28**	**1.14**	**1.08**	**1.08**	**1.09**	**1.08**
General Services Support Estimate (GSSE)[2]	**3 108**	**4 241**	**9 072**	**6 640**	**9 873**	**10 702**
Agricultural knowledge and innovation system	1 129	1 479	2 453	2 413	2 368	2 577
Inspection and control	372	559	1 150	1 058	1 201	1 191
Development and maintenance of infrastructure	13	30	1 978	-233	2 780	3 387
Marketing and promotion	495	654	1 339	1 250	1 373	1 395
Cost of public stockholding	0	52	1	1	0	1
Miscellaneous	1 100	1 468	2 151	2 151	2 151	2 151
Percentage GSSE (% of TSE)	**6.3**	**8.8**	**11.3**	**8.9**	**12.0**	**12.9**
Consumer Support Estimate (CSE)	**-3 794**	**4 452**	**34 381**	**33 927**	**31 837**	**37 379**
Transfers to producers from consumers	-12 746	-12 129	-3 884	-1 975	-5 976	-3 702
Other transfers from consumers	-1 432	-1 243	-826	-1 382	-815	-280
Transfers to consumers from taxpayers	10 089	17 816	39 091	37 285	38 628	41 360
Excess feed cost	294	8	0	0	0	0
Percentage CSE (%)	**-3.2**	**2.9**	**11.9**	**11.9**	**10.5**	**13.2**
Consumer NPC (coeff.)	**1.12**	**1.08**	**1.01**	**1.01**	**1.02**	**1.01**
Consumer NAC (coeff.)	**1.03**	**0.97**	**0.89**	**0.89**	**0.90**	**0.88**
Total Support Estimate (TSE)	**49 608**	**48 671**	**80 032**	**74 963**	**82 049**	**83 084**
Transfers from consumers	14 177	13 372	4 710	3 358	6 791	3 981
Transfers from taxpayers	36 862	36 542	76 148	72 988	76 073	79 383
Budget revenues	-1 432	-1 243	-826	-1 382	-815	-280
Percentage TSE (% of GDP)	**1.1**	**0.6**	**0.5**	**0.5**	**0.5**	**0.5**
GDP deflator (1986-88=100)	**100**	**128**	**174**	**172**	**175**	**177**

Note: p: provisional. NPC: Nominal Protection Coefficient. NAC: Nominal Assistance Coefficient. A/An/R/I: Area planted/Animal numbers/Receipts/Income.

1. Market Price Support (MPS) is net of producer levies and excess feed cost. MPS commodities for the United States are: wheat, maize, barley, sorghum, cotton, rice, soybean, sugar, milk, beef and veal, sheep meat, wool, pigmeat, poultry and eggs.
2. A revised GSSE definition with new categories was introduced in 2014. When possible, the revision was implemented for the whole time series. The GSSE series and the resulting TSE are not comparable with the series published previously (for more details, see Annex 1.A2).

Source: OECD (2014), "Producer and Consumer Support Estimates", OECD *Agriculture Statistics Database, doi: http://dx.doi.org/10.1787/agr-pcse-data-en.*

StatLink ᴍᴤ᠊ *http://dx.doi.org/10.1787/888933110809*

Box 16.1. Main changes in the United States' GSSE and TSE estimates resulting from the change in the definition of the General Services Support Estimate*

As a result of the change in the definition of the General Services Support Estimate, there have been major changes in the classification of some large US programmes and as a result a very significant reduction of the US GSSE and TSE. For the year 2011, these indicators drop by 91% and 48%, respectively (Table 16.3). The reduction results from the clarification in the new methodology that the GSSE encompasses only general services to the domestic primary agriculture sector. For the US, that narrowing of the GSSE boundaries leads to removal of two major sources of previously reported expenditures from the GSSE: 1) the share of the US Supplemental Nutrition Assistance Program (SNAP) expenditures (USD 62 billion in 2013) attributable to the food supply chain beyond the farm; and 2) expenditures on international food assistance (USD 1.6 billion in 2013), both of which had been included under "Marketing and Promotion" under the previous GSSE. The share of SNAP expenditures attributable to farm level production (USD 16 billion) continues to be reported in the CSE. In addition to these two major items, some small additional changes have been made, including i) moving reported expenditures for the Renewable Energy Program (USD 56 million for 2013) to the PSE under payments based on input use, fixed capital formation; ii) moving reported expenditures for the Bioenergy Program for Advanced Biofuels (USD 31 million for 2013) to the CSE under non-commodity-specific transfers to consumers; and iii) removing expenditures for watershed and flood prevention programs (USD 235 million for 2013).

Table 16.3. Comparison of the 2011 estimate of support to agriculture for the United States as published in the 2013 report and in the current report

	Total Support Estimate	Producer Support Estimate	Consumer Support Estimate	General Services Support Estimate	GSSE categories[1]						
					A1	A2	B	C	D	E	F
United States (Million USD)											
2014 Monitoring report	74 963	31 038	33 927	6 640	2 227	186	1 058	-233	1 250	1	2 151
2013 Monitoring report	143 778	31 596	35 694	71 539	2 324	0	1 079	320	65 664	1	2 151
%diff	-48	-2	-5	-91	-4	-	-2	-173	-98	0	0

1. See Table 1.A2.1 in the Annex 1.A2 for descriptive labels of the GSSE categories under the 2014 and 2013 monitoring report. The 2013 estimates utilise the previous GSSE methodology and definitions. The estimates from the 2014 report use the revised GSSE methodology and may contain updated information across all agriculture support categories.
Source: OECD (2013a and 2014), Producer and Consumer Support Estimates, OECD Agriculture Statistics Database, http://dx.doi.org/10.1787/agr-pcse-data-en.

StatLink 🔗 http://dx.doi.org/10.1787/888933110828

* A full description of the change in the definition of the General Services Support Estimate and the resulting changes is provided in Annex 1.A2. Revised General Services Support Estimate: Overview of Main Changes of this report.

Description of policy developments

Main policy instruments

The Food, Conservation and, Energy Act of 2008 (the **2008 Farm Act***), provided the basic legislation governing farm policy for the period 2008-13. A new farm law, the Agricultural Act of 2014 (**2014 Farm Act**), was enacted on 7 February 2014, and will remain in force through 2018, and in the case of some provisions beyond 2018.

The main policy instruments under the 2008 Farm Act for the crop sector are Direct Payments (DP), Counter-Cyclical Payments (CCP), Average Crop Revenue Election (ACRE), and support-price provisions operating through non-recourse marketing loans for cereals, rice, upland cotton, oilseeds, peanuts and pulses (small chickpeas, lentils and dry peas). DPs were based on pre-determined rates and historical production. CCPs were based on current prices and historical production. Sugar is supported by a tariff-rate-quota (TRQ), together with provisions for non-recourse loans and marketing allotments. Milk and dairy products are supported by minimum prices with government purchases of butter, SMP and cheddar cheese, as well as by tariffs, TRQs and export subsidies. There are marketing loans for wool, mohair and honey, and border measures (including TRQs) for beef and sheep meat. Since the enactment of the 1985 Farm Act, eligibility for most federal commodity programme payments is subject to cross-compliance requirements.

Environmental programmes focus on measures to convert highly erodible cropland to approved conservation uses (including long-term retirement), to re-convert farmland back into wetlands, and to encourage crop and livestock producers to adopt practices that reduce environmental problems. Ethanol production is mainly supported in the form of mandated fuel use, tax incentives, loan and grant programmes. Research and advice are increasingly focused on food safety and promoting sustainable farming practices. Payments and loans for natural disasters, support for public grazing land management and irrigation infrastructures, interest concessions and tax concessions are also provided. The 2008 Farm Act also increased funding for most domestic food assistance programmes, particularly the former food stamps, now renamed the Supplemental Nutrition Assistance Program (SNAP).

The 2014 Farm Act makes major changes in commodity programmes, adds new crop insurance options, streamlines conservation programmes, modifies some provisions of the Supplemental Nutrition Assistance Program (SNAP, formerly known as food stamps), and expands programmes for specialty crops, organic farmers, bioenergy, rural development, and beginning farmers and ranchers (see Box 16.2). The Act ends fixed annual payments based on historical production, removes upland cotton from coverage under Title I programmes and introduces a new dairy margin insurance programme. The legislation also renews the Supplemental Disaster Assistance programmes for livestock and for orchard and nursery trees, vines, and bushes. The Congressional Budget Office projects these changes in commodity programmes will reduce outlays by USD 6 billion (nominal USD), or 25%, over the projected costs of continuing commodity previous programmes.

Domestic policy developments in 2013-14

Significant policy developments during 2013 included the effects of budget sequestration, mandated under the Budget Control Act of 2011, on commodity program payments and the first-ever use of the Feedstock Flexibility Programme authorised under the 2008 Farm Act.

---

* For a detailed analysis of the 2008 Farm Act, see OECD (2011), *Evaluation of Agricultural Policy Reforms in the United States.*

Box 16.2. **2014 Farm Act highlights***

Commodity programmes

- Repeals Direct Payments, Countercyclical Payments and the Average Crop Revenue Election programme (ACRE).

- Creates two new programmes – Price Loss Coverage (PLC) and Agriculture Risk Coverage (ARC). Although each of these programmes is available to producers with historical base acres of covered commodities (wheat, feed grains, rice oilseeds, peanuts and pulses), participating producers must make a choice between the two programmes, on a commodity-by-commodity basis, which holds for the life of the 2014 Farm Act. The PLC programme makes payments to enrolled producers when market prices fall below fixed reference prices. The ARC programme makes payments to enrolled producers when actual revenue falls below rolling average benchmark revenues. Payments are made on base acres, not current plantings. To receive payments under these programmes producers must comply with applicable conservation requirements, which also apply to producers participating in conservation and crop insurance programmes.

- Upland cotton producers are not eligible for PLC or ARC, but they are eligible for a new crop insurance product under Title XI – the Stacked Income Protection Plan (STAX). Cotton producers will receive transition payments while new STAX policies are implemented.

- Revises payment limitations and adjusted gross income eligibility rules.

- Continues the marketing assistance loan programme unchanged, except for an adjustment in the loan rate for upland cotton.

- Continues the sugar programme unchanged.

Dairy and livestock

- The Dairy Product Price Support Program and the Dairy Export Incentive Program are repealed.

- New programmes include the Margin Protection Program (MPP) for dairy producers and the Dairy Product Donation Program (DPDP). MPP makes payments when the difference between milk prices and feed costs falls below the coverage level elected by participating dairy operations. Under the DPDP, the government will purchase dairy products at prevailing market prices for distribution to low-income Americans through food banks and feeding programs when dairy margins fall below legislated targets.

- The Milk Income Loss Contract Program continues until MPP is operational, but is then repealed.

- The Livestock Indemnity Program, Livestock Forage Disaster Program, Emergency Assistance for Livestock Honeybees, and Farm-Raised Fish Program and Tree Assistance Program are renewed with mandatory funding and made permanent and retroactive to cover losses in fiscal years 2012 and 2013, when many producers were impacted by severe weather.

- The Supplemental Revenue Assistance Program, which covered eligible losses incurred through 30 September 2011, is not reinstated.

- Country of origin labelling (COOL) regulations remain in place and are extended to include venison.

Crop insurance

- The Stacked Income Protection Plan (STAX) provides premium subsidies to upland cotton producers to purchase area-based revenue insurance policies. The programme seeks to address the WTO ruling that the US upland cotton programme under previous US farm legislation affected world prices and thus distorted trade.

- The Supplemental Coverage Option (SCO) offers producers additional area-based insurance coverage in combination with traditional crop insurance policies. Producers who elect to participate in the ARC programme or the STAX programme are not eligible to purchase SCO coverage.

- The Non-insured Crop Assistance Program, which provides weather-related coverage for commodities for which crop insurance policies are not available, is expanded. Additional "buy-up" coverage above catastrophic loss levels will be allowed for commodities that otherwise would not have additional coverage available to them.

Box 16.2. **2014 Farm Act highlights*** *(cont.)*

Conservation programmes

- Maintains strong overall funding for USDA conservation programmes. The Congressional Budget Office estimates that between 2014 and 2018, mandatory spending on USDA conservation programmes will decline by USD 200 million – less than 1% of the USD 28 billion (nominal USD) that would have been spent if the 2008 Farm Act had continued through 2018. All major conservation programmes, with the exception of Conservation Technical Assistance, have mandatory funding.

- Continues emphasis on conservation on working lands. Funding for working land programmes (the Environmental Quality Incentives Program (EQIP) and Conservation Stewardship Program) is projected to be more than 50% of conservation spending during 2014-18. These programmes accounted for just over 40% of spending during 2008-13.

- Gradually reduces Conservation Reserve Program (CRP) cap from 32 million acres to 24 million acres by 2017.

- Consolidates many conservation programmes into new programmes or merges them into existing programmes, reducing the number of USDA conservation programmes from 23 to 13. In particular, the new Agricultural Conservation Easement Program (ACEP) consolidates the Wetland Reserve Program, Grassland Reserve Program, and the Farmland Protection Program. Funding for ACEP is just over half of what was provided for the three previous programmes in the 2008 Farm Act.

- Re-links crop insurance premium subsidies to conservation compliance (conservation of highly erodible land and wetlands) for the first time since 1996.

- The Wildlife Habitat Incentives Program is repealed, although 5% of EQIP funds will be set aside for habitat related practices.

Specialty crops and organic agriculture

- Expands programmes for specialty crops, particularly in the areas of research, disease prevention and management, and availability of fruits and vegetables through nutrition programmes.

- Expands and adds new programmes for organic agriculture, locally and regionally produced foods, and beginning farmers and ranchers.

- Increases funding to assist organic producers and handlers with the cost of organic certification.

- Expands total mandatory organic research funding.

- Exempts certified organic producers from having to pay for conventional commodity promotion programmes on their organic production, and establishes the option for an organic promotion programme.

- Requires improvements in crop insurance for organic producers and strengthens enforcement of organic regulations.

Nutrition programmes

- Re-authorises the Supplemental Nutrition Assistance programme (SNAP), the largest food and nutrition assistance programme in the United States, maintaining the programme's basic eligibility guidelines while restricting access to an income deduction related to heating and cooling expenses that boosted benefits for some households.

- Provides additional SNAP funding for enhanced employment and training activities, increased healthy food options and expanded anti-fraud efforts.

Rural development

- Continues most of USDA rural development programmes with reduced funding authorisations.

- Reduces funding to support rural business development and growth through the Rural Micro-entrepreneur Assistance Program from USD 10 million to USD 3 million per fiscal year.

- Increases mandatory funding for Value-Added Agricultural Market Development Grants Program from USD 15 million to USD 63 million per fiscal year.

- Reserves 10% of certain programmes for regional, long-term investments to better promote economic development through regional planning and leveraging of resources.

Box 16.2. **2014 Farm Act highlights**[*] *(cont.)*

Research

- Provides initial funding of USD 200 million, to be matched by outside funds, for the Foundation for Food and Agriculture Research, a new non-profit institution to foster research and technology transfer through public-private collaborations.

- Broadens support for animal health and disease research and veterinary services, and sets aside USD 5 million per year for capacity and infrastructure grants.

- Mandatory funding for specialty crops research and extension will increase to USD 80 million per year, including at least USD 25 million for emergency citrus disease research.

- High-priority research areas include pulses, coffee plants, maize and soymeal and other grain by products, and food safety training, and pollinator research is expanded.

Renewable energy and energy efficiency

- Re-authorises energy programmes established in the 2008 Farm Act.

- Expands Biorefinery Assistance Program to include bio-based product and renewable chemical manufacturing.

- Expands the Biobased Markets Programme to include forestry products

- The Biomass Crop Assistance Program now allows enrolment of land under the Conservation Reserve Program or Agricultural Conservation Easement Program contracts that are set to expire in any given fiscal year.

International trade

- Continues authorisation for USD 200 million annually for international market development.

- Re-authorises international food assistance programmes, including the McGovern-Dole Food for Education and Food for Progress programmes.

- Authorises up to USD 80 million per year for a Local and Regional Purchase Food Aid Procurement projects.

Beginning farmers and ranchers in agriculture

- Re-authorises and increases funding to USD 100 million during 2014-18 for the Beginning Farmer and Rancher Development Programme.

- Increases access to credit and supports crop insurance and risk management tools, including reducing crop insurance premiums during the first five years of farming.

[*] For more information see: *http://ers.usda.gov/agricultural-act-of-2014-highlights-and-implications.aspx*

Source: Based on information available on the USDA-ERS website at: *http://ers.usda.gov/agricultural-act-of-2014-highlights-and-implications.aspx*

On **market price support and commodity loans**, crop year 2013 marketing assistance loans issued in FY 2014 were reduced by 5.1% under mandated budget sequestration. Crop year 2013 loan deficiency payments, if any, paid under the *Marketing Assistance Loan Program* will be reduced 5.1%. Due to large sugar supplies in the domestic market, the Commodity Credit Corporation (CCC) took several actions in 2013 to reduce the likelihood of forfeitures under the sugar loan programme. First, two actions, in May and June, increased flexibility and limits on licenses under the *Refined Sugar Re-export Program* to temporarily increase processors' ability to use domestic, rather than imported, raw sugar for refining for export. In July, the CCC purchased refined sugar from US processors, which was subsequently exchanged for import access credits under the Re-export program, which permit imports of raw sugar to be refined for re-export onto the global market, and for Certificates of Quota Eligibility (CQE) under the US-Colombia Free Trade Agreement. In August, the CCC purchased refined sugar under the *Feedstock Flexibility Program* (FFP) to be sold for ethanol production. When some loan forfeitures took place despite previous actions, in September, the CCC traded its inventory of sugar for further import access credits under the Re-export program and in November and December, remaining sugar inventory was sold for ethanol and animal feed production. No such actions are anticipated for 2014.

On **direct income payments**, Direct Payments for 2013 were reduced by 8.6% under mandated budget sequestration; Countercyclical Payments and ACRE payments, if any, will be reduced 5.1%. Payments under the Milk Income Loss Contract programme expired at the end of fiscal year 2013 (30 September 2013) under provisions of the American Taxpayers Relief Act of 2012 that extended most programs of the 2008 Farm Act.

On **farm credit**, the new microloan programme was implemented beginning January 2013. The programme is designed to help small and family operations, and beginning and socially disadvantaged farmers secure loans under USD 35 000.

On **disaster assistance**, the Livestock Indemnity Program (LIP), the Livestock Forage Assistance Program, the Emergency Livestock Assistance Program and the Tree Assistance Program were extended through fiscal year 2013 (ending 30 September 2013), but no funds were appropriated to implement them. Under the 2014 Farm Act, these programmes are made permanent and retroactive to cover eligible livestock losses back to fiscal year 2012.

On **farm inspection**, the US Food and Drug Administration (FDA) implemented a plan to help phase out the use of medically important antimicrobials in food animals for food production purposes, such as to enhance growth or improve feed efficiency. The plan operates through voluntary removal by animal pharmaceutical companies of such uses from FDA-approved use conditions on labels for these products.

On **renewable energy**, the American Taxpayer Relief Act of 2012, signed into law in early 2013, extended the USD 1.01 per gallon cellulosic tax credit through 31 December 2013. It also extended the credit for alternative vehicle re-fuelling property, incentives for renewable biodiesel and renewable diesel, (the biodiesel tax credit in the amount of USD 1.00 per gallon of biodiesel, agri-biodiesel, or renewable diesel through 31 December 2013). While the Biomass Crop Assistance Program authority was extended through fiscal year 2013 under ATRA, no funds were appropriated.

On **food safety**, several initiatives took place during 2013 by the USDA Food Safety and Inspection Service (FSIS), including: i) amending regulations governing meat and poultry product labelling to expand the circumstances in which FSIS will generically approve the labels of meat and poultry products; and ii) requested public comment on draft guidelines on changes to ongoing equivalence verifications of foreign food regulatory systems.

Actions taken by the FDA include: i) proposed standards for the growing, harvesting, packing and holding of produce for human consumption, as part of its implementation of the Food Safety Modernisation Act; ii) a plan outlining the goals, objectives and key actions that will provide a strategic framework for the FDA in setting priorities and managing international food safety capacity-building programmes; iii) proposal to amend its animal drug regulations regarding the Veterinary Feed Directive drugs; and iv) issued guidance for industry on new animal drugs and new animal drug combination products administered in or on medicated feed or drinking water of food-producing animals.

On **domestic food assistance**, on 1 November 2013, the temporary increase in Supplemental Nutrition Assistance Program payments established under the 2009 American Recovery and Reinvestment Act was ended.

Trade policy developments in 2013-14

On **trade agreements**, the **European Union** and the United States launched negotiations on a comprehensive trade and investment agreement, the **Transatlantic Trade and Investment Partnership** (TTIP). By March 2014, four rounds had taken place between the United States and the European Union. New **Trade and Investment Framework Agreements** (TIFA) were signed with the **Caribbean Community** and **Myanmar** in May 2013. TIFAs provide strategic frameworks and principles for dialogue on trade and investment issues between the United States and the other parties to the TIFA. The United States also participates in the **Trans-Pacific Partnership** (TPP) negotiations.

In July 2013, the US Generalized System of Preferences (GSP) expired. GSP is a trade preference programme which provides preferential, duty-free entry for up to 5 000 products when imported from one of 127 designated beneficiary countries and territories. Extension of the programme is still under consideration in the US Congress. GSP authorisation has expired on several previous occasions, most recently in 2011. In the past, when Congress acted to extend the program, it applied the duty-free treatment to GSP-eligible products retroactively to the expiration of the program, thereby allowing importers to seek refunds of duties paid.

Japan and the United States completed an agreement to allow organic products certified in Japan or in the United States to be sold as organic in either region. The agreement, reached in September 2013, became effective on 1 January 2014.

The United States and **Morocco** signed a **Trade Facilitation Agreement** in November that addresses modernising customs practices. The agreement, which builds on the United States-Morocco Free Trade Agreement, includes provisions covering internet publication, transit, transparency with respect to penalties, and other issues that will further boost Morocco's competitiveness and benefit its trade environment.

On **labelling**, a new rule for the Country of Origin Labelling (COOL) program was promulgated, effective 23 May 2013, in response to the 23 July 2012 finding by the WTO Appellate Body that US COOL requirements for muscle cut meat were inconsistent with US obligations under the WTO Agreement on Technical Barriers to Trade. The new rule is being evaluated for compliance with WTO obligations by the WTO Dispute Settlement Body.

ANNEX II.A1

Sources and definitions of contextual indicators

Table X.1. Contextual indicators

Gross domestic product – GDP (USD billion): OECD National Accounts, Gross domestic product, national currency, current prices. Spot exchange rates used for conversion in USD.

Population (million): OECD.stat, Demography and population, Population statistics, Population and vital statistics, series on Total population mid-year estimates. For EU member countries, data come from EUROSTAT, population/demography/demography national data/population.

Land area (thousands km^2): FAO, Land use database, Land area (000 ha) recalculated to thousands km^2. Land area excludes water areas.

Population density (inhabitants/km^2): UN *World Population Prospects, 2010 Revision*, Population density by major area, region and country, 1950-2010 (persons per square km). For EU members calculated from EUROSTAT population and area.

GDP per capita, PPP (USD): OECD.stat, National accounts, Main aggregates, Gross domestic product (output approach), Per head, USD, current prices, current PPPs. EU countries, EUROSTAT, GDP and main components – Current prices.

Trade as % of GDP: Trade data from OECD ITCS Database. Customs data; Average trade: (exports + imports)/2. EU does not account for intra-EU trade.

Agriculture share in GDP (%): OECD.stat, Country statistical profiles 2011; Value added in agriculture, hunting, forestry and fishing as % total value added. EU countries: EUROSTAT, Gross value added – Agriculture and fishing – % of all branches (NACE).

Agriculture share in employment (%): OECD.stat, Employment by activities and status (ALFS), share of Agriculture, hunting, forestry (ISIC rev. 3,A), Employment ('000) (which does not include fishing) in Employment in all activities (ISIC rev. 3, A-X) ('000). EUROSTAT for the EU corresponds to the share of employed persons aged 15-64, in agriculture, hunting and forestry in total NACE activities.

Agro-food exports in total exports (%): Comtrade SAS extraction (March 2013) from OECD ITCS database. Extraction does not include fish and fish products.

Agro-food imports in total imports (%): Comtrade SAS extraction (March 2013) from OECD ITCS database. Extraction does not include fish and fish products.

Agro-food trade balance (USD million): Comtrade SAS extraction (March 2013) from OECD ITCS database. Extraction does not include fish and fish products.

Crop in total agricultural production (%): Share of value of total crop production (including horticulture) in total agricultural production. National data.

Livestock in total agricultural production (%): Share of value of total livestock production in total agricultural production. National data.

Agricultural area (AA) (thousand ha): FAO, Land use database, Agricultural area.

Share of arable land in AA (%): FAO, Land use database, arable land in percentage of agricultural area.

Share of irrigated area in AA (%): OECD, *Environmental Indicators Database.*

Share of agriculture in water consumption (%): OECD, *Environmental Indicators Database.*

Nitrogen balance (kg/ha): OECD, *Environmental Indicators Database.*

Figure X.2 Main macroeconomic indicators.

Real GDP growth (%): OECD (2014), "OECD Factbook", OECD Factbook Statistics (database, *http://dx.doi.org/10.1787/data-00590-en.*

OECD.stat, Country statistical profiles, real GDP growth.

Inflation rate (%): OECD Analytical DataBase (ADB), Annual average rate of change in Harmonised Indices of Consumer Prices (HICPs), EUROSTAT for the European Union.

Unemployment rate (%): OECD Analytical DataBase (ADB), labour force statistics; EUROSTAT for the European Union.

Figure X.3. Agro-food trade

Agro-food exports (USD billion): Comtrade SAS extraction (March 2013) from OECD ITCS database. Extraction does not include fish and fish products.

Agro-food imports (USD billion): Comtrade SAS extraction (March 2013) from OECD ITCS database. Extraction does not include fish and fish products.

Statistical annex
Summary tables of estimation of support*

A.1. Producer Support Estimate by country 203
A.2. Consumer Support Estimate by country. 205
A.3. General Services Support Estimate by country 207
A.4. Total Support Estimate by country 208
A.5. Composition of Producer Support Estimate by country 209
A.6. Characteristics of policy support by country 211
A.7. Composition of General Services Support Estimate 213
A.8. OECD: Producer Single Commodity Transfer 217
A.9. Australia: Producer Single Commodity Transfers 219
A.10. Canada: Producer Single Commodity Transfers 220
A.11. Chile: Producer Single Commodity Transfers. 221
A.12. European Union: Producer Single Commodity Transfers 222
A.13. Iceland: Producer Single Commodity Transfers. 224
A.14. Israel: Producer Single Commodity Transfers 225
A.15. Japan: Producer Single Commodity Transfers 227
A.16. Korea: Producer Single Commodity Transfers 229
A.17. Mexico: Producer Single Commodity Transfers. 230
A.18. New Zealand: Producer Single Commodity Transfers. 231
A.19. Norway: Producer Single Commodity Transfers 232
A.20. Switzerland: Producer Single Commodity Transfers. 233
A.21. Turkey: Producer Single Commodity Transfers 234
A.22. United States: Producer Single Commodity Transfers 235
A.23. OECD: Consumer Single Commodity Transfers 236
A.24. Australia: Consumer Single Commodity Transfers 238
A.25. Canada: Consumer Single Commodity Transfers 239
A.26. Chile: Consumer Single Commodity Transfers 240
A.27. European Union: Consumer Single Commodity Transfers. 241
A.28. Iceland: Consumer Single Commodity Transfers 242
A.29. Israel: Consumer Single Commodity Transfers 243
A.30. Japan: Consumer Single Commodity Transfers 244
A.31. Korea: Consumer Single Commodity Transfers 245
A.32. Mexico: Consumer Single Commodity Transfers. 246
A.33. New Zealand: Consumer Single Commodity Transfers 247
A.34. Norway: Consumer Single Commodity Transfers 248

* The statistical data for Israel are supplied by and under the responsibility of the relevant Israeli authorities. The use of such data by the OECD is without prejudice to the status of the Golan Heights, East Jerusalem and Israeli settlements in the West Bank under the terms of international law.

A.35. Switzerland: Consumer Single Commodity Transfers 249

A.36. Turkey: Consumer Single Commodity Transfers 250

A.37. United States: Consumer Single Commodity Transfers 251

A.38. Australia: Payments made on the basis of area, animal numbers,
receipts or income 252

A.39. Canada: Payments made on the basis of area, animal numbers,
receipts or income 252

A.40. Chile: Payments made on the basis of area, animal numbers,
receipts or income 253

A.41. European Union: Payments made on the basis of area, animal numbers,
receipts or income 253

A.42. Iceland: Payments made on the basis of area, animal numbers,
receipts or income 254

A.43. Israel: Payments made on the basis of area, animal numbers,
receipts or income 254

A.44. Japan: Payments made on the basis of area, animal numbers,
receipts or income 255

A.45. Korea: Payments made on the basis of area, animal numbers,
receipts or income 255

A.46. Mexico: Payments made on the basis of area, animal numbers,
receipts or income 256

A.47. New Zealand: Payments made on the basis of area, animal numbers,
receipts or income 256

A.48. Norway: Payments made on the basis of area, animal numbers,
receipts or income 257

A.49. Switzerland: Payments made on the basis of area, animal numbers,
receipts or income 257

A.50. Turkey: Payments made on the basis of area, animal numbers,
receipts or income 258

A.51. United States: Payments made on the basis of area, animal numbers,
receipts or income 258

A.52. Contribution to change in Producer Support Estimate
by country, 2012 to 2013 259

A.53. Contribution of budgetary payments to change
in Producer Support Estimate by country, 2012 to 2013 260

A.54. Contribution to change in border price by country, 2012 to 2013 261

Table A.1. **Producer Support Estimate by country**

	1986-88	1995-97	2011-13	2011	2012	2013p
Australia						
PSE (million USD)	1 444	1 282	1 186	1 591	1 005	961
PSE (million EUR)	1 318	1 031	883	1 145	782	724
Percentage PSE (%)	10.1	5.8	2.3	3.1	2.0	1.9
Producer NPC (coeff.)	1.08	1.03	1.00	1.00	1.00	1.00
Producer NAC (coeff.)	1.11	1.06	1.02	1.03	1.02	1.02
Canada						
PSE (million USD)	6 056	3 576	7 115	7 516	7 801	6 028
PSE (million EUR)	5 519	2 882	5 339	5 406	6 069	4 541
Percentage PSE (%)	35.8	16.3	13.7	14.8	14.5	11.6
Producer NPC (coeff.)	1.39	1.10	1.10	1.10	1.11	1.09
Producer NAC (coeff.)	1.56	1.20	1.16	1.17	1.17	1.13
Chile[1]						
PSE (million USD)	..	416	388	354	398	413
PSE (million EUR)	..	338	292	254	310	311
Percentage PSE (%)	..	8.0	2.7	2.6	2.8	2.7
Producer NPC (coeff.)	..	1.07	1.00	1.00	1.00	1.00
Producer NAC (coeff.)	..	1.09	1.03	1.03	1.03	1.03
European Union[2]						
PSE (million USD)	97 318	116 732	111 847	108 331	110 952	116 257
PSE (million EUR)	88 006	94 287	83 935	77 907	86 321	87 576
Percentage PSE (%)	39.2	33.8	19.2	18.3	19.6	19.8
Producer NPC (coeff.)	1.70	1.33	1.05	1.03	1.05	1.06
Producer NAC (coeff.)	1.65	1.51	1.24	1.22	1.24	1.25
Iceland						
PSE (million USD)	193	131	145	140	149	146
PSE (million EUR)	174	106	109	101	116	110
Percentage PSE (%)	77.2	60.4	44.2	44.2	47.2	41.3
Producer NPC (coeff.)	4.22	2.32	1.57	1.57	1.65	1.50
Producer NAC (coeff.)	4.44	2.52	1.80	1.79	1.89	1.70
Israel[1,3]						
PSE (million USD)	..	782	838	1 035	802	677
PSE (million EUR)	..	635	626	744	624	510
Percentage PSE (%)	..	20.0	10.3	12.6	10.3	8.1
Producer NPC (coeff.)	..	1.19	1.08	1.11	1.08	1.06
Producer NAC (coeff.)	..	1.25	1.12	1.14	1.11	1.09
Japan						
PSE (million USD)	49 757	58 891	59 966	60 384	65 567	53 947
PSE (million EUR)	45 112	47 302	45 025	43 425	51 012	40 638
Percentage PSE (%)	64.0	58.1	54.0	51.3	55.1	55.6
Producer NPC (coeff.)	2.65	2.31	1.99	1.86	2.06	2.05
Producer NAC (coeff.)	2.78	2.40	2.18	2.05	2.23	2.25
Korea						
PSE (million USD)	12 040	23 080	21 203	20 991	20 483	22 134
PSE (million EUR)	10 803	18 630	15 902	15 096	15 936	16 674
Percentage PSE (%)	69.7	67.1	52.0	53.3	50.2	52.5
Producer NPC (coeff.)	3.35	2.97	2.00	2.03	1.94	2.03
Producer NAC (coeff.)	3.38	3.09	2.08	2.14	2.01	2.11
Mexico[4]						
PSE (million USD)	8 437	1 589	7 257	6 964	6 993	7 814
PSE (million EUR)	6 867	1 395	5 445	5 008	5 441	5 886
Percentage PSE (%)	28.4	5.2	12.3	12.6	12.1	12.3
Producer NPC (coeff.)	1.34	1.00	1.04	1.03	1.05	1.04
Producer NAC (coeff.)	1.40	1.06	1.14	1.14	1.14	1.14
New Zealand						
PSE (million USD)	435	63	139	159	145	111
PSE (million EUR)	416	51	104	115	113	84
Percentage PSE (%)	10.4	1.0	0.8	0.9	0.8	0.5
Producer NPC (coeff.)	1.02	1.01	1.01	1.01	1.01	1.00
Producer NAC (coeff.)	1.12	1.01	1.01	1.01	1.01	1.01
Norway						
PSE (million USD)	2 801	2 910	3 847	3 858	4 019	3 663
PSE (million EUR)	2 530	2 358	2 887	2 775	3 127	2 759
Percentage PSE (%)	70.3	66.3	57.1	58.3	60.2	52.9
Producer NPC (coeff.)	4.08	2.50	1.68	1.74	1.75	1.54
Producer NAC (coeff.)	3.38	2.97	2.34	2.40	2.51	2.12
Switzerland						
PSE (million USD)	5 437	5 748	5 815	6 133	5 937	5 376
PSE (million EUR)	4 900	4 644	4 360	4 411	4 619	4 049
Percentage PSE (%)	77.7	68.4	53.2	53.9	56.2	49.4
Producer NPC (coeff.)	4.54	2.79	1.41	1.44	1.49	1.30
Producer NAC (coeff.)	4.51	3.18	2.14	2.17	2.28	1.98

Table A.1. **Producer Support Estimate by country** (cont.)

	1986-88	1995-97	2011-13	2011	2012	2013p
Turkey						
PSE (million USD)	3 952	7 428	15 851	16 564	15 302	15 687
PSE (million EUR)	3 558	6 052	11 878	11 912	11 905	11 817
Percentage PSE (%)	20.5	25.9	19.3	19.8	18.9	19.2
Producer NPC (coeff.)	1.21	1.25	1.17	1.19	1.15	1.16
Producer NAC (coeff.)	1.26	1.35	1.24	1.25	1.23	1.24
United States						
PSE (million USD)	36 411	26 614	31 869	31 038	33 548	31 022
PSE (million EUR)	33 299	21 765	23 930	22 321	26 100	23 369
Percentage PSE (%)	21.9	12.3	7.6	7.6	7.9	7.4
Producer NPC (coeff.)	1.13	1.07	1.01	1.01	1.02	1.01
Producer NAC (coeff.)	1.28	1.14	1.08	1.08	1.09	1.08
OECD[5]						
PSE (million USD)	239 543	253 959	260 935	258 473	266 382	257 950
PSE (million EUR)	217 332	205 293	195 814	185 883	207 246	194 314
Percentage PSE (%)	37.0	29.7	18.4	18.2	18.8	18.2
Producer NPC (coeff.)	1.50	1.31	1.10	1.09	1.11	1.10
Producer NAC (coeff.)	1.59	1.42	1.23	1.22	1.23	1.22

.. Not available.

Note: p: provisional. NPC: Nominal Protection Coefficient. NAC: Nominal Assistance Coefficient.

1. Data are presented from 1995 onwards.

2. EU12 for 1986-88; EU15 for 1995-97; and EU27 from 2007.

3. The statistical data for Israel are supplied by and under the responsibility of the relevant Israeli authorities. The use of such data by the OECD is without prejudice to the status of the Golan Heights, East Jerusalem and Israeli settlements in the West Bank under the terms of international law.

4. For Mexico, the period 1986-88 is replaced by 1991-93.

5. OECD EU countries are included individually in the OECD total for all years prior to their accession to the EU. Slovenia is only included from 1992. The OECD total does not include the non-OECD EU member states.

Source: OECD (2014), "Producer and Consumer Support Estimates", OECD *Agriculture Statistics Database, doi: http://dx.doi.org/10.1787/agr-pcse-data-en.*

StatLink ⟶ *http://dx.doi.org/10.1787/888933110847*

Table A.2. **Consumer Support Estimate by country**

	1986-88	1995-97	2011-13	2011	2012	2013p
Australia						
CSE (million USD)	-608	-292	0	0	0	0
CSE (million EUR)	-553	-236	0	0	0	0
Percentage CSE (%)	-11.6	-3.3	0.0	0.0	0.0	0.0
Consumer NPC (coeff.)	1.13	1.03	1.00	1.00	1.00	1.00
Consumer NAC (coeff.)	1.13	1.03	1.00	1.00	1.00	1.00
Canada						
CSE (million USD)	-2 860	-1 758	-4 981	-4 749	-5 481	-4 715
CSE (million EUR)	-2 586	-1 429	-3 744	-3 415	-4 264	-3 552
Percentage CSE (%)	-22.8	-11.2	-14.7	-14.3	-15.4	-14.2
Consumer NPC (coeff.)	1.33	1.13	1.17	1.17	1.18	1.17
Consumer NAC (coeff.)	1.30	1.13	1.17	1.17	1.18	1.17
Chile[1]						
CSE (million USD)	..	-422	-29	-37	-30	-20
CSE (million EUR)	..	-342	-22	-27	-24	-15
Percentage CSE (%)	..	-8.2	-0.2	-0.3	-0.2	-0.2
Consumer NPC (coeff.)	..	1.09	1.00	1.00	1.00	1.00
Consumer NAC (coeff.)	..	1.09	1.00	1.00	1.00	1.00
European Union[2]						
CSE (million USD)	-72 556	-58 450	-20 904	-13 227	-22 540	-26 945
CSE (million EUR)	-65 589	-47 130	-15 782	-9 513	-17 536	-20 298
Percentage CSE (%)	-35.7	-20.8	-4.4	-2.7	-4.8	-5.6
Consumer NPC (coeff.)	1.70	1.30	1.05	1.03	1.05	1.06
Consumer NAC (coeff.)	1.56	1.26	1.05	1.03	1.05	1.06
Iceland						
CSE (million USD)	-112	-59	-53	-48	-58	-52
CSE (million EUR)	-102	-48	-40	-35	-45	-39
Percentage CSE (%)	-70.4	-42.9	-25.9	-25.0	-29.5	-23.3
Consumer NPC (coeff.)	4.44	1.82	1.37	1.36	1.44	1.32
Consumer NAC (coeff.)	3.50	1.75	1.35	1.33	1.42	1.30
Israel[1,3]						
CSE (million USD)	..	-655	-745	-952	-682	-599
CSE (million EUR)	..	-537	-556	-685	-531	-451
Percentage CSE (%)	..	-22.6	-12.7	-15.6	-12.5	-10.1
Consumer NPC (coeff.)	..	1.30	1.15	1.19	1.14	1.11
Consumer NAC (coeff.)	..	1.29	1.15	1.18	1.14	1.11
Japan						
CSE (million USD)	-61 284	-76 199	-63 603	-64 117	-71 058	-55 634
CSE (million EUR)	-55 383	-61 242	-47 767	-46 110	-55 284	-41 909
Percentage CSE (%)	-62.3	-53.6	-45.9	-44.3	-47.9	-45.6
Consumer NPC (coeff.)	2.66	2.17	1.85	1.80	1.92	1.84
Consumer NAC (coeff.)	2.65	2.16	1.85	1.79	1.92	1.84
Korea						
CSE (million USD)	-11 786	-23 777	-25 249	-26 752	-24 701	-24 294
CSE (million EUR)	-10 594	-19 120	-18 919	-19 239	-19 218	-18 301
Percentage CSE (%)	-65.7	-64.8	-49.0	-50.0	-48.0	-49.1
Consumer NPC (coeff.)	2.94	2.91	1.96	2.00	1.93	1.97
Consumer NAC (coeff.)	2.93	2.89	1.96	2.00	1.92	1.96
Mexico[4]						
CSE (million USD)	-6 298	61	-1 888	-1 254	-2 361	-2 049
CSE (million EUR)	-5 126	-48	-1 428	-902	-1 837	-1 544
Percentage CSE (%)	-24.3	1.3	-3.2	-2.3	-3.8	-3.4
Consumer NPC (coeff.)	1.38	1.02	1.04	1.03	1.04	1.04
Consumer NAC (coeff.)	1.32	0.99	1.03	1.02	1.04	1.04
New Zealand						
CSE (million USD)	-63	-34	-109	-125	-116	-86
CSE (million EUR)	-58	-28	-81	-90	-90	-65
Percentage CSE (%)	-6.6	-2.2	-3.5	-3.9	-3.9	-2.7
Consumer NPC (coeff.)	1.07	1.02	1.04	1.04	1.04	1.03
Consumer NAC (coeff.)	1.07	1.02	1.04	1.04	1.04	1.03
Norway						
CSE (million USD)	-1 333	-1 261	-1 666	-1 738	-1 803	-1 458
CSE (million EUR)	-1 207	-1 022	-1 250	-1 250	-1 403	-1 098
Percentage CSE (%)	-55.8	-47.5	-34.9	-38.4	-36.2	-30.2
Consumer NPC (coeff.)	3.24	2.13	1.58	1.67	1.61	1.47
Consumer NAC (coeff.)	2.27	1.91	1.54	1.62	1.57	1.43
Switzerland						
CSE (million USD)	-4 823	-3 913	-2 328	-2 548	-2 502	-1 933
CSE (million EUR)	-4 340	-3 154	-1 745	-1 832	-1 946	-1 456
Percentage CSE (%)	-73.1	-58.7	-27.1	-28.6	-30.3	-22.3
Consumer NPC (coeff.)	4.50	2.91	1.38	1.41	1.44	1.29
Consumer NAC (coeff.)	3.74	2.42	1.37	1.40	1.43	1.29

Table A.2. **Consumer Support Estimate by country** (*cont.*)

	1986-88	1995-97	2011-13	2011	2012	2013p
Turkey						
CSE (million USD)	-2 931	-5 186	-8 810	-10 911	-7 708	-7 811
CSE (million EUR)	-2 640	-4 224	-6 576	-7 846	-5 997	-5 884
Percentage CSE (%)	-19.2	-21.3	-14.4	-17.1	-13.0	-13.1
Consumer NPC (coeff.)	1.26	1.29	1.17	1.21	1.15	1.16
Consumer NAC (coeff.)	1.24	1.27	1.17	1.21	1.15	1.15
United States						
CSE (million USD)	-3 794	4 452	34 381	33 927	31 837	37 379
CSE (million EUR)	-3 494	3 550	25 775	24 399	24 769	28 157
Percentage CSE (%)	-3.2	2.9	11.9	11.9	10.5	13.2
Consumer NPC (coeff.)	1.12	1.08	1.01	1.01	1.02	1.01
Consumer NAC (coeff.)	1.03	0.97	0.89	0.89	0.90	0.88
OECD[5]						
CSE (million USD)	-159 865	-171 139	-94 833	-91 578	-105 929	-86 992
CSE (million EUR)	-144 680	-137 960	-71 268	-65 859	-82 413	-65 531
Percentage CSE (%)	-29.7	-23.2	-8.3	-8.0	-9.2	-7.7
Consumer NPC (coeff.)	1.52	1.35	1.13	1.12	1.14	1.13
Consumer NAC (coeff.)	1.42	1.30	1.09	1.09	1.10	1.08

.. Not available.

Note: p: provisional. NPC: Nominal Protection Coefficient. NAC: Nominal Assistance Coefficient.

1. Data are presented from 1995 onwards.

2. EU12 for 1986-88; EU15 for 1995-97; and EU27 from 2007.

3. The statistical data for Israel are supplied by and under the responsibility of the relevant Israeli authorities. The use of such data by the OECD is without prejudice to the status of the Golan Heights, East Jerusalem and Israeli settlements in the West Bank under the terms of international law.

4. For Mexico, the period 1986-88 is replaced by 1991-93.

5. OECD EU countries are included individually in the OECD total for all years prior to their accession to the EU. Slovenia is only included from 1992. The OECD total does not include the non-OECD EU member states.

Source: OECD (2014), "Producer and Consumer Support Estimates", OECD *Agriculture Statistics Database, doi: http://dx.doi.org/10.1787/agr-pcse-data-en.*

StatLink ᴹᔕᴾ *http://dx.doi.org/10.1787/888933110866*

Table A.3. **General Services Support Estimate by country**

	1986-88	1995-97	2011-13	2011	2012	2013p
Australia						
GSSE (million USD)	95	384	1 064	1 091	1 098	1 003
GSSE (million EUR)	86	315	798	785	855	756
Percentage GSSE (% of TSE)	6.2	23.6	48.0	40.7	52.2	51.1
Canada						
GSSE (million USD)	1 138	1 234	2 528	2 619	2 469	2 496
GSSE (million EUR)	1 033	998	1 895	1 884	1 921	1 880
Percentage GSSE (% of TSE)	15.8	25.7	26.4	25.8	24.0	29.3
Chile[1]						
GSSE (million USD)	..	79	384	398	356	397
GSSE (million EUR)	..	66	288	287	277	299
Percentage GSSE (% of TSE)	..	15.6	49.7	53.0	47.2	49.0
European Union[2]						
GSSE (million USD)	9 223	10 664	14 170	14 719	13 779	14 012
GSSE (million EUR)	8 309	8 669	10 620	10 585	10 720	10 555
Percentage GSSE (% of TSE)	8.2	8.1	11.2	11.8	11.0	10.7
Iceland						
GSSE (million USD)	18	14	7	7	7	8
GSSE (million EUR)	16	11	5	5	5	6
Percentage GSSE (% of TSE)	6.8	9.1	4.7	4.7	4.4	4.8
Israel[1,3]						
GSSE (million USD)	..	121	174	175	178	168
GSSE (million EUR)	..	98	130	126	139	127
Percentage GSSE (% of TSE)	..	13.4	17.5	14.5	18.2	19.9
Japan						
GSSE (million USD)	8 775	19 447	11 189	12 594	11 549	9 425
GSSE (million EUR)	7 889	15 611	8 381	9 057	8 985	7 100
Percentage GSSE (% of TSE)	14.9	24.7	15.7	17.3	15.0	14.9
Korea						
GSSE (million USD)	1 066	3 351	2 799	2 493	2 867	3 036
GSSE (million EUR)	951	2 740	2 104	1 793	2 231	2 287
Percentage GSSE (% of TSE)	7.9	12.7	11.6	10.6	12.3	12.0
Mexico[4]						
GSSE (million USD)	1 048	382	802	801	955	649
GSSE (million EUR)	853	308	603	576	743	489
Percentage GSSE (% of TSE)	10.1	9.6	9.7	9.9	11.7	7.5
New Zealand						
GSSE (million USD)	119	120	367	361	385	354
GSSE (million EUR)	108	98	275	259	299	267
Percentage GSSE (% of TSE)	26.4	65.8	72.7	69.3	72.7	76.1
Norway						
GSSE (million USD)	124	159	346	341	336	361
GSSE (million EUR)	112	128	260	245	261	272
Percentage GSSE (% of TSE)	3.9	5.0	8.1	8.0	7.6	8.8
Switzerland						
GSSE (million USD)	431	461	544	544	549	539
GSSE (million EUR)	390	372	408	391	427	406
Percentage GSSE (% of TSE)	6.6	6.5	8.6	8.1	8.5	9.1
Turkey						
GSSE (million USD)	298	2 296	781	1 430	91	821
GSSE (million EUR)	268	1 871	572	1 028	71	618
Percentage GSSE (% of TSE)	7.0	23.6	4.5	7.9	0.6	5.0
United States						
GSSE (million USD)	3 108	4 241	9 072	6 640	9 873	10 702
GSSE (million EUR)	2 825	3 447	6 840	4 775	7 681	8 062
Percentage GSSE (% of TSE)	6.3	8.8	11.3	8.9	12.0	12.9
OECD[5]						
GSSE (million USD)	25 621	43 464	43 919	43 888	44 192	43 675
GSSE (million EUR)	23 119	35 153	32 948	31 563	34 382	32 901
Percentage GSSE (% of TSE)	9.0	13.5	12.7	12.8	12.6	12.7

.. Not available.

Note: p: provisional. TSE: Total Support Estimate.

A revised GSSE definition with new categories was introduced in 2014. When possible, the revision was implemented for the whole time series. The GSSE series and the resulting TSE are not comparable with the series published previously (for more details, see Annex 1.A1).

1. Data are presented from 1995 onwards.
2. EU12 for 1986-88; EU15 for 1995-97; and EU27 from 2007.
3. The statistical data for Israel are supplied by and under the responsibility of the relevant Israeli authorities. The use of such data by the OECD is without prejudice to the status of the Golan Heights, East Jerusalem and Israeli settlements in the West Bank under the terms of international law.
4. For Mexico, the period 1986-88 is replaced by 1991-93.
5. OECD EU countries are included individually in the OECD total for all years prior to their accession to the EU. Slovenia is only included from 1992. The OECD total does not include the non-OECD EU member states.

Source: OECD (2014), "Producer and Consumer Support Estimates", OECD *Agriculture Statistics Database, doi: http://dx.doi.org/10.1787/agr-pcse-data-en.*

Table A.4. **Total Support Estimate by country**

	1986-88	1995-97	2011-13	2011	2012	2013p
Australia						
TSE (million USD)	1 538	1 666	2 250	2 683	2 104	1 964
TSE (million EUR)	1 404	1 345	1 682	1 929	1 637	1 479
Percentage TSE (% of GDP)	0.7	0.4	0.1	0.2	0.1	0.1
Canada						
TSE (million USD)	7 225	4 814	9 644	10 136	10 272	8 526
TSE (million EUR)	6 583	3 883	7 234	7 289	7 991	6 422
Percentage TSE (% of GDP)	1.7	0.8	0.5	0.6	0.6	0.5
Chile[1]						
TSE (million USD)	..	495	772	752	754	810
TSE (million EUR)	..	403	579	541	587	610
Percentage TSE (% of GDP)	..	0.6	0.3	0.3	0.3	0.3
European Union[2]						
TSE (million USD)	111 453	132 251	127 073	124 531	125 515	131 171
TSE (million EUR)	100 756	106 888	95 340	89 558	97 652	98 811
Percentage TSE (% of GDP)	2.6	1.5	0.7	0.7	0.8	0.8
Iceland						
TSE (million USD)	257	150	156	150	159	157
TSE (million EUR)	231	122	117	108	124	118
Percentage TSE (% of GDP)	5.0	2.1	1.1	1.1	1.2	1.1
Israel[1,3]						
TSE (million USD)	..	903	1 012	1 210	980	845
TSE (million EUR)	..	734	756	870	762	636
Percentage TSE (% of GDP)	..	0.9	0.4	0.5	0.4	0.3
Japan						
TSE (million USD)	58 424	78 578	71 165	72 988	77 125	63 382
TSE (million EUR)	52 904	63 106	53 413	52 490	60 004	47 745
Percentage TSE (% of GDP)	2.3	1.6	1.3	1.2	1.3	1.3
Korea						
TSE (million USD)	13 179	26 740	24 045	23 526	23 394	25 214
TSE (million EUR)	11 820	21 621	18 038	16 919	18 201	18 994
Percentage TSE (% of GDP)	8.8	4.9	2.1	2.1	2.1	2.1
Mexico[4]						
TSE (million USD)	10 337	2 581	8 313	8 079	8 165	8 693
TSE (million EUR)	8 411	2 203	6 237	5 810	6 353	6 549
Percentage TSE (% of GDP)	2.6	0.6	0.7	0.7	0.7	0.7
New Zealand						
TSE (million USD)	554	183	505	520	530	466
TSE (million EUR)	524	149	379	374	412	351
Percentage TSE (% of GDP)	1.6	0.3	0.3	0.3	0.3	0.3
Norway						
TSE (million USD)	3 145	3 150	4 268	4 277	4 430	4 098
TSE (million EUR)	2 844	2 553	3 203	3 076	3 447	3 087
Percentage TSE (% of GDP)	3.5	2.0	0.9	0.9	0.9	0.8
Switzerland						
TSE (million USD)	6 569	7 038	6 367	6 683	6 491	5 927
TSE (million EUR)	5 923	5 682	4 774	4 806	5 050	4 465
Percentage TSE (% of GDP)	3.7	2.3	1.0	1.0	1.0	0.9
Turkey						
TSE (million USD)	4 250	9 724	16 631	17 993	15 392	16 508
TSE (million EUR)	3 826	7 923	12 450	12 940	11 975	12 435
Percentage TSE (% of GDP)	3.7	4.0	2.1	2.3	1.9	2.0
United States						
TSE (million USD)	49 608	48 671	80 032	74 963	82 049	83 084
TSE (million EUR)	45 293	39 685	60 111	53 911	63 834	62 587
Percentage TSE (% of GDP)	1.1	0.6	0.5	0.5	0.5	0.5
OECD[5]						
TSE (million USD)	285 040	322 184	345 378	341 570	350 329	344 234
TSE (million EUR)	258 481	260 546	259 171	245 643	272 558	259 311
Percentage TSE (% of GDP)	2.8	1.5	0.8	0.8	0.8	0.8

.. Not available.

Note: p: provisional.

1. Data are presented from 1995 onwards.

2. EU12 for 1986-88; EU15 for 1995-97; and EU27 from 2007.

3. The statistical data for Israel are supplied by and under the responsibility of the relevant Israeli authorities. The use of such data by the OECD is without prejudice to the status of the Golan Heights, East Jerusalem and Israeli settlements in the West Bank under the terms of international law.

4. For Mexico, the period 1986-88 is replaced by 1991-93.

5. OECD EU countries are included individually in the OECD total for all years prior to their accession to the EU. Slovenia is only included from 1992. The OECD total does not include the non-OECD EU member states.

Source: OECD (2014), "Producer and Consumer Support Estimates", OECD Agriculture Statistics Database, doi: http://dx.doi.org/10.1787/agr-pcse-data-en.

StatLink ⬛⬛⬛ http://dx.doi.org/10.1787/888933110904

Table A.5. **Composition of Producer Support Estimate by country**

As percentage of PSE

	1986-88	1995-97	2011-13	2011	2012	2013p
Australia						
Support based on commodity output	71.4	50.2	0.0	0.0	0.0	0.0
Payments based on input use	16.0	34.8	48.6	35.0	54.9	56.1
Payments based on current A/An/R/I, production required	0.0	1.1	15.5	26.8	10.1	9.6
Payments based on non-current A/An/R/I, production required	0.0	0.0	0.0	0.0	0.0	0.0
Payments based on non-current A/An/R/I, production not required	12.6	13.8	34.6	36.2	34.0	33.5
Payments based on non-commodity criteria	0.0	0.0	1.3	2.0	1.1	0.8
Miscellaneous payments	0.0	0.0	0.0	0.0	0.0	0.0
Memo items: Percentage PSE (% of gross farm receipts)	10.1	5.8	2.3	3.1	2.0	1.9
Canada						
Support based on commodity output	57.6	51.1	63.5	57.3	63.7	69.6
Payments based on input use	18.1	14.2	6.6	6.7	6.4	6.7
Payments based on current A/An/R/I, production required	21.6	17.2	27.0	29.9	28.1	22.9
Payments based on non-current A/An/R/I, production required	0.0	0.0	0.0	0.0	0.0	0.0
Payments based on non-current A/An/R/I, production not required	0.0	15.1	1.8	4.9	0.6	0.0
Payments based on non-commodity criteria	0.1	0.0	0.1	0.2	0.0	0.0
Miscellaneous payments	2.5	2.4	1.0	0.9	1.2	0.9
Memo items: Percentage PSE (% of gross farm receipts)	35.8	16.3	13.7	14.8	14.5	11.6
Chile[1]						
Support based on commodity output	..	82.4	3.1	4.3	2.8	2.2
Payments based on input use	..	15.1	96.0	95.5	97.0	95.5
Payments based on current A/An/R/I, production required	..	2.5	0.9	0.2	0.2	2.3
Payments based on non-current A/An/R/I, production required	..	0.0	0.0	0.0	0.0	0.0
Payments based on non-current A/An/R/I, production not required	..	0.0	0.0	0.0	0.0	0.0
Payments based on non-commodity criteria	..	0.0	0.0	0.0	0.0	0.0
Miscellaneous payments	..	0.0	0.0	0.0	0.0	0.0
Memo items: Percentage PSE (% of gross farm receipts)	..	8.0	2.7	2.6	2.8	2.7
European Union[2]						
Support based on commodity output	90.7	61.1	20.3	15.1	21.7	24.1
Payments based on input use	5.2	6.9	14.4	15.2	14.6	13.3
Payments based on current A/An/R/I, production required	3.6	31.6	17.3	18.7	16.7	16.5
Payments based on non-current A/An/R/I, production required	0.0	0.0	0.1	0.1	0.1	0.1
Payments based on non-current A/An/R/I, production not required	0.0	0.0	45.3	48.2	44.1	43.7
Payments based on non-commodity criteria	0.5	1.0	2.5	2.3	2.6	2.5
Miscellaneous payments	0.0	-0.7	0.2	0.4	0.2	-0.1
Memo items: Percentage PSE (% of gross farm receipts)	39.2	33.8	19.2	18.3	19.6	19.8
Iceland						
Support based on commodity output	93.3	86.7	71.9	71.5	73.1	71.1
Payments based on input use	6.8	3.8	6.3	6.3	6.0	6.7
Payments based on current A/An/R/I, production required	-0.6	-2.0	1.2	0.9	1.5	1.3
Payments based on non-current A/An/R/I, production required	0.0	11.4	20.5	21.2	19.5	20.8
Payments based on non-current A/An/R/I, production not required	0.6	0.2	0.0	0.0	0.0	0.0
Payments based on non-commodity criteria	0.0	0.0	0.0	0.0	0.0	0.0
Miscellaneous payments	0.0	0.0	0.0	0.0	0.0	0.0
Memo items: Percentage PSE (% of gross farm receipts)	77.2	60.4	44.2	44.2	47.2	41.3
Israel[1,3]						
Support based on commodity output	..	65.8	77.8	82.1	78.0	73.2
Payments based on input use	..	27.6	14.2	12.5	13.7	16.3
Payments based on current A/An/R/I, production required	..	4.1	6.9	4.4	7.1	9.1
Payments based on non-current A/An/R/I, production required	..	0.0	0.0	0.0	0.0	0.0
Payments based on non-current A/An/R/I, production not required	..	2.4	1.2	0.9	1.1	1.4
Payments based on non-commodity criteria	..	0.0	0.0	0.0	0.0	0.0
Miscellaneous payments	..	0.1	0.0	0.0	0.0	0.0
Memo items: Percentage PSE (% of gross farm receipts)	..	20.0	10.3	12.6	10.3	8.1
Japan						
Support based on commodity output	92.7	93.3	83.5	81.1	85.8	83.5
Payments based on input use	4.1	4.8	2.8	2.6	2.7	3.0
Payments based on current A/An/R/I, production required	0.0	0.0	6.4	8.7	4.4	6.1
Payments based on non-current A/An/R/I, production required	0.0	0.0	0.0	0.0	0.0	0.0
Payments based on non-current A/An/R/I, production not required	3.1	1.9	7.3	7.6	7.0	7.4
Payments based on non-commodity criteria	0.0	0.0	0.0	0.0	0.0	0.0
Miscellaneous payments	0.0	0.0	0.0	0.0	0.0	0.0
Memo items: Percentage PSE (% of gross farm receipts)	64.0	58.1	54.0	51.3	55.1	55.6
Korea						
Support based on commodity output	99.0	94.4	92.3	90.0	93.7	93.2
Payments based on input use	0.7	4.5	2.5	2.5	2.4	2.5
Payments based on current A/An/R/I, production required	0.3	1.1	2.3	4.6	1.1	1.3
Payments based on non-current A/An/R/I, production required	0.0	0.0	0.0	0.0	0.0	0.0
Payments based on non-current A/An/R/I, production not required	0.0	0.0	2.9	2.8	2.8	3.0
Payments based on non-commodity criteria	0.0	0.0	0.0	0.0	0.0	0.0
Miscellaneous payments	0.0	0.0	0.0	0.0	0.0	0.0
Memo items: Percentage PSE (% of gross farm receipts)	69.7	67.1	52.0	53.3	50.2	52.5

Table A.5. **Composition of Producer Support Estimate by country** (cont.)

As percentage of PSE

	1986-88	1995-97	2011-13	2011	2012	2013p
Mexico[4]						
Support based on commodity output	82.9	98.3	28.4	21.8	33.8	29.6
Payments based on input use	17.1	2.5	45.5	51.9	40.5	44.2
Payments based on current A/An/R/I, production required	0.0	0.5	7.0	5.7	5.1	10.2
Payments based on non-current A/An/R/I, production required	0.0	0.0	4.2	4.6	4.4	3.5
Payments based on non-current A/An/R/I, production not required	0.0	-1.4	14.9	16.0	16.3	12.5
Payments based on non-commodity criteria	0.0	0.0	0.0	0.0	0.0	0.0
Miscellaneous payments	0.0	0.0	0.0	0.0	0.0	0.0
Memo items: Percentage PSE (% of gross farm receipts)	28.4	5.2	12.3	12.6	12.1	12.3
New Zealand						
Support based on commodity output	19.9	60.8	81.6	85.2	82.7	76.8
Payments based on input use	47.9	38.5	18.1	14.4	17.2	22.7
Payments based on current A/An/R/I, production required	11.4	0.7	0.3	0.4	0.1	0.4
Payments based on non-current A/An/R/I, production required	20.8	0.0	0.0	0.0	0.0	0.0
Payments based on non-current A/An/R/I, production not required	0.0	0.0	0.0	0.0	0.0	0.0
Payments based on non-commodity criteria	0.0	0.0	0.0	0.0	0.0	0.0
Miscellaneous payments	0.0	0.0	0.0	0.0	0.0	0.0
Memo items: Percentage PSE (% of gross farm receipts)	10.4	1.0	0.8	0.9	0.8	0.5
Norway						
Support based on commodity output	72.4	62.3	47.7	47.9	51.8	43.3
Payments based on input use	9.0	5.0	5.7	5.8	5.4	5.9
Payments based on current A/An/R/I, production required	18.6	32.5	33.1	33.1	30.7	35.3
Payments based on non-current A/An/R/I, production required	0.0	0.0	13.3	12.9	11.9	15.2
Payments based on non-current A/An/R/I, production not required	0.0	0.0	0.0	0.0	0.0	0.0
Payments based on non-commodity criteria	0.0	0.2	0.2	0.2	0.2	0.3
Miscellaneous payments	0.0	0.0	0.0	0.0	0.0	0.0
Memo items: Percentage PSE (% of gross farm receipts)	70.3	66.3	57.1	58.3	60.2	52.9
Switzerland						
Support based on commodity output	83.3	66.8	39.6	41.0	42.3	35.5
Payments based on input use	6.6	5.6	3.8	3.6	3.6	4.1
Payments based on current A/An/R/I, production required	7.2	16.3	24.6	24.0	23.5	26.3
Payments based on non-current A/An/R/I, production required	0.3	7.7	1.9	1.9	1.8	2.0
Payments based on non-current A/An/R/I, production not required	0.0	0.0	22.6	22.4	21.5	24.0
Payments based on non-commodity criteria	0.0	0.8	3.8	3.5	3.7	4.1
Miscellaneous payments	2.5	2.7	3.7	3.6	3.5	4.0
Memo items: Percentage PSE (% of gross farm receipts)	77.7	68.4	53.2	53.9	56.2	49.4
Turkey						
Support based on commodity output	77.6	71.7	83.2	81.4	83.9	84.1
Payments based on input use	22.4	27.6	6.6	9.0	5.3	5.5
Payments based on current A/An/R/I, production required	0.0	0.7	10.2	9.6	10.8	10.4
Payments based on non-current A/An/R/I, production required	0.0	0.0	0.0	0.0	0.0	0.0
Payments based on non-current A/An/R/I, production not required	0.0	0.0	0.0	0.0	0.0	0.0
Payments based on non-commodity criteria	0.0	0.0	0.0	0.0	0.0	0.0
Miscellaneous payments	0.0	0.0	0.0	0.0	0.0	0.0
Memo items: Percentage PSE (% of gross farm receipts)	20.5	25.9	19.3	19.8	18.9	19.2
United States						
Support based on commodity output	44.2	46.6	13.2	6.7	19.8	13.2
Payments based on input use	19.6	25.7	31.9	32.8	29.9	33.1
Payments based on current A/An/R/I, production required	33.5	7.7	28.8	33.3	25.4	27.6
Payments based on non-current A/An/R/I, production required	0.0	0.0	0.0	0.0	0.0	0.0
Payments based on non-current A/An/R/I, production not required	0.9	12.9	17.8	18.7	17.2	17.5
Payments based on non-commodity criteria	1.7	7.1	8.3	8.6	7.8	8.5
Miscellaneous payments	0.0	0.0	0.0	0.0	0.0	0.0
Memo items: Percentage PSE (% of gross farm receipts)	21.9	12.3	7.6	7.6	7.9	7.4
OECD[5]						
Support based on commodity output	82.1	70.2	46.1	42.6	49.0	46.7
Payments based on input use	8.4	9.5	12.9	13.5	12.3	12.8
Payments based on current A/An/R/I, production required	7.8	16.4	14.7	16.6	13.4	14.0
Payments based on non-current A/An/R/I, production required	0.2	0.2	0.4	0.4	0.3	0.4
Payments based on non-current A/An/R/I, production not required	0.9	2.7	23.6	24.7	22.6	23.7
Payments based on non-commodity criteria	0.4	1.2	2.1	2.1	2.1	2.2
Miscellaneous payments	0.1	-0.2	0.2	0.2	0.2	0.2
Memo items: Percentage PSE (% of gross farm receipts)	37.0	29.7	18.4	18.2	18.8	18.2

.. Not available.

Note: p: provisional. A/An/R/I: Area planted/Animal numbers/Receipts/Income.

1. Data are presented from 1995 onwards.
2. EU12 for 1986-88; EU15 for 1995-97; and EU27 from 2007.
3. The statistical data for Israel are supplied by and under the responsibility of the relevant Israeli authorities. The use of such data by the OECD is without prejudice to the status of the Golan Heights, East Jerusalem and Israeli settlements in the West Bank under the terms of international law.
4. For Mexico, the period 1986-88 is replaced by 1991-93.
5. OECD EU countries are included individually in the OECD total for all years prior to their accession to the EU. Slovenia is only included from 1992. The OECD total does not include the non-OECD EU member states.

Source: OECD (2014), "Producer and Consumer Support Estimates", OECD *Agriculture Statistics Database, doi: http://dx.doi.org/10.1787/agr-pcse-data-en.*

StatLink ⟨ᵐˢˡ⟩ http://dx.doi.org/10.1787/888933110923

Table A.6. **Characteristics of policy support by country**

As percentage of PSE

	1986-88	1995-97	2011-13	2011	2012	2013p
Australia						
Support with output and payment limits	0.0	2.4	35.2	31.0	36.4	38.1
Support with input constraints	0.0	2.4	20.7	21.2	20.9	20.0
Support based on single commodities	71.4	52.6	0.1	0.2	0.0	0.0
Support not requiring production	12.6	13.9	35.9	38.2	35.0	34.3
Canada						
Support with output and payment limits	35.7	43.7	74.2	73.9	73.7	75.1
Support with input constraints	0.1	0.0	0.1	0.2	0.0	0.1
Support based on single commodities	71.0	58.8	78.0	73.3	78.3	82.5
Support not requiring production	2.6	17.5	2.9	6.0	1.8	0.9
Chile[1]						
Support with output and payment limits	..	0.0	0.3	0.0	0.6	0.5
Support with input constraints	..	6.6	36.6	37.9	35.6	36.4
Support based on single commodities	..	82.4	3.1	4.3	2.8	2.2
Support not requiring production	..	0.0	0.0	0.0	0.0	0.0
European Union[2]						
Support with output and payment limits	31.7	49.6	53.6	57.4	52.0	51.4
Support with input constraints	1.5	13.7	62.3	66.0	60.6	60.1
Support based on single commodities	93.2	70.3	23.7	18.9	24.9	27.1
Support not requiring production	0.5	0.3	47.9	50.9	46.8	46.1
Iceland						
Support with output and payment limits	0.0	46.7	52.9	54.7	50.2	53.7
Support with input constraints	0.0	0.0	0.0	0.0	0.0	0.0
Support based on single commodities	94.7	99.5	98.6	99.1	98.5	98.4
Support not requiring production	0.6	0.2	0.0	0.0	0.0	0.0
Israel[1,3]						
Support with output and payment limits	..	2.6	3.4	2.6	3.4	4.2
Support with input constraints	..	0.0	0.0	0.0	0.0	0.0
Support based on single commodities	..	67.7	79.0	83.4	79.3	74.1
Support not requiring production	..	2.4	1.2	0.9	1.1	1.4
Japan						
Support with output and payment limits	2.1	2.2	7.3	9.6	5.3	7.0
Support with input constraints	0.0	0.0	6.1	6.6	5.8	5.9
Support based on single commodities	92.7	93.3	88.3	88.0	88.9	88.2
Support not requiring production	3.1	1.9	7.3	7.6	7.0	7.4
Korea						
Support with output and payment limits	0.0	0.0	2.9	2.8	2.8	3.0
Support with input constraints	0.0	0.4	3.6	3.5	3.5	3.7
Support based on single commodities	99.0	94.4	93.5	93.4	93.7	93.2
Support not requiring production	0.0	0.0	2.9	2.8	2.8	3.0
Mexico[4]						
Support with output and payment limits	0.5	-2.0	28.8	30.0	30.2	26.3
Support with input constraints	0.0	0.0	4.2	4.6	4.4	3.5
Support based on single commodities	84.4	99.6	44.9	43.2	46.7	44.8
Support not requiring production	0.0	-1.4	14.9	16.0	16.3	12.5
New Zealand						
Support with output and payment limits	0.2	0.0	0.0	0.0	0.0	0.0
Support with input constraints	0.0	0.0	0.0	0.0	0.0	0.0
Support based on single commodities	19.9	60.8	81.6	85.2	82.7	76.8
Support not requiring production	0.0	0.0	0.0	0.0	0.0	0.0
Norway						
Support with output and payment limits	32.3	34.9	28.0	27.1	29.0	27.9
Support with input constraints	0.0	0.7	10.6	10.4	9.6	11.9
Support based on single commodities	72.4	62.4	53.3	53.4	56.9	49.6
Support not requiring production	0.0	0.2	0.2	0.2	0.2	0.3
Switzerland						
Support with output and payment limits	33.6	28.3	8.7	8.8	11.4	5.9
Support with input constraints	4.8	26.1	53.6	52.4	51.2	57.2
Support based on single commodities	85.7	69.0	39.8	41.2	42.5	35.7
Support not requiring production	2.5	3.5	30.1	29.5	28.7	32.1
Turkey						
Support with output and payment limits	77.6	72.4	84.5	82.6	85.4	85.6
Support with input constraints	0.0	0.0	0.1	0.1	0.1	0.1
Support based on single commodities	77.8	72.7	86.9	84.9	87.9	87.9
Support not requiring production	0.0	0.0	0.0	0.0	0.0	0.0
United States						
Support with output and payment limits	72.6	66.6	42.2	36.5	47.6	42.5
Support with input constraints	24.0	28.1	59.9	65.2	55.2	59.3
Support based on single commodities	71.3	51.4	35.9	30.4	40.6	36.7
Support not requiring production	2.6	20.0	26.1	27.3	25.0	26.0

Table A.6. **Characteristics of policy support by country** (cont.)

As percentage of PSE

	1986-88	1995-97	2011-13	2011	2012	2013p
OECD[5]						
Support with output and payment limits	27.8	34.7	37.4	38.5	36.5	37.1
Support with input constraints	4.3	10.1	35.7	37.4	33.9	35.8
Support based on single commodities	87.7	75.1	52.6	50.2	54.7	52.8
Support not requiring production	1.4	3.7	26.0	26.9	24.8	26.1

.. Not available.

Note: p: provisional.

The shares may add up to more than 100% as different characteristics may apply to the same payment.

1. Data are presented from 1995 onwards.

2. EU12 for 1986-88; EU15 for 1995-97; and EU27 from 2007.

3. The statistical data for Israel are supplied by and under the responsibility of the relevant Israeli authorities. The use of such data by the OECD is without prejudice to the status of the Golan Heights, East Jerusalem and Israeli settlements in the West Bank under the terms of international law.

4. For Mexico, the period 1986-88 is replaced by 1991-93.

5. OECD EU countries are included individually in the OECD total for all years prior to their accession to the EU. Slovenia is only included from 1992. The OECD total does not include the non-OECD EU member states.

Source: OECD (2014), "Producer and Consumer Support Estimates", OECD *Agriculture Statistics Database, doi: http://dx.doi.org/10.1787/agr-pcse-data-en.*

StatLink ⟪≣⟫ *http://dx.doi.org/10.1787/888933110942*

Table A.7. **Composition of General Services Support Estimate**

As percentage of GSSE

	1986-88	1995-97	2011-13	2011	2012	2013p
Australia						
Agricultural knowledge and innovation system	100.0	77.0	59.3	57.5	59.7	60.7
Agricultural knowledge generation	100.0	77.0	56.5	54.2	57.2	58.2
Agricultural knowledge transfer	0.0	0.0	2.7	3.3	2.5	2.5
Inspection and control	0.0	5.1	9.7	10.3	9.3	9.5
Agricultural product safety and inspection	0.0	0.0	1.1	1.3	1.1	1.1
Pest and disease inspection and control	0.0	5.1	8.5	9.0	8.2	8.4
Input control	0.0	0.0	0.0	0.0	0.0	0.0
Development and maintenance of infrastructure	0.0	12.9	30.3	31.5	30.3	29.0
Hydrological infrastructure	0.0	5.9	23.7	24.2	24.0	22.8
Storage, marketing and other physical infrastructure	0.0	4.4	6.6	7.3	6.2	6.2
Institutional infrastructure	0.0	1.8	0.0	0.0	0.0	0.0
Farm restructuring	0.0	0.9	0.0	0.0	0.0	0.0
Marketing and promotion	0.0	5.0	0.8	0.7	0.8	0.8
Collective schemes for processing and marketing	0.0	2.5	0.4	0.3	0.5	0.5
Promotion of agricultural products	0.0	2.5	0.3	0.3	0.3	0.3
Cost of public stockholding	0.0	0.0	0.0	0.0	0.0	0.0
Miscellaneous	0.0	0.0	0.0	0.0	0.0	0.0
Canada						
Agricultural knowledge and innovation system	41.6	41.0	36.9	35.6	38.7	36.4
Agricultural knowledge generation	23.5	25.4	27.6	26.2	28.6	28.1
Agricultural knowledge transfer	18.1	15.7	9.3	9.4	10.2	8.3
Inspection and control	24.9	21.0	39.2	38.9	40.3	38.4
Agricultural product safety and inspection	23.9	20.1	37.3	37.1	37.9	37.0
Pest and disease inspection and control	1.0	0.9	1.9	1.8	2.3	1.4
Input control	0.0	0.0	0.0	0.0	0.0	0.0
Development and maintenance of infrastructure	24.5	14.4	10.8	13.6	10.1	8.8
Hydrological infrastructure	7.6	2.5	2.2	2.5	2.4	1.7
Storage, marketing and other physical infrastructure	11.6	9.0	6.0	8.6	4.8	4.5
Institutional infrastructure	4.1	2.7	2.6	2.4	2.9	2.5
Farm restructuring	1.2	0.2	0.0	0.1	0.0	0.0
Marketing and promotion	7.4	21.3	7.9	9.2	8.0	6.5
Collective schemes for processing and marketing	5.2	20.5	6.1	6.8	6.1	5.3
Promotion of agricultural products	2.3	0.8	1.8	2.4	1.9	1.2
Cost of public stockholding	0.0	0.0	0.0	0.0	0.0	0.0
Miscellaneous	1.6	2.2	5.2	2.7	3.0	9.8
Chile[1]						
Agricultural knowledge and innovation system	..	35.8	25.3	24.2	27.3	24.4
Agricultural knowledge generation	..	34.2	23.7	22.7	25.5	22.8
Agricultural knowledge transfer	..	1.6	1.6	1.5	1.7	1.6
Inspection and control	..	1.0	19.7	19.2	20.8	19.1
Agricultural product safety and inspection	..	1.0	11.3	10.6	12.0	11.4
Pest and disease inspection and control	..	0.0	0.0	0.0	0.0	0.0
Input control	..	0.0	8.4	8.6	8.7	7.7
Development and maintenance of infrastructure	..	57.6	50.6	53.8	46.5	51.6
Hydrological infrastructure	..	49.4	35.5	38.2	31.0	37.2
Storage, marketing and other physical infrastructure	..	0.0	0.0	0.0	0.0	0.1
Institutional infrastructure	..	0.0	0.0	0.0	0.0	0.0
Farm restructuring	..	8.2	15.1	15.6	15.4	14.3
Marketing and promotion	..	4.8	4.4	2.8	5.5	4.9
Collective schemes for processing and marketing	..	0.0	0.0	0.0	0.0	0.0
Promotion of agricultural products	..	4.8	4.4	2.8	5.5	4.9
Cost of public stockholding	..	0.0	0.0	0.0	0.0	0.0
Miscellaneous	..	0.7	0.0	0.0	0.0	0.0
European Union[2]						
Agricultural knowledge and innovation system	19.8	36.3	44.3	43.9	43.9	45.2
Agricultural knowledge generation	12.0	17.1	17.7	17.7	17.4	18.0
Agricultural knowledge transfer	7.7	19.2	26.6	26.2	26.5	27.2
Inspection and control	2.1	2.6	6.1	6.1	6.1	6.1
Agricultural product safety and inspection	0.8	0.7	2.0	2.2	1.9	1.8
Pest and disease inspection and control	1.3	2.0	3.1	3.0	3.2	3.2
Input control	0.0	0.0	1.0	0.9	1.0	1.0
Development and maintenance of infrastructure	15.0	19.8	29.2	28.8	29.9	28.9
Hydrological infrastructure	1.9	2.7	1.9	1.9	1.9	1.9
Storage, marketing and other physical infrastructure	7.4	6.6	7.0	7.8	7.2	6.1
Institutional infrastructure	2.4	1.0	3.8	3.7	3.8	3.9
Farm restructuring	3.3	9.4	16.5	15.4	17.0	17.0
Marketing and promotion	13.5	19.4	19.8	20.4	19.6	19.4
Collective schemes for processing and marketing	1.8	2.8	9.6	9.3	9.9	9.7
Promotion of agricultural products	11.6	16.5	10.1	11.0	9.7	9.6
Cost of public stockholding	49.4	21.3	0.1	0.3	0.1	0.1
Miscellaneous	0.3	0.5	0.4	0.5	0.4	0.3

Table A.7. **Composition of General Services Support Estimate** (*cont.*)

As percentage of GSSE

	1986-88	1995-97	2011-13	2011	2012	2013p
Iceland						
Agricultural knowledge and innovation system	26.7	35.5	9.6	10.8	8.7	9.4
Agricultural knowledge generation	20.0	25.2	9.6	10.8	8.7	9.4
Agricultural knowledge transfer	6.7	10.3	0.0	0.0	0.0	0.0
Inspection and control	5.2	9.5	41.9	42.1	42.6	41.2
Agricultural product safety and inspection	0.0	0.0	0.0	0.0	0.0	0.0
Pest and disease inspection and control	5.2	9.5	41.9	42.1	42.6	41.2
Input control	0.0	0.0	0.0	0.0	0.0	0.0
Development and maintenance of infrastructure	12.9	19.4	1.6	0.6	1.7	2.5
Hydrological infrastructure	0.0	0.0	0.0	0.0	0.0	0.0
Storage, marketing and other physical infrastructure	10.2	13.0	1.6	0.6	1.7	2.5
Institutional infrastructure	0.0	0.0	0.0	0.0	0.0	0.0
Farm restructuring	2.7	6.4	0.0	0.0	0.0	0.0
Marketing and promotion	8.1	8.0	3.4	2.5	3.5	4.3
Collective schemes for processing and marketing	0.0	0.0	0.0	0.0	0.0	0.0
Promotion of agricultural products	8.1	8.0	3.4	2.5	3.5	4.3
Cost of public stockholding	47.1	27.6	43.4	44.1	43.5	42.6
Miscellaneous	0.0	0.0	0.0	0.0	0.0	0.0
Israel[1,3]						
Agricultural knowledge and innovation system	..	39.8	42.6	45.2	38.7	43.9
Agricultural knowledge generation	..	39.1	42.4	45.0	38.5	43.6
Agricultural knowledge transfer	..	0.8	0.3	0.2	0.2	0.3
Inspection and control	..	14.3	15.4	15.1	17.6	13.6
Agricultural product safety and inspection	..	3.6	2.8	2.6	2.9	2.9
Pest and disease inspection and control	..	10.7	12.6	12.5	14.8	10.7
Input control	..	0.0	0.0	0.0	0.0	0.0
Development and maintenance of infrastructure	..	2.8	32.5	32.2	33.7	31.6
Hydrological infrastructure	..	1.7	20.3	32.0	25.4	3.6
Storage, marketing and other physical infrastructure	..	1.1	4.4	0.2	8.2	4.7
Institutional infrastructure	..	0.0	0.0	0.0	0.0	0.0
Farm restructuring	..	0.0	7.8	0.0	0.0	23.3
Marketing and promotion	..	15.3	0.5	0.2	0.5	0.8
Collective schemes for processing and marketing	..	0.0	0.0	0.0	0.0	0.0
Promotion of agricultural products	..	15.3	0.5	0.2	0.5	0.8
Cost of public stockholding	..	27.7	8.2	7.2	8.6	9.0
Miscellaneous	..	0.0	0.7	0.1	0.9	1.1
Japan						
Agricultural knowledge and innovation system	6.0	4.8	12.8	11.9	14.5	12.0
Agricultural knowledge generation	3.6	3.4	8.5	8.2	9.9	7.5
Agricultural knowledge transfer	2.3	1.4	4.3	3.6	4.7	4.5
Inspection and control	0.6	0.5	1.2	1.4	1.0	1.3
Agricultural product safety and inspection	0.0	0.0	0.0	0.0	0.0	0.1
Pest and disease inspection and control	0.6	0.5	1.0	1.4	0.6	0.9
Input control	0.0	0.0	0.2	0.0	0.4	0.3
Development and maintenance of infrastructure	88.2	90.3	82.9	83.7	80.6	84.3
Hydrological infrastructure	33.6	30.4	47.7	54.4	40.4	48.3
Storage, marketing and other physical infrastructure	47.2	55.2	28.9	23.2	33.3	30.3
Institutional infrastructure	0.0	0.0	0.0	0.0	0.0	0.0
Farm restructuring	7.4	4.6	6.2	6.1	6.8	5.8
Marketing and promotion	1.8	1.3	1.4	1.4	2.3	0.6
Collective schemes for processing and marketing	0.9	0.7	0.4	0.7	0.2	0.2
Promotion of agricultural products	0.9	0.7	1.1	0.7	2.1	0.4
Cost of public stockholding	3.4	3.1	1.7	1.6	1.6	1.8
Miscellaneous	0.0	0.0	0.0	0.0	0.0	0.0
Korea						
Agricultural knowledge and innovation system	6.6	11.6	25.3	26.2	23.4	26.5
Agricultural knowledge generation	6.0	9.9	22.4	24.4	21.7	21.1
Agricultural knowledge transfer	0.6	1.6	2.9	1.7	1.7	5.3
Inspection and control	2.6	2.3	6.1	6.1	6.0	6.1
Agricultural product safety and inspection	1.8	1.7	3.5	3.7	3.4	3.3
Pest and disease inspection and control	0.6	0.4	2.6	2.4	2.7	2.7
Input control	0.3	0.1	0.0	0.0	0.0	0.0
Development and maintenance of infrastructure	46.5	75.0	49.0	51.9	50.1	45.1
Hydrological infrastructure	44.9	62.2	36.9	36.9	38.2	35.6
Storage, marketing and other physical infrastructure	1.5	12.4	10.0	12.7	9.7	7.6
Institutional infrastructure	0.0	0.0	0.0	0.0	0.0	0.0
Farm restructuring	0.1	0.5	2.1	2.4	2.1	2.0
Marketing and promotion	0.0	0.4	2.3	2.5	2.2	2.1
Collective schemes for processing and marketing	0.0	0.0	0.0	0.0	0.0	0.0
Promotion of agricultural products	0.0	0.4	2.3	2.5	2.2	2.1
Cost of public stockholding	44.2	10.7	17.2	13.3	18.2	20.2
Miscellaneous	0.0	0.0	0.0	0.0	0.0	0.0

Table A.7. **Composition of General Services Support Estimate** (cont.)

As percentage of GSSE

	1986-88	1995-97	2011-13	2011	2012	2013p
Mexico[4]						
Agricultural knowledge and innovation system	27.5	55.7	56.1	53.3	44.1	71.0
Agricultural knowledge generation	10.5	20.8	14.7	13.4	11.7	19.0
Agricultural knowledge transfer	17.0	35.0	41.4	39.9	32.4	52.0
Inspection and control	0.0	6.2	13.1	7.7	13.6	17.9
Agricultural product safety and inspection	0.0	2.0	4.4	2.6	4.5	6.0
Pest and disease inspection and control	0.0	2.1	4.4	2.6	4.6	6.0
Input control	0.0	2.1	4.4	2.6	4.5	6.0
Development and maintenance of infrastructure	27.7	17.1	28.0	37.2	38.7	7.9
Hydrological infrastructure	24.6	14.3	24.0	32.0	36.8	3.3
Storage, marketing and other physical infrastructure	1.4	0.7	0.0	0.0	0.0	0.0
Institutional infrastructure	0.0	0.0	3.9	5.2	2.0	4.7
Farm restructuring	1.7	2.1	0.0	0.0	0.0	0.0
Marketing and promotion	7.9	6.0	2.8	1.8	3.5	3.1
Collective schemes for processing and marketing	7.9	6.0	0.0	0.0	0.0	0.0
Promotion of agricultural products	0.0	0.0	2.8	1.7	3.5	3.1
Cost of public stockholding	36.9	15.0	0.0	0.0	0.0	0.0
Miscellaneous	0.0	0.0	0.0	0.0	0.0	0.0
New Zealand						
Agricultural knowledge and innovation system	50.7	64.7	38.3	34.1	41.4	39.5
Agricultural knowledge generation	50.7	61.6	32.2	28.6	35.2	32.7
Agricultural knowledge transfer	0.0	3.2	6.1	5.5	6.1	6.8
Inspection and control	26.3	24.0	39.7	45.6	35.5	38.0
Agricultural product safety and inspection	0.0	0.0	0.0	0.0	0.0	0.0
Pest and disease inspection and control	4.0	21.7	38.4	44.1	34.3	36.9
Input control	22.4	2.3	1.2	1.5	1.2	1.1
Development and maintenance of infrastructure	23.0	11.2	22.0	20.3	23.2	22.5
Hydrological infrastructure	23.0	5.6	14.5	13.3	15.5	14.8
Storage, marketing and other physical infrastructure	0.0	5.6	7.4	7.0	7.6	7.7
Institutional infrastructure	0.0	0.0	0.0	0.0	0.0	0.0
Farm restructuring	0.0	0.0	0.0	0.0	0.0	0.0
Marketing and promotion	0.0	0.0	0.0	0.0	0.0	0.0
Collective schemes for processing and marketing	0.0	0.0	0.0	0.0	0.0	0.0
Promotion of agricultural products	0.0	0.0	0.0	0.0	0.0	0.0
Cost of public stockholding	0.0	0.0	0.0	0.0	0.0	0.0
Miscellaneous	0.0	0.0	0.0	0.0	0.0	0.0
Norway						
Agricultural knowledge and innovation system	55.7	59.7	52.4	52.5	53.0	51.6
Agricultural knowledge generation	15.3	18.6	12.7	13.1	13.0	12.1
Agricultural knowledge transfer	40.4	41.1	39.6	39.4	40.1	39.5
Inspection and control	3.8	16.4	33.6	33.7	33.0	34.2
Agricultural product safety and inspection	0.0	0.5	33.6	33.7	33.0	34.2
Pest and disease inspection and control	3.8	15.9	0.0	0.0	0.0	0.0
Input control	0.0	0.0	0.0	0.0	0.0	0.0
Development and maintenance of infrastructure	23.9	10.4	10.9	11.0	11.3	10.4
Hydrological infrastructure	0.0	0.0	0.0	0.0	0.0	0.0
Storage, marketing and other physical infrastructure	8.1	2.9	0.0	0.0	0.0	0.0
Institutional infrastructure	15.8	7.5	6.2	6.1	6.4	6.1
Farm restructuring	0.0	0.0	4.7	4.9	4.8	4.4
Marketing and promotion	16.6	11.4	3.1	2.8	2.7	3.7
Collective schemes for processing and marketing	0.0	0.0	0.0	0.0	0.0	0.0
Promotion of agricultural products	16.6	11.4	3.1	2.8	2.7	3.7
Cost of public stockholding	0.0	2.1	0.0	0.0	0.0	0.0
Miscellaneous	0.0	0.0	0.0	0.0	0.0	0.0
Switzerland						
Agricultural knowledge and innovation system	25.5	27.9	24.7	23.5	25.9	24.5
Agricultural knowledge generation	19.9	21.4	22.3	21.1	23.6	22.1
Agricultural knowledge transfer	5.6	6.4	2.4	2.5	2.3	2.4
Inspection and control	2.1	2.5	2.2	2.3	2.2	2.2
Agricultural product safety and inspection	2.1	2.5	2.2	2.3	2.2	2.2
Pest and disease inspection and control	0.0	0.0	0.0	0.0	0.0	0.0
Input control	0.0	0.0	0.0	0.0	0.0	0.0
Development and maintenance of infrastructure	18.6	14.1	17.4	17.2	16.9	18.0
Hydrological infrastructure	0.0	0.0	0.0	0.0	0.0	0.0
Storage, marketing and other physical infrastructure	18.6	14.1	17.4	17.2	16.9	18.0
Institutional infrastructure	0.0	0.0	0.0	0.0	0.0	0.0
Farm restructuring	0.0	0.0	0.0	0.0	0.0	0.0
Marketing and promotion	6.6	7.6	11.8	11.5	12.5	11.4
Collective schemes for processing and marketing	0.0	0.0	0.0	0.0	0.0	0.0
Promotion of agricultural products	6.6	7.6	11.8	11.5	12.5	11.4
Cost of public stockholding	15.2	14.0	7.8	8.2	7.5	7.8
Miscellaneous	31.9	33.9	36.1	37.3	35.0	36.1

Table A.7. **Composition of General Services Support Estimate** (cont.)

As percentage of GSSE

	1986-88	1995-97	2011-13	2011	2012	2013p
Turkey						
Agricultural knowledge and innovation system	15.7	2.1	16.8	1.4	43.8	5.2
Agricultural knowledge generation	14.7	1.8	16.8	1.4	43.8	5.2
Agricultural knowledge transfer	1.0	0.2	0.0	0.0	0.0	0.0
Inspection and control	16.7	3.2	22.1	3.2	56.2	6.7
Agricultural product safety and inspection	0.0	0.0	0.0	0.0	0.0	0.0
Pest and disease inspection and control	16.7	3.2	22.1	3.2	56.2	6.7
Input control	0.0	0.0	0.0	0.0	0.0	0.0
Development and maintenance of infrastructure	2.6	0.5	0.0	0.0	0.0	0.0
Hydrological infrastructure	1.3	0.3	0.0	0.0	0.0	0.0
Storage, marketing and other physical infrastructure	1.3	0.3	0.0	0.0	0.0	0.0
Institutional infrastructure	0.0	0.0	0.0	0.0	0.0	0.0
Farm restructuring	0.0	0.0	0.0	0.0	0.0	0.0
Marketing and promotion	28.8	89.8	61.1	95.4	0.0	88.0
Collective schemes for processing and marketing	0.0	0.0	0.0	0.0	0.0	0.0
Promotion of agricultural products	28.8	89.8	61.1	95.4	0.0	88.0
Cost of public stockholding	0.0	0.0	0.0	0.0	0.0	0.0
Miscellaneous	36.2	4.5	0.0	0.0	0.0	0.0
United States						
Agricultural knowledge and innovation system	36.3	34.9	28.1	36.3	24.0	24.1
Agricultural knowledge generation	33.3	32.1	26.1	33.5	22.2	22.5
Agricultural knowledge transfer	3.0	2.8	2.1	2.8	1.8	1.6
Inspection and control	12.0	13.2	13.1	15.9	12.2	11.1
Agricultural product safety and inspection	12.0	13.2	12.0	15.9	10.3	9.7
Pest and disease inspection and control	0.0	0.0	0.0	0.0	0.0	0.0
Input control	0.0	0.0	1.1	0.0	1.8	1.4
Development and maintenance of infrastructure	0.4	0.7	18.8	-3.5	28.2	31.6
Hydrological infrastructure	0.0	0.0	0.0	0.0	0.0	0.0
Storage, marketing and other physical infrastructure	0.4	0.6	0.2	0.3	0.2	0.2
Institutional infrastructure	0.0	0.1	18.5	-3.8	27.9	31.5
Farm restructuring	0.0	0.0	0.0	0.0	0.0	0.0
Marketing and promotion	15.9	15.4	15.3	18.8	13.9	13.0
Collective schemes for processing and marketing	0.0	0.0	0.0	0.0	0.0	0.0
Promotion of agricultural products	15.9	15.4	15.3	18.8	13.9	13.0
Cost of public stockholding	0.0	1.2	0.0	0.0	0.0	0.0
Miscellaneous	35.4	34.6	24.8	32.4	21.8	20.1
OECD[5]						
Agricultural knowledge and innovation system	19.0	19.4	30.8	31.0	30.4	30.8
Agricultural knowledge generation	13.1	12.3	18.8	19.0	18.8	18.7
Agricultural knowledge transfer	5.9	7.1	11.9	12.1	11.7	12.1
Inspection and control	4.2	3.5	8.8	8.8	8.8	8.8
Agricultural product safety and inspection	3.0	2.3	5.9	6.1	5.8	5.9
Pest and disease inspection and control	1.1	1.2	2.3	2.5	2.2	2.2
Input control	0.1	0.0	0.6	0.3	0.8	0.7
Development and maintenance of infrastructure	39.9	52.1	40.8	39.2	42.8	40.5
Hydrological infrastructure	15.2	19.4	16.9	20.3	15.7	14.6
Storage, marketing and other physical infrastructure	19.9	27.7	10.9	10.9	12.2	9.7
Institutional infrastructure	1.1	0.4	5.9	0.9	7.7	9.2
Farm restructuring	3.8	4.5	7.1	7.1	7.3	7.0
Marketing and promotion	8.5	12.7	12.1	13.9	10.6	11.8
Collective schemes for processing and marketing	1.4	1.7	3.4	3.6	3.4	3.4
Promotion of agricultural products	7.1	11.0	8.7	10.4	7.2	8.5
Cost of public stockholding	22.9	8.2	1.7	1.4	1.8	2.0
Miscellaneous	5.4	4.2	5.8	5.7	5.6	6.0

.. Not available.

Note: p: provisional.

A revised GSSE definition with new categories was introduced in 2014. When possible, the revision was implemented for the whole time series. The GSSE series and the resulting TSE are not comparable with the series published previously (for more details, see Annex 1.A1).

1. Data are presented from 1995 onwards.

2. EU12 for 1986-88; EU15 for 1995-97; and EU27 from 2007.

3. The statistical data for Israel are supplied by and under the responsibility of the relevant Israeli authorities. The use of such data by the OECD is without prejudice to the status of the Golan Heights, East Jerusalem and Israeli settlements in the West Bank under the terms of international law.

4. For Mexico, the period 1986-88 is replaced by 1991-93.

5. OECD EU countries are included individually in the OECD total for all years prior to their accession to the EU. Slovenia is only included from 1992. The OECD total does not include the non-OECD EU member states.

Source: OECD (2014), "Producer and Consumer Support Estimates", OECD Agriculture Statistics Database, doi: http://dx.doi.org/10.1787/agr-pcse-data-en.

StatLink ⟨⟩ http://dx.doi.org/10.1787/888933110961

Table A.8. OECD: Producer Single Commodity Transfer

	1986-88	1995-97	2011-13	2011	2012	2013p
TOTAL						
PSE (million USD)	239 543	253 959	260 935	258 473	266 382	257 950
PSE (million EUR)	217 332	205 293	195 814	185 883	207 246	194 314
Producer SCT (million USD)	210 051	190 853	137 217	129 657	145 681	136 313
Producer SCT (million EUR)	190 609	154 114	103 089	93 244	113 341	102 684
Share of Producer SCT in PSE (%)	87.7	75.1	52.6	50.2	54.7	52.8
Wheat						
Producer SCT (million USD)	16 022	3 674	3 264	3 237	3 429	3 126
Producer SCT (million EUR)	14 649	2 955	2 450	2 328	2 668	2 355
Percentage SCT (%)	43.2	8.8	4.2	4.3	4.4	4.0
Producer NPC (coeff.)	1.63	1.05	1.02	1.02	1.03	1.02
Maize						
Producer SCT (million USD)	11 012	2 724	3 315	3 584	3 027	3 334
Producer SCT (million EUR)	10 121	2 193	2 482	2 577	2 355	2 512
Percentage SCT (%)	36.2	7.4	3.3	3.4	2.9	3.7
Producer NPC (coeff.)	1.29	1.04	1.00	1.00	1.00	1.00
Barley						
Producer SCT (million USD)	8 340	1 824	645	591	610	733
Producer SCT (million EUR)	7 627	1 460	484	425	475	552
Percentage SCT (%)	52.3	12.7	3.0	3.0	2.7	3.3
Producer NPC (coeff.)	2.19	1.15	1.03	1.03	1.03	1.03
Oats						
Producer SCT (million USD)	573	326	46	49	45	45
Producer SCT (million EUR)	529	262	35	35	35	34
Percentage SCT (%)	31.7	17.4	1.5	1.7	1.5	1.4
Producer NPC (coeff.)	1.49	1.21	1.01	1.01	1.01	1.00
Sorghum						
Producer SCT (million USD)	871	50	294	307	263	314
Producer SCT (million EUR)	806	38	220	221	204	236
Percentage SCT (%)	31.0	2.2	7.6	8.2	6.4	8.1
Producer NPC (coeff.)	1.18	1.01	1.00	1.00	1.00	1.00
Rice						
Producer SCT (million USD)	25 346	31 241	23 004	23 092	24 409	21 512
Producer SCT (million EUR)	23 037	25 136	17 267	16 607	18 991	16 205
Percentage SCT (%)	79.8	75.4	62.8	62.4	64.3	61.5
Producer NPC (coeff.)	4.90	4.17	2.45	2.29	2.66	2.41
Rapeseed						
Producer SCT (million USD)	1 833	51	177	134	239	158
Producer SCT (million EUR)	1 662	41	134	96	186	119
Percentage SCT (%)	47.5	1.2	0.8	0.6	1.1	0.8
Producer NPC (coeff.)	1.88	1.01	1.00	1.00	1.00	1.00
Sunflower						
Producer SCT (million USD)	1 161	76	653	653	648	656
Producer SCT (million EUR)	1 054	63	489	470	504	494
Percentage SCT (%)	47.3	4.5	15.1	13.6	15.5	16.2
Producer NPC (coeff.)	1.92	1.05	1.18	1.16	1.18	1.19
Soyabean						
Producer SCT (million USD)	1 101	355	2 515	2 645	2 321	2 581
Producer SCT (million EUR)	1 001	285	1 884	1 902	1 806	1 944
Percentage SCT (%)	8.7	2.0	5.3	6.0	4.7	5.4
Producer NPC (coeff.)	1.09	1.02	1.02	1.02	1.02	1.02
Sugar						
Producer SCT (million USD)	4 988	5 727	1 473	1 665	1 852	901
Producer SCT (million EUR)	4 544	4 662	1 106	1 197	1 441	679
Percentage SCT (%)	50.8	41.2	9.8	10.6	12.0	6.8
Producer NPC (coeff.)	2.18	1.74	1.10	1.11	1.13	1.06
Milk						
Producer SCT (million USD)	45 278	42 246	14 976	11 922	18 080	14 926
Producer SCT (million EUR)	41 116	34 216	11 295	8 574	14 066	11 243
Percentage SCT (%)	59.3	44.7	9.9	7.8	12.3	9.6
Producer NPC (coeff.)	2.79	1.84	1.11	1.08	1.14	1.10
Beef and Veal						
Producer SCT (million USD)	18 033	19 786	18 278	12 847	19 416	22 571
Producer SCT (million EUR)	16 398	16 079	13 783	9 239	15 106	17 003
Percentage SCT (%)	27.8	25.0	14.2	10.3	15.0	17.3
Producer NPC (coeff.)	1.41	1.25	1.14	1.09	1.15	1.18
Sheepmeat						
Producer SCT (million USD)	4 285	4 086	982	498	946	1 502
Producer SCT (million EUR)	3 844	3 283	742	358	736	1 132
Percentage SCT (%)	51.7	39.8	8.3	3.9	8.3	12.6
Producer NPC (coeff.)	1.81	1.37	1.07	1.02	1.06	1.12
Wool						
Producer SCT (million USD)	112	97	23	24	23	22
Producer SCT (million EUR)	105	77	17	18	18	17
Percentage SCT (%)	2.9	3.7	0.7	0.7	0.7	0.7
Producer NPC (coeff.)	1.01	1.02	1.01	1.01	1.01	1.01

Table A.8. **OECD: Producer Single Commodity Transfers** (cont.)

	1986-88	1995-97	2011-13	2011	2012	2013p
Pigmeat						
Producer SCT (million USD)	4 211	5 911	7 503	8 001	7 387	7 121
Producer SCT (million EUR)	3 634	4 742	5 622	5 754	5 747	5 364
Percentage SCT (%)	9.0	9.8	8.4	9.1	8.4	7.8
Producer NPC (coeff.)	1.20	1.13	1.09	1.10	1.09	1.08
Poultry						
Producer SCT (million USD)	3 232	5 022	6 357	7 510	6 823	4 739
Producer SCT (million EUR)	2 851	4 037	4 760	5 401	5 309	3 570
Percentage SCT (%)	13.3	13.7	9.0	11.1	9.7	6.3
Producer NPC (coeff.)	1.26	1.17	1.10	1.13	1.11	1.07
Eggs						
Producer SCT (million USD)	3 352	2 376	1 575	1 707	1 330	1 689
Producer SCT (million EUR)	3 032	1 899	1 178	1 228	1 035	1 272
Percentage SCT (%)	21.4	12.3	4.6	5.5	3.8	4.6
Producer NPC (coeff.)	1.34	1.16	1.05	1.06	1.04	1.05
Other Commodities[1]						
Producer SCT (million USD)	60 300	65 283	52 136	51 191	54 833	50 384
Producer SCT (million EUR)	54 601	52 684	39 143	36 815	42 660	37 954
Percentage SCT (%)	26.3	21.0	11.0	10.7	11.6	10.7
Producer NPC (coeff.)	1.57	1.33	1.12	1.11	1.12	1.11

Note: p: provisional. SCT: Single Commodity Transfers. PSE: Producer Support Estimate. NPC: Nominal Protection Coefficient.

1. Producer SCT for Other Commodities: Total Producer SCT minus the Producer SCTs for the commodities listed above.

Source: OECD (2014), "Producer and Consumer Support Estimates", OECD *Agriculture Statistics Database, doi: http://dx.doi.org/10.1787/agr-pcse-data-en.*

StatLink 🖳🖵 *http://dx.doi.org/10.1787/888933110980*

Table A.9. **Australia: Producer Single Commodity Transfers**

	1986-88	1995-97	2011-13	2011	2012	2013p
TOTAL						
PSE (million AUD)	2 022	1 694	1 170	1 542	971	996
Producer SCT (million AUD)	1 447	873	1	2	0	0
Share of Producer SCT in PSE (%)	71.4	52.6	0.1	0.2	0.0	0.0
Wheat						
Producer SCT (million AUD)	109	43	0	0	0	0
Percentage SCT (%)	4.5	1.0	0.0	0.0	0.0	0.0
Producer NPC (coeff.)	1.05	1.01	1.00	1.00	1.00	1.00
Barley						
Producer SCT (million AUD)	1	0	0	0	0	0
Percentage SCT (%)	0.1	0.0	0.0	0.0	0.0	0.0
Producer NPC (coeff.)	1.00	1.00	1.00	1.00	1.00	1.00
Oats						
Producer SCT (million AUD)	0	0	0	0	0	0
Percentage SCT (%)	0.0	0.0	0.0	0.0	0.0	0.0
Producer NPC (coeff.)	1.00	1.00	1.00	1.00	1.00	1.00
Sorghum						
Producer SCT (million AUD)	0	0	0	0	0	0
Percentage SCT (%)	0.0	0.0	0.0	0.0	0.0	0.0
Producer NPC (coeff.)	1.00	1.00	1.00	1.00	1.00	1.00
Rice						
Producer SCT (million AUD)	13	6	0	0	0	0
Percentage SCT (%)	11.1	2.3	0.0	0.0	0.0	0.0
Producer NPC (coeff.)	1.13	1.02	1.00	1.00	1.00	1.00
Rapeseed						
Producer SCT (million AUD)	0	0	0	0	0	0
Percentage SCT (%)	0.0	0.0	0.0	0.0	0.0	0.0
Producer NPC (coeff.)	1.00	1.00	1.00	1.00	1.00	1.00
Sunflower						
Producer SCT (million AUD)	0	0	0	0	0	0
Percentage SCT (%)	0.0	0.0	0.0	0.0	0.0	0.0
Producer NPC (coeff.)	1.00	1.00	1.00	1.00	1.00	1.00
Soyabean						
Producer SCT (million AUD)	0	0	0	0	0	0
Percentage SCT (%)	0.0	0.0	0.0	0.0	0.0	0.0
Producer NPC (coeff.)	1.00	1.00	1.00	1.00	1.00	1.00
Sugar						
Producer SCT (million AUD)	66	30	0	0	0	0
Percentage SCT (%)	10.4	2.6	0.0	0.0	0.0	0.0
Producer NPC (coeff.)	1.12	1.03	1.00	1.00	1.00	1.00
Milk						
Producer SCT (million AUD)	971	515	0	0	0	0
Percentage SCT (%)	62.2	18.3	0.0	0.0	0.0	0.0
Producer NPC (coeff.)	2.71	1.22	1.00	1.00	1.00	1.00
Beef and Veal						
Producer SCT (million AUD)	-2	-1	1	2	0	0
Percentage SCT (%)	-0.1	0.0	0.0	0.0	0.0	0.0
Producer NPC (coeff.)	1.00	1.00	1.00	1.00	1.00	1.00
Sheepmeat						
Producer SCT (million AUD)	10	0	0	0	0	0
Percentage SCT (%)	1.3	0.0	0.0	0.0	0.0	0.0
Producer NPC (coeff.)	1.01	1.00	1.00	1.00	1.00	1.00
Wool						
Producer SCT (million AUD)	26	74	0	0	0	0
Percentage SCT (%)	0.6	2.8	0.0	0.0	0.0	0.0
Producer NPC (coeff.)	1.01	1.01	1.00	1.00	1.00	1.00
Pigmeat						
Producer SCT (million AUD)	0	0	0	0	0	0
Percentage SCT (%)	0.0	0.0	0.0	0.0	0.0	0.0
Producer NPC (coeff.)	1.00	1.00	1.00	1.00	1.00	1.00
Poultry						
Producer SCT (million AUD)	0	0	0	0	0	0
Percentage SCT (%)	0.0	0.0	0.0	0.0	0.0	0.0
Producer NPC (coeff.)	1.00	1.00	1.00	1.00	1.00	1.00
Eggs						
Producer SCT (million AUD)	43	1	0	0	0	0
Percentage SCT (%)	14.3	0.6	0.0	0.0	0.0	0.0
Producer NPC (coeff.)	1.18	1.01	1.00	1.00	1.00	1.00
Cotton						
Producer SCT (million AUD)	10	0	0	0	0	0
Percentage SCT (%)	2.7	0.0	0.0	0.0	0.0	0.0
Producer NPC (coeff.)	1.03	1.00	1.00	1.00	1.00	1.00
Other Commodities[1]						
Producer SCT (million AUD)	201	206	0	0	0	0
Percentage SCT (%)	6.2	2.9	0.0	0.0	0.0	0.0
Producer NPC (coeff.)	1.07	1.03	1.00	1.00	1.00	1.00

Note: p: provisional. SCT: Single Commodity Transfers. PSE: Producer Support Estimate. NPC: Nominal Protection Coefficient.
   1. Producer SCT for Other Commodities: Total Producer SCT minus the Producer SCTs for the commodities listed above.
Source: OECD (2014), "Producer and Consumer Support Estimates", OECD *Agriculture Statistics Database, doi: http://dx.doi.org/10.1787/agr-pcse-data-en.*

StatLink *http://dx.doi.org/10.1787/888933110999*

Table A.10. Canada: Producer Single Commodity Transfers

	1986-88	1995-97	2011-13	2011	2012	2013p
TOTAL						
PSE (million CAD)	7 982	4 910	7 147	7 435	7 795	6 210
Producer SCT (million CAD)	5 682	2 840	5 559	5 449	6 107	5 122
Share of Producer SCT in PSE (%)	71.0	58.8	78.0	73.3	78.3	82.5
Wheat						
Producer SCT (million CAD)	1 274	54	78	69	43	122
Percentage SCT (%)	33.2	1.2	1.1	1.3	0.6	1.5
Producer NPC (coeff.)	1.32	1.00	1.00	1.00	1.00	1.00
Maize						
Producer SCT (million CAD)	169	32	44	24	37	70
Percentage SCT (%)	20.6	2.7	1.5	0.9	1.1	2.5
Producer NPC (coeff.)	1.13	1.00	1.00	1.00	1.00	1.00
Barley						
Producer SCT (million CAD)	536	26	29	37	10	40
Percentage SCT (%)	47.4	1.9	2.0	2.9	0.6	2.5
Producer NPC (coeff.)	1.76	1.00	1.00	1.00	1.00	1.00
Oats						
Producer SCT (million CAD)	27	10	29	31	22	34
Percentage SCT (%)	7.5	1.7	3.8	4.0	3.0	4.4
Producer NPC (coeff.)	1.00	1.00	1.00	1.00	1.00	1.00
Rapeseed						
Producer SCT (million CAD)	170	36	151	102	216	136
Percentage SCT (%)	17.0	1.6	1.8	1.3	2.5	1.5
Producer NPC (coeff.)	1.11	1.00	1.00	1.00	1.00	1.00
Soyabean						
Producer SCT (million CAD)	8	9	16	14	10	25
Percentage SCT (%)	3.1	1.0	0.7	0.7	0.4	1.0
Producer NPC (coeff.)	1.02	1.00	1.00	1.00	1.00	1.00
Milk						
Producer SCT (million CAD)	2 591	1 909	2 793	2 606	3 071	2 701
Percentage SCT (%)	73.6	48.2	45.8	43.3	50.4	43.8
Producer NPC (coeff.)	6.33	2.03	1.85	1.76	2.02	1.78
Beef and Veal						
Producer SCT (million CAD)	-17	73	143	174	132	122
Percentage SCT (%)	-0.5	1.7	2.7	3.4	2.5	2.2
Producer NPC (coeff.)	1.03	1.00	1.00	1.00	1.00	1.00
Pigmeat						
Producer SCT (million CAD)	-39	84	189	218	203	146
Percentage SCT (%)	-1.7	3.1	4.6	5.3	5.1	3.5
Producer NPC (coeff.)	1.02	1.00	1.00	1.00	1.00	1.00
Poultry						
Producer SCT (million CAD)	123	50	829	791	920	777
Percentage SCT (%)	12.2	3.4	32.8	32.8	36.2	29.3
Producer NPC (coeff.)	1.19	1.04	1.49	1.49	1.57	1.42
Eggs						
Producer SCT (million CAD)	78	135	217	206	244	200
Percentage SCT (%)	16.5	23.6	25.0	25.6	27.7	21.8
Producer NPC (coeff.)	1.28	1.31	1.34	1.34	1.38	1.28
Dried Beans						
Producer SCT (million CAD)	7	2	2	1	0	3
Percentage SCT (%)	9.5	1.8	0.9	0.7	0.2	1.7
Producer NPC (coeff.)	1.13	1.00	1.00	1.00	1.00	1.00
Dried Peas						
Producer SCT (million CAD)	2	3	14	14	18	11
Percentage SCT (%)	3.7	0.9	1.5	1.7	1.5	1.1
Producer NPC (coeff.)	1.00	1.00	1.00	1.00	1.00	1.00
Flax						
Producer SCT (million CAD)	4	3	5	5	6	3
Percentage SCT (%)	2.9	0.8	1.7	2.3	2.1	0.8
Producer NPC (coeff.)	1.00	1.00	1.00	1.00	1.00	1.00
Lentils						
Producer SCT (million CAD)	2	2	10	16	10	5
Percentage SCT (%)	8.8	1.0	1.4	2.1	1.5	0.6
Producer NPC (coeff.)	1.00	1.00	1.00	1.00	1.00	1.00
Potatoes						
Producer SCT (million CAD)	5	5	21	23	25	16
Percentage SCT (%)	1.2	0.8	1.8	2.0	2.1	1.2
Producer NPC (coeff.)	1.00	1.00	1.00	1.00	1.00	1.00
Other Commodities[1]						
Producer SCT (million CAD)	739	409	989	1 118	1 140	709
Percentage SCT (%)	54.8	120.7	17.9	17.1	21.4	15.1
Producer NPC (coeff.)	2.72	1.13	1.15	1.12	1.17	1.16

Note: p: provisional. SCT: Single Commodity Transfers. PSE: Producer Support Estimate. NPC: Nominal Protection Coefficient.
  1. Producer SCT for Other Commodities: Total Producer SCT minus the Producer SCTs for the commodities listed above.
Source: OECD (2014), "Producer and Consumer Support Estimates", OECD Agriculture Statistics Database, doi: http://dx.doi.org/10.1787/agr-pcse-data-en.

StatLink ⬛⬛⬛ http://dx.doi.org/10.1787/888933111018

Table A.11. **Chile: Producer Single Commodity Transfers**

	1995-97	2011-13	2011	2012	2013p
TOTAL					
PSE (million CLP)	170 102	189 733	170 959	193 802	204 438
Producer SCT (million CLP)	140 034	5 752	7 331	5 447	4 477
Share of Producer SCT in PSE (%)	82.4	3.1	4.3	2.8	2.2
Wheat					
Producer SCT (million CLP)	7 631	0	0	0	0
Percentage SCT (%)	6.1	0.0	0.0	0.0	0.0
Producer NPC (coeff.)	1.07	1.00	1.00	1.00	1.00
Maize					
Producer SCT (million CLP)	3 166	0	0	0	0
Percentage SCT (%)	4.6	0.0	0.0	0.0	0.0
Producer NPC (coeff.)	1.05	1.00	1.00	1.00	1.00
Sugar					
Producer SCT (million CLP)	27 124	3 461	4 391	3 229	2 761
Percentage SCT (%)	27.7	2.5	2.8	2.6	2.2
Producer NPC (coeff.)	1.39	1.03	1.03	1.03	1.02
Milk					
Producer SCT (million CLP)	35 564	0	0	0	0
Percentage SCT (%)	19.1	0.0	0.0	0.0	0.0
Producer NPC (coeff.)	1.24	1.00	1.00	1.00	1.00
Beef and Veal					
Producer SCT (million CLP)	18 693	0	0	0	0
Percentage SCT (%)	8.7	0.0	0.0	0.0	0.0
Producer NPC (coeff.)	1.10	1.00	1.00	1.00	1.00
Pigmeat					
Producer SCT (million CLP)	-589	0	0	0	0
Percentage SCT (%)	-0.5	0.0	0.0	0.0	0.0
Producer NPC (coeff.)	1.00	1.00	1.00	1.00	1.00
Poultry					
Producer SCT (million CLP)	-1 178	0	0	0	0
Percentage SCT (%)	-0.7	0.0	0.0	0.0	0.0
Producer NPC (coeff.)	1.00	1.00	1.00	1.00	1.00
Apples					
Producer SCT (million CLP)	0	0	0	0	0
Percentage SCT (%)	0.0	0.0	0.0	0.0	0.0
Producer NPC (coeff.)	1.00	1.00	1.00	1.00	1.00
Grapes					
Producer SCT (million CLP)	0	0	0	0	0
Percentage SCT (%)	0.0	0.0	0.0	0.0	0.0
Producer NPC (coeff.)	1.00	1.00	1.00	1.00	1.00
Tomatoes					
Producer SCT (million CLP)	0	0	0	0	0
Percentage SCT (%)	0.0	0.0	0.0	0.0	0.0
Producer NPC (coeff.)	1.00	1.00	1.00	1.00	1.00
Other Commodities[1]					
Producer SCT (million CLP)	49 623	2 291	2 939	2 218	1 715
Percentage SCT (%)	6.7	0.1	0.1	0.1	0.1
Producer NPC (coeff.)	1.07	1.00	1.00	1.00	1.00

Note: p: provisional. SCT: Single Commodity Transfers. PSE: Producer Support Estimate. NPC: Nominal Protection Coefficient.

1. Producer SCT for Other Commodities: Total Producer SCT minus the Producer SCTs for the commodities listed above.

Source: OECD (2014), "Producer and Consumer Support Estimates", OECD *Agriculture Statistics Database, doi: http://dx.doi.org/10.1787/agr-pcse-data-en.*

StatLink ᴹᶳᴵ *http://dx.doi.org/10.1787/888933111037*

Table A.12. **European Union: Producer Single Commodity Transfers**

	1986-88	1995-97	2011-13	2011	2012	2013p
TOTAL						
PSE (million EUR)	88 006	94 287	83 935	77 907	86 321	87 576
Producer SCT (million EUR)	81 991	66 345	20 008	14 731	21 532	23 762
Share of Producer SCT in PSE (%)	93.2	70.3	23.7	18.9	24.9	27.1
Wheat						
Producer SCT (million EUR)	7 228	1 558	27	25	29	26
Percentage SCT (%)	49.3	11.2	0.1	0.1	0.1	0.1
Producer NPC (coeff.)	2.04	1.05	1.00	1.00	1.00	1.00
Maize						
Producer SCT (million EUR)	2 697	2 204	1	1	0	0
Percentage SCT (%)	51.0	34.9	0.0	0.0	0.0	0.0
Producer NPC (coeff.)	2.15	1.28	1.00	1.00	1.00	1.00
Barley						
Producer SCT (million EUR)	4 569	734	0	0	0	0
Percentage SCT (%)	57.5	12.6	0.0	0.0	0.0	0.0
Producer NPC (coeff.)	2.55	1.17	1.00	1.00	1.00	1.00
Oats						
Producer SCT (million EUR)	291	201	0	0	0	0
Percentage SCT (%)	33.3	24.6	0.0	0.0	0.0	0.0
Producer NPC (coeff.)	1.58	1.33	1.00	1.00	1.00	1.00
Rice						
Producer SCT (million EUR)	412	290	92	267	3	4
Percentage SCT (%)	58.9	33.5	7.2	20.9	0.4	0.4
Producer NPC (coeff.)	2.55	1.52	1.04	1.11	1.00	1.00
Rapeseed						
Producer SCT (million EUR)	1 267	4	1	2	0	0
Percentage SCT (%)	58.2	0.2	0.0	0.0	0.0	0.0
Producer NPC (coeff.)	2.40	1.00	1.00	1.00	1.00	1.00
Sunflower						
Producer SCT (million EUR)	971	2	0	1	0	0
Percentage SCT (%)	56.0	0.2	0.0	0.0	0.0	0.0
Producer NPC (coeff.)	2.30	1.00	1.00	1.00	1.00	1.00
Soyabean						
Producer SCT (million EUR)	479	1	0	0	0	0
Percentage SCT (%)	60.9	0.3	0.0	0.0	0.0	0.0
Producer NPC (coeff.)	2.63	1.00	1.00	1.00	1.00	1.00
Sugar						
Producer SCT (million EUR)	2 582	2 800	69	42	52	114
Percentage SCT (%)	58.8	49.7	2.0	1.0	1.3	3.6
Producer NPC (coeff.)	2.99	2.14	1.01	1.00	1.00	1.02
Milk						
Producer SCT (million EUR)	21 363	18 689	778	669	885	780
Percentage SCT (%)	69.6	50.1	1.5	1.3	1.7	1.5
Producer NPC (coeff.)	4.51	2.06	1.01	1.01	1.01	1.01
Beef and Veal						
Producer SCT (million EUR)	10 476	12 171	8 590	4 231	9 659	11 879
Percentage SCT (%)	50.5	48.5	28.9	15.0	31.9	39.8
Producer NPC (coeff.)	2.07	1.66	1.36	1.11	1.39	1.58
Sheepmeat						
Producer SCT (million EUR)	3 568	3 093	745	317	731	1 186
Percentage SCT (%)	69.1	56.1	14.9	6.6	14.5	23.5
Producer NPC (coeff.)	2.70	1.71	1.11	1.00	1.10	1.23
Pigmeat						
Producer SCT (million EUR)	-270	1 381	253	23	28	709
Percentage SCT (%)	-1.4	5.3	0.7	0.1	0.1	1.9
Producer NPC (coeff.)	1.13	1.08	1.01	1.00	1.00	1.02
Poultry						
Producer SCT (million EUR)	963	2 399	2 747	3 472	3 181	1 588
Percentage SCT (%)	13.3	30.6	17.8	23.1	20.2	9.9
Producer NPC (coeff.)	1.46	1.51	1.22	1.30	1.25	1.11
Eggs						
Producer SCT (million EUR)	1 682	456	59	75	98	5
Percentage SCT (%)	32.7	9.4	0.7	1.0	0.9	0.0
Producer NPC (coeff.)	1.64	1.14	1.01	1.01	1.01	1.00
Flowers						
Producer SCT (million EUR)	714	784	390	429	369	373
Percentage SCT (%)	8.0	5.9	2.1	2.4	2.0	2.0
Producer NPC (coeff.)	1.09	1.06	1.02	1.02	1.02	1.02
Potatoes						
Producer SCT (million EUR)	616	940	1 036	1 249	967	892
Percentage SCT (%)	14.4	12.1	9.2	9.6	8.9	9.0
Producer NPC (coeff.)	1.17	1.14	1.10	1.10	1.10	1.10

Table A.12. **European Union: Producer Single Commodity Transfers** (cont.)

	1986-88	1995-97	2011-13	2011	2012	2013p
Tomatoes						
Producer SCT (million EUR)	935	72	333	346	290	361
Percentage SCT (%)	13.5	0.7	2.9	3.3	2.4	3.1
Producer NPC (coeff.)	1.16	1.01	1.03	1.03	1.02	1.03
Wine						
Producer SCT (million EUR)	751	704	26	30	26	22
Percentage SCT (%)	8.3	4.9	0.2	0.2	0.2	0.1
Producer NPC (coeff.)	1.09	1.05	1.00	1.00	1.00	1.00
Other Commodities[1]						
Producer SCT (million EUR)	20 697	17 864	4 862	3 549	5 213	5 823
Percentage SCT (%)	32.0	28.0	5.1	3.8	5.4	5.9
Producer NPC (coeff.)	1.56	1.41	1.05	1.03	1.05	1.06

Note: p: provisional. SCT: Single Commodity Transfers. PSE: Producer Support Estimate. NPC: Nominal Protection Coefficient. EU12 for 1986-88; EU15 for 1995-97; and EU27 from 2007.

1. Producer SCT for Other Commodities: Total Producer SCT minus the Producer SCTs for the commodities listed above.

Source: OECD (2014), "Producer and Consumer Support Estimates", OECD *Agriculture Statistics Database, doi: http://dx.doi.org/10.1787/agr-pcse-data-en.*

StatLink ⟶ *http://dx.doi.org/10.1787/888933111056*

Table A.13. Iceland: Producer Single Commodity Transfers

	1986-88	1995-97	2011-13	2011	2012	2013p
TOTAL						
PSE (million ISK)	7 909	8 825	17 570	16 248	18 597	17 866
Producer SCT (million ISK)	7 495	8 782	17 328	16 095	18 316	17 572
Share of Producer SCT in PSE (%)	94.7	99.5	98.6	99.1	98.5	98.4
Milk						
Producer SCT (million ISK)	2 643	3 996	8 054	7 781	8 827	7 555
Percentage SCT (%)	88.5	73.9	52.2	51.0	58.1	47.7
Producer NPC (coeff.)	9.45	3.89	2.01	1.94	2.26	1.82
Beef and Veal						
Producer SCT (million ISK)	327	305	153	146	154	158
Percentage SCT (%)	58.0	34.4	6.6	6.8	6.4	6.6
Producer NPC (coeff.)	2.40	1.58	1.00	1.00	1.00	1.00
Sheepmeat						
Producer SCT (million ISK)	2 176	1 770	3 739	3 563	3 770	3 883
Percentage SCT (%)	71.9	54.9	42.3	43.6	42.1	41.2
Producer NPC (coeff.)	3.57	1.51	1.00	1.00	1.00	1.00
Wool						
Producer SCT (million ISK)	27	138	42	40	85	0
Percentage SCT (%)	15.6	47.9	9.1	8.7	18.4	0.0
Producer NPC (coeff.)	1.20	2.05	1.11	1.10	1.23	1.00
Pigmeat						
Producer SCT (million ISK)	348	459	770	658	822	829
Percentage SCT (%)	74.4	50.4	31.8	30.1	33.5	31.9
Producer NPC (coeff.)	4.08	2.05	1.47	1.43	1.50	1.47
Poultry						
Producer SCT (million ISK)	227	498	2 201	1 842	2 365	2 396
Percentage SCT (%)	84.0	84.6	69.9	68.7	71.1	70.0
Producer NPC (coeff.)	6.38	6.39	3.30	3.15	3.42	3.31
Eggs						
Producer SCT (million ISK)	306	415	796	806	706	875
Percentage SCT (%)	81.9	74.3	58.4	65.0	52.7	57.7
Producer NPC (coeff.)	5.63	4.00	2.44	2.86	2.11	2.36
Other Commodities[1]						
Producer SCT (million ISK)	1 441	1 202	1 575	1 260	1 588	1 876
Percentage SCT (%)	73.7	43.9	28.2	28.0	31.9	24.7
Producer NPC (coeff.)	3.96	1.78	1.39	1.39	1.47	1.33

Note: p: provisional. SCT: Single Commodity Transfers. PSE: Producer Support Estimate. NPC: Nominal Protection Coefficient.

1. Producer SCT for Other Commodities: Total Producer SCT minus the Producer SCTs for the commodities listed above.

Source: OECD (2014), "Producer and Consumer Support Estimates", OECD *Agriculture Statistics Database*, doi: *http://dx.doi.org/10.1787/agr-pcse-data-en*.

StatLink ᵐˢ᷄ᵖ *http://dx.doi.org/10.1787/888933111075*

Table A.14. **Israel: Producer Single Commodity Transfers**

	1995-97	2011-13	2011	2012	2013p
TOTAL					
PSE (million ILS)	2 517	3 076	3 697	3 087	2 442
Producer SCT (million ILS)	1 715	2 448	3 085	2 448	1 811
Share of Producer SCT in PSE (%)	67.7	79.0	83.4	79.3	74.1
Wheat					
Producer SCT (million ILS)	20	23	28	14	28
Percentage SCT (%)	16.2	14.4	20.3	6.8	16.3
Producer NPC (coeff.)	1.22	1.17	1.25	1.07	1.19
Milk					
Producer SCT (million ILS)	800	776	631	1 051	647
Percentage SCT (%)	58.1	26.6	23.7	34.6	21.5
Producer NPC (coeff.)	2.48	1.37	1.32	1.53	1.27
Beef and Veal					
Producer SCT (million ILS)	135	689	712	638	716
Percentage SCT (%)	29.1	42.0	41.7	39.3	44.8
Producer NPC (coeff.)	1.42	1.73	1.73	1.65	1.81
Sheepmeat					
Producer SCT (million ILS)	51	227	266	211	204
Percentage SCT (%)	32.3	26.2	32.6	22.9	23.1
Producer NPC (coeff.)	1.50	1.37	1.50	1.30	1.30
Poultry					
Producer SCT (million ILS)	278	-27	180	-41	-221
Percentage SCT (%)	18.9	-1.0	5.4	-1.2	-7.3
Producer NPC (coeff.)	1.30	1.00	1.07	0.99	0.93
Eggs					
Producer SCT (million ILS)	43	-37	93	-137	-66
Percentage SCT (%)	9.5	-3.9	11.2	-15.7	-7.2
Producer NPC (coeff.)	1.13	0.99	1.16	0.87	0.93
Apples					
Producer SCT (million ILS)	0	32	86	28	-18
Percentage SCT (%)	0.0	4.8	12.6	4.5	-2.8
Producer NPC (coeff.)	1.00	1.05	1.14	1.05	0.97
Avocado					
Producer SCT (million ILS)	0	0	0	0	0
Percentage SCT (%)	0.0	0.0	0.0	0.0	0.0
Producer NPC (coeff.)	1.00	1.00	1.00	1.00	1.00
Bananas					
Producer SCT (million ILS)	-36	128	185	99	100
Percentage SCT (%)	-21.7	28.1	42.1	20.5	21.7
Producer NPC (coeff.)	0.85	1.42	1.73	1.26	1.28
Cotton					
Producer SCT (million ILS)	-36	-5	10	-22	-4
Percentage SCT (%)	-11.9	-3.7	5.8	-13.7	-3.2
Producer NPC (coeff.)	0.90	0.97	1.06	0.88	0.97
Grapefruit					
Producer SCT (million ILS)	0	0	0	0	0
Percentage SCT (%)	0.0	0.0	0.0	0.0	0.0
Producer NPC (coeff.)	1.00	1.00	1.00	1.00	1.00
Grapes					
Producer SCT (million ILS)	0	0	0	0	0
Percentage SCT (%)	0.0	0.0	0.0	0.0	0.0
Producer NPC (coeff.)	1.00	1.00	1.00	1.00	1.00
Orange					
Producer SCT (million ILS)	0	0	0	0	0
Percentage SCT (%)	0.0	0.0	0.0	0.0	0.0
Producer NPC (coeff.)	1.00	1.00	1.00	1.00	1.00
Peppers					
Producer SCT (million ILS)	0	0	0	0	0
Percentage SCT (%)	0.0	0.0	0.0	0.0	0.0
Producer NPC (coeff.)	1.00	1.00	1.00	1.00	1.00
Peanuts					
Producer SCT (million ILS)	0	0	0	0	0
Percentage SCT (%)	0.0	0.0	0.0	0.0	0.0
Producer NPC (coeff.)	1.00	1.00	1.00	1.00	1.00
Potatoes					
Producer SCT (million ILS)	0	0	0	0	0
Percentage SCT (%)	0.0	0.0	0.0	0.0	0.0
Producer NPC (coeff.)	1.00	1.00	1.00	1.00	1.00
Tomatoes					
Producer SCT (million ILS)	0	0	0	0	0
Percentage SCT (%)	0.0	0.0	0.0	0.0	0.0
Producer NPC (coeff.)	1.00	1.00	1.00	1.00	1.00

Table A.14. **Israel: Producer Single Commodity Transfers** (*cont.*)

	1995-97	2011-13	2011	2012	2013p
Other Commodities[1]					
Producer SCT (million ILS)	460	641	892	606	425
Percentage SCT (%)	8.8	5.0	7.0	4.7	3.2
Producer NPC (coeff.)	1.10	1.04	1.05	1.04	1.03

Note: p: provisional. SCT: Single Commodity Transfers. PSE: Producer Support Estimate. NPC: Nominal Protection Coefficient.

The statistical data for Israel are supplied by and under the responsibility of the relevant Israeli authorities. The use of such data by the OECD is without prejudice to the status of the Golan Heights, East Jerusalem and Israeli settlements in the West Bank under the terms of international law.

1. Producer SCT for Other Commodities: Total Producer SCT minus the Producer SCTs for the commodities listed above.

Source: OECD (2014), "Producer and Consumer Support Estimates", OECD *Agriculture Statistics Database, doi: http://dx.doi.org/10.1787/agr-pcse-data-en.*

StatLink ⬛ᶆᵉ *http://dx.doi.org/10.1787/888933111094*

Table A.15. **Japan: Producer Single Commodity Transfers**

	1986-88	1995-97	2011-13	2011	2012	2013p
TOTAL						
PSE (billion JPY)	7 267	6 239	5 104	4 813	5 233	5 265
Producer SCT (billion JPY)	6 740	5 822	4 508	4 233	4 650	4 642
Share of Producer SCT in PSE (%)	92.7	93.3	88.3	88.0	88.9	88.2
Wheat						
Producer SCT (billion JPY)	135	61	37	37	37	37
Percentage SCT (%)	84.7	81.2	47.8	51.5	43.8	48.1
Producer NPC (coeff.)	6.56	5.34	1.92	2.06	1.78	1.93
Barley						
Producer SCT (billion JPY)	52	24	16	16	16	15
Percentage SCT (%)	84.1	77.3	70.0	72.5	71.3	66.2
Producer NPC (coeff.)	6.30	4.49	3.36	3.64	3.48	2.96
Rice						
Producer SCT (billion JPY)	2 720	2 385	1 541	1 439	1 595	1 589
Percentage SCT (%)	82.6	79.9	75.8	75.1	77.6	74.6
Producer NPC (coeff.)	5.81	5.12	3.64	3.32	4.12	3.49
Soyabean						
Producer SCT (billion JPY)	29	5	24	25	24	23
Percentage SCT (%)	64.7	19.8	47.5	46.7	49.6	46.3
Producer NPC (coeff.)	2.96	1.26	1.91	1.87	1.99	1.86
Sugar						
Producer SCT (billion JPY)	81	54	42	41	42	42
Percentage SCT (%)	65.1	58.6	56.4	55.0	56.2	57.8
Producer NPC (coeff.)	2.88	2.42	2.29	2.22	2.29	2.37
Milk						
Producer SCT (billion JPY)	621	501	413	362	443	435
Percentage SCT (%)	86.0	69.8	60.9	54.0	64.6	63.9
Producer NPC (coeff.)	7.43	3.40	2.59	2.18	2.83	2.78
Beef and Veal						
Producer SCT (billion JPY)	357	155	201	179	175	248
Percentage SCT (%)	71.5	34.4	37.5	36.0	33.6	43.1
Producer NPC (coeff.)	3.65	1.53	1.61	1.56	1.51	1.76
Pigmeat						
Producer SCT (billion JPY)	285	255	335	342	361	301
Percentage SCT (%)	41.5	50.5	64.1	65.9	68.3	58.1
Producer NPC (coeff.)	1.73	2.07	2.84	2.94	3.17	2.40
Poultry						
Producer SCT (billion JPY)	45	29	27	27	28	27
Percentage SCT (%)	11.3	10.5	10.2	10.2	10.1	10.2
Producer NPC (coeff.)	1.13	1.12	1.12	1.12	1.12	1.12
Eggs						
Producer SCT (billion JPY)	70	71	66	68	64	67
Percentage SCT (%)	17.0	16.1	15.2	15.0	15.3	15.3
Producer NPC (coeff.)	1.21	1.19	1.18	1.18	1.18	1.18
Apples						
Producer SCT (billion JPY)	36	25	30	48	19	22
Percentage SCT (%)	24.9	17.8	22.9	36.8	14.8	17.1
Producer NPC (coeff.)	1.36	1.22	1.32	1.58	1.17	1.21
Chinese cabbage						
Producer SCT (billion JPY)	10	50	73	72	72	76
Percentage SCT (%)	10.0	51.5	73.8	75.5	71.6	74.4
Producer NPC (coeff.)	1.12	2.09	3.83	4.08	3.52	3.91
Cucumbers						
Producer SCT (billion JPY)	36	33	4	4	4	4
Percentage SCT (%)	20.5	18.9	3.2	3.0	3.3	3.2
Producer NPC (coeff.)	1.26	1.24	1.03	1.03	1.03	1.03
Grapes						
Producer SCT (billion JPY)	39	62	64	65	61	65
Percentage SCT (%)	35.7	50.9	63.6	65.8	60.5	64.4
Producer NPC (coeff.)	1.56	2.04	2.76	2.93	2.53	2.81
Mandarins						
Producer SCT (billion JPY)	29	75	76	74	75	78
Percentage SCT (%)	17.5	33.4	50.3	48.3	51.2	51.2
Producer NPC (coeff.)	1.21	1.56	2.01	1.93	2.05	2.05
Pears						
Producer SCT (billion JPY)	23	31	44	36	51	47
Percentage SCT (%)	25.9	27.5	54.7	44.4	62.7	57.1
Producer NPC (coeff.)	1.36	1.43	2.27	1.80	2.68	2.33
Spinach						
Producer SCT (billion JPY)	48	80	3	3	3	3
Percentage SCT (%)	54.0	71.3	3.2	3.0	3.3	3.2
Producer NPC (coeff.)	2.20	4.20	1.03	1.03	1.03	1.03

Table A.15. **Japan: Producer Single Commodity Transfers** (cont.)

	1986-88	1995-97	2011-13	2011	2012	2013p
Strawberries						
Producer SCT (billion JPY)	14	39	33	31	38	31
Percentage SCT (%)	10.0	22.0	21.8	20.0	24.8	20.6
Producer NPC (coeff.)	1.11	1.29	1.28	1.25	1.33	1.26
Welsh Onion						
Producer SCT (billion JPY)	33	65	102	98	103	107
Percentage SCT (%)	37.4	48.4	72.8	73.0	71.2	74.0
Producer NPC (coeff.)	1.65	1.94	3.68	3.71	3.47	3.85
Other Commodities[1]						
Producer SCT (billion JPY)	2 077	1 822	1 376	1 267	1 439	1 422
Percentage SCT (%)	62.3	53.1	45.1	39.9	46.4	48.9
Producer NPC (coeff.)	2.66	2.15	1.83	1.67	1.87	1.96

Note: p: provisional. SCT: Single Commodity Transfers. PSE: Producer Support Estimate. NPC: Nominal Protection Coefficient.

1. Producer SCT for Other Commodities: Total Producer SCT minus the Producer SCTs for the commodities listed above.

Source: OECD (2014), "Producer and Consumer Support Estimates", OECD Agriculture Statistics Database, doi: http://dx.doi.org/10.1787/agr-pcse-data-en.

StatLink ᵐᵖᵃ http://dx.doi.org/10.1787/888933111113

Table A.16. **Korea: Producer Single Commodity Transfers**

	1986-88	1995-97	2011-13	2011	2012	2013p
TOTAL						
PSE (billion KRW)	9 605	19 277	23 514	23 243	23 063	24 236
Producer SCT (billion KRW)	9 511	18 199	21 975	21 721	21 605	22 598
Share of Producer SCT in PSE (%)	99.0	94.4	93.5	93.4	93.7	93.2
Barley						
Producer SCT (billion KRW)	220	208	21	25	18	18
Percentage SCT (%)	72.8	79.4	46.8	49.3	47.7	43.4
Producer NPC (coeff.)	3.69	4.89	1.88	1.97	1.91	1.77
Rice						
Producer SCT (billion KRW)	4 509	6 886	5 233	5 103	4 928	5 668
Percentage SCT (%)	82.0	82.1	58.4	56.4	58.0	60.7
Producer NPC (coeff.)	5.59	5.89	2.34	2.09	2.38	2.54
Soyabean						
Producer SCT (billion KRW)	156	235	739	792	598	828
Percentage SCT (%)	78.7	85.2	89.0	90.8	87.7	88.3
Producer NPC (coeff.)	4.75	6.97	9.20	10.91	8.14	8.55
Milk						
Producer SCT (billion KRW)	306	512	990	727	1 081	1 161
Percentage SCT (%)	67.8	59.9	50.7	44.1	53.8	54.3
Producer NPC (coeff.)	3.11	2.50	2.05	1.79	2.16	2.19
Beef and Veal						
Producer SCT (billion KRW)	496	1 294	1 328	1 042	1 390	1 551
Percentage SCT (%)	53.8	64.9	31.3	31.2	31.0	31.7
Producer NPC (coeff.)	2.23	2.89	1.46	1.45	1.45	1.47
Pigmeat						
Producer SCT (billion KRW)	307	775	2 401	2 877	2 059	2 266
Percentage SCT (%)	32.2	39.5	55.5	63.9	52.0	50.6
Producer NPC (coeff.)	1.50	1.69	2.29	2.77	2.08	2.02
Poultry						
Producer SCT (billion KRW)	132	385	601	718	551	534
Percentage SCT (%)	49.4	56.5	42.2	49.5	40.3	36.9
Producer NPC (coeff.)	2.09	2.33	1.75	1.98	1.67	1.58
Eggs						
Producer SCT (billion KRW)	-28	63	216	180	38	429
Percentage SCT (%)	-10.8	10.7	15.2	12.7	3.0	30.0
Producer NPC (coeff.)	0.92	1.12	1.20	1.15	1.03	1.43
Chinese cabbage						
Producer SCT (billion KRW)	76	108	200	151	208	240
Percentage SCT (%)	23.1	22.7	21.3	21.3	21.3	21.3
Producer NPC (coeff.)	1.30	1.29	1.27	1.27	1.27	1.27
Garlic						
Producer SCT (billion KRW)	261	534	371	453	298	362
Percentage SCT (%)	71.5	56.1	59.7	72.9	49.2	56.9
Producer NPC (coeff.)	3.50	2.62	2.66	3.69	1.97	2.32
Red pepper						
Producer SCT (billion KRW)	398	702	1 061	1 037	1 206	940
Percentage SCT (%)	63.6	59.8	76.4	80.2	75.5	73.7
Producer NPC (coeff.)	2.75	2.55	4.31	5.04	4.08	3.80
Other Commodities[1]						
Producer SCT (billion KRW)	2 679	6 497	8 815	8 616	9 229	8 600
Percentage SCT (%)	76.8	64.6	50.0	50.2	48.5	51.3
Producer NPC (coeff.)	9.17	2.91	2.00	2.01	1.94	2.05

Note: p: provisional. SCT: Single Commodity Transfers. PSE: Producer Support Estimate. NPC: Nominal Protection Coefficient.

1. Producer SCT for Other Commodities: Total Producer SCT minus the Producer SCTs for the commodities listed above.

Source: OECD (2014), "Producer and Consumer Support Estimates", OECD *Agriculture Statistics Database, doi: http://dx.doi.org/10.1787/agr-pcse-data-en.*

StatLink 🔗 *http://dx.doi.org/10.1787/888933111132*

Table A.17. **Mexico: Producer Single Commodity Transfers**

	1991-93	1995-97	2011-13	2011	2012	2013p
TOTAL						
PSE (million MXN)	25 995	12 953	92 778	86 593	91 962	99 779
Producer SCT (million MXN)	21 975	630	41 664	37 415	42 906	44 672
Share of Producer SCT in PSE (%)	84.4	99.6	44.9	43.2	46.7	44.8
Wheat						
Producer SCT (million MXN)	492	-176	2 388	3 798	1 645	1 721
Percentage SCT (%)	22.0	-7.6	15.4	21.4	12.5	12.1
Producer NPC (coeff.)	1.29	0.95	1.00	1.00	1.01	1.00
Maize						
Producer SCT (million MXN)	5 225	-732	3 898	5 842	2 298	3 553
Percentage SCT (%)	42.9	-2.7	5.2	8.6	2.5	4.5
Producer NPC (coeff.)	1.75	0.99	1.00	1.00	1.00	1.00
Barley						
Producer SCT (million MXN)	144	26	3	9	0	0
Percentage SCT (%)	38.4	1.2	0.2	0.5	0.0	0.0
Producer NPC (coeff.)	1.64	1.04	1.00	1.00	1.00	1.00
Sorghum						
Producer SCT (million MXN)	458	109	1 840	2 140	1 634	1 746
Percentage SCT (%)	24.8	4.2	8.0	9.2	6.4	8.2
Producer NPC (coeff.)	1.33	1.05	1.00	1.00	1.00	1.00
Rice						
Producer SCT (million MXN)	17	2	59	86	59	31
Percentage SCT (%)	6.9	1.2	8.5	12.9	8.6	3.9
Producer NPC (coeff.)	1.08	1.02	1.09	1.15	1.09	1.04
Soyabean						
Producer SCT (million MXN)	75	-15	64	130	4	57
Percentage SCT (%)	14.4	-7.1	4.5	9.7	0.3	3.6
Producer NPC (coeff.)	1.17	0.94	1.02	1.07	1.00	1.00
Sugar						
Producer SCT (million MXN)	2 114	1 745	2 316	962	5 986	0
Percentage SCT (%)	56.1	19.5	6.3	2.8	16.2	0.0
Producer NPC (coeff.)	2.07	1.28	1.07	1.03	1.19	1.00
Milk						
Producer SCT (million MXN)	2 236	1 075	861	-130	2 712	0
Percentage SCT (%)	35.6	4.5	1.5	-0.3	4.8	0.0
Producer NPC (coeff.)	1.62	1.07	1.02	1.00	1.05	1.00
Beef and Veal						
Producer SCT (million MXN)	1 795	397	4 001	4 043	4 252	3 709
Percentage SCT (%)	24.6	-0.9	7.9	8.4	8.3	7.1
Producer NPC (coeff.)	1.34	1.04	1.00	1.00	1.00	1.00
Pigmeat						
Producer SCT (million MXN)	25	-1 305	2 880	1 981	2 303	4 356
Percentage SCT (%)	0.6	-17.6	8.7	6.8	7.1	12.2
Producer NPC (coeff.)	1.06	0.86	1.00	1.00	1.00	1.00
Poultry						
Producer SCT (million MXN)	1 685	1 992	10 913	9 774	11 546	11 419
Percentage SCT (%)	33.1	11.2	15.6	15.8	16.3	14.8
Producer NPC (coeff.)	1.62	1.14	1.19	1.19	1.19	1.17
Eggs						
Producer SCT (million MXN)	88	26	1 136	-144	0	3 551
Percentage SCT (%)	2.5	0.2	2.0	-0.4	0.0	6.3
Producer NPC (coeff.)	1.05	1.00	1.02	1.00	1.00	1.07
Dried Beans						
Producer SCT (million MXN)	665	-650	2 440	2 670	36	4 615
Percentage SCT (%)	29.1	-29.3	20.9	34.0	0.3	28.5
Producer NPC (coeff.)	1.45	0.85	1.31	1.52	1.00	1.40
Coffee						
Producer SCT (million MXN)	-55	-593	30	0	0	90
Percentage SCT (%)	-5.2	-13.0	0.5	0.0	0.0	1.5
Producer NPC (coeff.)	0.95	0.88	1.00	1.00	1.00	1.00
Tomatoes						
Producer SCT (million MXN)	308	-1 400	0	0	0	0
Percentage SCT (%)	13.2	-48.4	0.0	0.0	0.0	0.0
Producer NPC (coeff.)	1.17	0.75	1.00	1.00	1.00	1.00
Other Commodities[1]						
Producer SCT (million MXN)	6 703	129	8 836	6 254	10 431	9 824
Percentage SCT (%)	19.2	-1.2	3.4	2.6	4.3	3.3
Producer NPC (coeff.)	1.23	1.02	1.03	1.03	1.04	1.03

Note: p: provisional. SCT: Single Commodity Transfers. PSE: Producer Support Estimate. NPC: Nominal Protection Coefficient.

1. Producer SCT for Other Commodities: Total Producer SCT minus the Producer SCTs for the commodities listed above.

Source: OECD (2014), "Producer and Consumer Support Estimates", OECD *Agriculture Statistics Database*, doi: *http://dx.doi.org/10.1787/agr-pcse-data-en.*

StatLink ⧉ *http://dx.doi.org/10.1787/888933111151*

Table A.18. **New Zealand: Producer Single Commodity Transfers**

	1986-88	1995-97	2011-13	2011	2012	2013p
TOTAL						
PSE (million NZD)	786	94	172	202	179	136
Producer SCT (million NZD)	114	58	141	172	148	104
Share of Producer SCT in PSE (%)	19.9	60.8	81.6	85.2	82.7	76.8
Wheat						
Producer SCT (million NZD)	3	0	0	0	0	0
Percentage SCT (%)	2.8	0.0	0.0	0.0	0.0	0.0
Producer NPC (coeff.)	1.03	1.00	1.00	1.00	1.00	1.00
Maize						
Producer SCT (million NZD)	0	0	0	0	0	0
Percentage SCT (%)	0.0	0.0	0.0	0.0	0.0	0.0
Producer NPC (coeff.)	1.00	1.00	1.00	1.00	1.00	1.00
Milk						
Producer SCT (million NZD)	21	0	0	0	0	0
Percentage SCT (%)	1.7	0.0	0.0	0.0	0.0	0.0
Producer NPC (coeff.)	1.02	1.00	1.00	1.00	1.00	1.00
Beef and Veal						
Producer SCT (million NZD)	0	0	0	0	0	0
Percentage SCT (%)	0.0	0.0	0.0	0.0	0.0	0.0
Producer NPC (coeff.)	1.00	1.00	1.00	1.00	1.00	1.00
Sheepmeat						
Producer SCT (million NZD)	0	0	0	0	0	0
Percentage SCT (%)	0.0	0.0	0.0	0.0	0.0	0.0
Producer NPC (coeff.)	1.00	1.00	1.00	1.00	1.00	1.00
Wool						
Producer SCT (million NZD)	0	0	0	0	0	0
Percentage SCT (%)	0.0	0.0	0.0	0.0	0.0	0.0
Producer NPC (coeff.)	1.00	1.00	1.00	1.00	1.00	1.00
Pigmeat						
Producer SCT (million NZD)	2	0	0	0	0	0
Percentage SCT (%)	1.6	0.0	0.0	0.0	0.0	0.0
Producer NPC (coeff.)	1.02	1.00	1.00	1.00	1.00	1.00
Poultry						
Producer SCT (million NZD)	18	16	103	113	115	83
Percentage SCT (%)	17.4	9.0	23.5	27.0	25.3	18.3
Producer NPC (coeff.)	1.25	1.10	1.31	1.37	1.34	1.22
Eggs						
Producer SCT (million NZD)	40	26	7	21	0	0
Percentage SCT (%)	48.5	29.6	5.4	16.1	0.0	0.0
Producer NPC (coeff.)	1.97	1.43	1.06	1.19	1.00	1.00
Other Commodities[1]						
Producer SCT (million NZD)	32	16	31	38	33	21
Percentage SCT (%)	1.7	0.6	0.6	0.8	0.7	0.4
Producer NPC (coeff.)	1.02	1.01	1.01	1.01	1.01	1.00

Note: p: provisional. SCT: Single Commodity Transfers. PSE: Producer Support Estimate. NPC: Nominal Protection Coefficient.

1. Producer SCT for Other Commodities: Total Producer SCT minus the Producer SCTs for the commodities listed above.

Source: OECD (2014), "Producer and Consumer Support Estimates", OECD *Agriculture Statistics Database*, doi: *http://dx.doi.org/10.1787/agr-pcse-data-en*.

StatLink ᴴᴵᴸᴾ *http://dx.doi.org/10.1787/888933111170*

Table A.19. **Norway: Producer Single Commodity Transfers**

	1986-88	1995-97	2011-13	2011	2012	2013p
TOTAL						
PSE (million NOK)	19 175	19 246	22 173	21 623	23 371	21 527
Producer SCT (million NOK)	13 877	12 013	11 835	11 543	13 290	10 671
Share of Producer SCT in PSE (%)	72.4	62.4	53.3	53.4	56.9	49.6
Wheat						
Producer SCT (million NOK)	330	320	227	264	207	209
Percentage SCT (%)	73.1	51.6	32.8	35.4	32.1	31.0
Producer NPC (coeff.)	3.81	2.09	1.50	1.56	1.48	1.45
Barley						
Producer SCT (million NOK)	1 136	609	385	366	372	417
Percentage SCT (%)	83.1	52.4	30.5	33.1	28.0	30.4
Producer NPC (coeff.)	6.20	2.15	1.44	1.50	1.39	1.44
Oats						
Producer SCT (million NOK)	701	334	97	96	129	67
Percentage SCT (%)	68.5	54.4	20.2	20.7	26.1	13.7
Producer NPC (coeff.)	3.30	2.20	1.26	1.26	1.36	1.16
Milk						
Producer SCT (million NOK)	4 575	5 002	3 899	3 607	4 527	3 562
Percentage SCT (%)	71.2	65.8	46.6	45.5	54.0	40.2
Producer NPC (coeff.)	6.19	3.33	1.68	1.60	1.99	1.45
Beef and Veal						
Producer SCT (million NOK)	2 174	1 941	1 894	1 995	1 899	1 789
Percentage SCT (%)	69.3	60.6	48.1	51.9	49.7	42.7
Producer NPC (coeff.)	4.36	2.92	2.03	2.16	2.13	1.80
Sheepmeat						
Producer SCT (million NOK)	531	399	172	73	209	235
Percentage SCT (%)	54.1	45.4	15.1	6.7	18.7	19.9
Producer NPC (coeff.)	3.64	2.05	1.25	1.12	1.31	1.31
Wool						
Producer SCT (million NOK)	104	175	129	128	128	130
Percentage SCT (%)	48.7	66.4	53.7	53.2	57.8	50.2
Producer NPC (coeff.)	2.01	2.98	2.17	2.14	2.37	2.01
Pigmeat						
Producer SCT (million NOK)	1 138	732	1 430	1 557	1 470	1 262
Percentage SCT (%)	46.3	33.5	41.7	46.0	41.9	37.3
Producer NPC (coeff.)	3.09	1.77	1.89	2.00	1.96	1.70
Poultry						
Producer SCT (million NOK)	136	283	867	845	936	819
Percentage SCT (%)	43.2	57.8	50.4	54.9	53.1	43.0
Producer NPC (coeff.)	3.49	3.06	2.19	2.34	2.41	1.83
Eggs						
Producer SCT (million NOK)	447	225	369	495	348	264
Percentage SCT (%)	52.6	38.4	37.5	52.8	33.6	26.0
Producer NPC (coeff.)	4.67	2.30	1.84	2.41	1.69	1.41
Other Commodities[1]						
Producer SCT (million NOK)	2 604	1 993	2 367	2 116	3 066	1 918
Percentage SCT (%)	54.7	47.7	38.0	36.9	47.7	29.3
Producer NPC (coeff.)	3.34	2.18	1.53	1.69	1.43	1.49

Note: p: provisional. SCT: Single Commodity Transfers. PSE: Producer Support Estimate. NPC: Nominal Protection Coefficient. Total Consumer SCT may differ from the Total CSE by the amount of subsidies to consumers which are not specific to a single commodity.
1. Producer SCT for Other Commodities: Total Producer SCT minus the Producer SCTs for the commodities listed above.

StatLink ᴬᴵˢᴾ *http://dx.doi.org/10.1787/888933111189*

Table A.20. **Switzerland: Producer Single Commodity Transfers**

	1986-88	1995-97	2011-13	2011	2012	2013p
TOTAL						
PSE (million CHF)	8 509	7 362	5 330	5 442	5 566	4 983
Producer SCT (million CHF)	7 294	5 073	2 130	2 241	2 367	1 781
Share of Producer SCT in PSE (%)	85.7	69.0	39.8	41.2	42.5	35.7
Wheat						
Producer SCT (million CHF)	417	333	48	46	58	39
Percentage SCT (%)	76.0	54.1	19.3	17.2	23.1	17.5
Producer NPC (coeff.)	4.02	2.66	1.24	1.21	1.30	1.21
Maize						
Producer SCT (million CHF)	102	63	9	8	13	7
Percentage SCT (%)	70.9	52.8	17.9	15.2	23.7	14.8
Producer NPC (coeff.)	3.46	2.13	1.22	1.18	1.31	1.17
Barley						
Producer SCT (million CHF)	153	102	11	10	14	9
Percentage SCT (%)	78.9	57.9	17.8	15.0	22.7	15.6
Producer NPC (coeff.)	4.80	2.50	1.22	1.18	1.29	1.19
Rapeseed						
Producer SCT (million CHF)	80	57	23	25	21	24
Percentage SCT (%)	83.9	76.8	37.3	36.7	34.6	40.7
Producer NPC (coeff.)	6.45	4.32	1.60	1.58	1.53	1.69
Sugar						
Producer SCT (million CHF)	95	111	12	8	7	20
Percentage SCT (%)	72.9	71.4	9.9	5.4	5.3	19.1
Producer NPC (coeff.)	4.28	3.51	1.12	1.06	1.06	1.24
Milk						
Producer SCT (million CHF)	2 775	2 132	468	479	634	292
Percentage SCT (%)	85.7	65.0	22.1	22.0	30.2	14.1
Producer NPC (coeff.)	9.80	3.27	1.30	1.29	1.45	1.17
Beef and Veal						
Producer SCT (million CHF)	1 312	646	398	449	405	340
Percentage SCT (%)	75.0	55.5	34.3	38.4	35.0	29.3
Producer NPC (coeff.)	4.21	2.40	1.53	1.63	1.54	1.42
Sheepmeat						
Producer SCT (million CHF)	36	42	9	5	9	12
Percentage SCT (%)	68.5	63.4	22.6	13.1	23.9	30.8
Producer NPC (coeff.)	5.08	3.70	1.31	1.16	1.32	1.45
Pigmeat						
Producer SCT (million CHF)	717	458	352	391	363	301
Percentage SCT (%)	44.8	39.4	40.7	44.3	41.1	36.6
Producer NPC (coeff.)	2.45	2.17	1.73	1.83	1.75	1.60
Poultry						
Producer SCT (million CHF)	112	133	122	118	124	124
Percentage SCT (%)	73.5	74.9	75.9	76.6	75.9	75.1
Producer NPC (coeff.)	6.08	6.10	4.38	4.55	4.45	4.15
Eggs						
Producer SCT (million CHF)	185	135	123	134	117	117
Percentage SCT (%)	78.9	72.4	67.1	73.6	63.6	63.9
Producer NPC (coeff.)	6.87	5.28	3.32	4.10	2.97	2.88
Other Commodities[1]						
Producer SCT (million CHF)	1 310	862	555	569	601	495
Percentage SCT (%)	82.0	65.9	32.0	33.6	37.1	25.3
Producer NPC (coeff.)	4.50	2.90	1.27	1.30	1.34	1.18

Note: p: provisional. SCT: Single Commodity Transfers. PSE: Producer Support Estimate. NPC: Nominal Protection Coefficient.
  1. Producer SCT for Other Commodities: Total Producer SCT minus the Producer SCTs for the commodities listed above.
Source: OECD (2014), "Producer and Consumer Support Estimates", OECD *Agriculture Statistics Database*, doi: http://dx.doi.org/10.1787/agr-pcse-data-en.

StatLink ⟨⟨⟨ http://dx.doi.org/10.1787/888933111208

Table A.21. **Turkey: Producer Single Commodity Transfers**

	1986-88	1995-97	2011-13	2011	2012	2013p
TOTAL						
PSE (million TRY)	4	707	28 326	27 689	27 414	29 876
Producer SCT (million TRY)	3	520	24 622	23 513	24 104	26 249
Share of Producer SCT in PSE (%)	77.8	72.7	86.9	84.9	87.9	87.9
Wheat						
Producer SCT (million TRY)	1	54	2 257	1 871	2 768	2 133
Percentage SCT (%)	23.9	11.0	16.6	13.9	21.4	14.6
Producer NPC (coeff.)	1.36	1.14	1.20	1.16	1.27	1.17
Maize						
Producer SCT (million TRY)	0	8	258	307	181	287
Percentage SCT (%)	13.6	17.6	8.2	10.9	6.4	7.3
Producer NPC (coeff.)	1.16	1.23	1.09	1.12	1.07	1.08
Barley						
Producer SCT (million TRY)	0	21	518	362	451	743
Percentage SCT (%)	23.1	13.0	12.4	9.7	11.2	16.2
Producer NPC (coeff.)	1.36	1.16	1.14	1.11	1.13	1.19
Sunflower						
Producer SCT (million TRY)	0	11	1 167	1 090	1 161	1 249
Percentage SCT (%)	12.9	29.3	43.8	43.8	43.1	44.7
Producer NPC (coeff.)	1.16	1.43	1.78	1.78	1.76	1.81
Sugar						
Producer SCT (million TRY)	0	49	156	17	238	212
Percentage SCT (%)	12.6	38.9	7.0	0.8	10.1	10.1
Producer NPC (coeff.)	1.11	1.67	1.06	1.00	1.10	1.09
Milk						
Producer SCT (million TRY)	0	97	3 205	2 641	2 336	4 638
Percentage SCT (%)	52.9	50.3	22.3	21.9	15.2	29.9
Producer NPC (coeff.)	2.49	2.16	1.31	1.29	1.19	1.45
Beef and Veal						
Producer SCT (million TRY)	0	44	3 902	3 929	4 539	3 236
Percentage SCT (%)	8.1	29.3	39.6	44.9	42.1	31.9
Producer NPC (coeff.)	1.19	1.54	1.54	1.66	1.60	1.36
Sheepmeat						
Producer SCT (million TRY)	0	1	55	31	72	61
Percentage SCT (%)	11.2	4.8	3.9	2.1	5.3	4.3
Producer NPC (coeff.)	1.17	1.09	1.08	1.04	1.09	1.09
Poultry						
Producer SCT (million TRY)	0	14	76	68	35	124
Percentage SCT (%)	-15.9	23.1	1.4	1.5	0.7	2.1
Producer NPC (coeff.)	0.93	1.40	1.02	1.03	1.01	1.03
Eggs						
Producer SCT (million TRY)	0	18	25	180	-45	-61
Percentage SCT (%)	10.6	30.5	1.0	6.7	-1.6	-2.1
Producer NPC (coeff.)	1.21	1.59	1.03	1.10	1.00	1.00
Apples						
Producer SCT (million TRY)	0	3	1 702	1 818	1 506	1 782
Percentage SCT (%)	4.1	6.6	48.6	53.2	45.2	47.5
Producer NPC (coeff.)	1.04	1.07	1.96	2.14	1.83	1.90
Cotton						
Producer SCT (million TRY)	0	0	984	792	1 124	1 037
Percentage SCT (%)	0.0	0.0	22.4	14.1	28.3	24.8
Producer NPC (coeff.)	1.00	1.00	1.30	1.16	1.39	1.33
Grapes						
Producer SCT (million TRY)	0	8	0	0	0	0
Percentage SCT (%)	4.1	4.4	0.0	0.0	0.0	0.0
Producer NPC (coeff.)	1.05	1.05	1.00	1.00	1.00	1.00
Potatoes						
Producer SCT (million TRY)	0	17	1 553	2 044	1 363	1 252
Percentage SCT (%)	16.6	24.9	60.2	62.8	60.1	57.5
Producer NPC (coeff.)	1.23	1.39	2.52	2.69	2.51	2.35
Tobacco						
Producer SCT (million TRY)	0	45	2	7	0	0
Percentage SCT (%)	11.8	38.4	0.8	2.3	0.0	0.0
Producer NPC (coeff.)	1.14	1.57	1.00	1.00	1.00	1.00
Tomatoes						
Producer SCT (million TRY)	0	11	0	0	0	0
Percentage SCT (%)	28.2	5.3	0.0	0.0	0.0	0.0
Producer NPC (coeff.)	1.41	1.06	1.00	1.00	1.00	1.00
Other Commodities[1]						
Producer SCT (million TRY)	1	120	8 762	8 354	8 375	9 557
Percentage SCT (%)	16.1	19.1	15.0	15.1	14.7	15.1
Producer NPC (coeff.)	1.21	1.25	1.13	1.18	1.10	1.10

Note: p: provisional. SCT: Single Commodity Transfers. PSE: Producer Support Estimate. NPC: Nominal Protection Coefficient.

1. Producer SCT for Other Commodities: Total Producer SCT minus the Producer SCTs for the commodities listed above.

Source: OECD (2014), "Producer and Consumer Support Estimates", OECD *Agriculture Statistics Database, doi: http://dx.doi.org/10.1787/agr-pcse-data-en.*

StatLink ⟦≡⟧ *http://dx.doi.org/10.1787/888933111227*

Table A.22. **United States: Producer Single Commodity Transfers**

	1986-88	1995-97	2011-13	2011	2012	2013p
TOTAL						
PSE (million USD)	36 411	26 614	31 869	31 038	33 548	31 022
Producer SCT (million USD)	26 190	13 550	11 480	9 444	13 608	11 387
Share of Producer SCT in PSE (%)	71.3	51.4	35.9	30.4	40.6	36.7
Wheat						
Producer SCT (million USD)	4 337	545	1 168	1 140	1 116	1 249
Percentage SCT (%)	46.5	5.2	7.1	7.3	6.0	7.9
Producer NPC (coeff.)	1.33	1.01	1.00	1.00	1.00	1.00
Maize						
Producer SCT (million USD)	7 217	120	2 809	2 894	2 701	2 831
Percentage SCT (%)	34.8	0.5	3.8	3.6	3.5	4.3
Producer NPC (coeff.)	1.13	1.00	1.00	1.00	1.00	1.00
Barley						
Producer SCT (million USD)	412	18	48	40	54	51
Percentage SCT (%)	41.1	1.8	4.0	4.6	3.7	3.7
Producer NPC (coeff.)	1.81	1.01	1.00	1.00	1.00	1.00
Sorghum						
Producer SCT (million USD)	765	30	150	135	138	177
Percentage SCT (%)	36.2	1.8	9.1	9.5	8.1	9.7
Producer NPC (coeff.)	1.17	1.00	1.00	1.00	1.00	1.00
Rice						
Producer SCT (million USD)	816	168	51	55	48	51
Percentage SCT (%)	50.2	8.2	1.7	2.0	1.6	1.6
Producer NPC (coeff.)	1.45	1.01	1.00	1.00	1.00	1.00
Soyabean						
Producer SCT (million USD)	172	25	1 545	1 597	1 480	1 557
Percentage SCT (%)	1.7	0.2	3.6	4.0	3.3	3.6
Producer NPC (coeff.)	1.01	1.00	1.00	1.00	1.00	1.00
Sugar						
Producer SCT (million USD)	1 036	744	615	990	656	198
Percentage SCT (%)	55.9	36.6	17.3	29.0	17.5	5.5
Producer NPC (coeff.)	2.31	1.60	1.21	1.40	1.20	1.05
Milk						
Producer SCT (million USD)	6 340	7 500	2 482	514	4 400	2 534
Percentage SCT (%)	34.9	35.2	6.4	1.3	11.7	6.3
Producer NPC (coeff.)	1.53	1.57	1.07	1.01	1.13	1.07
Beef and Veal						
Producer SCT (million USD)	258	-3	106	0	0	318
Percentage SCT (%)	1.1	0.0	0.2	0.0	0.0	0.6
Producer NPC (coeff.)	1.02	1.00	1.00	1.00	1.00	1.01
Sheepmeat						
Producer SCT (million USD)	5	3	38	46	34	34
Percentage SCT (%)	1.1	0.8	9.0	9.0	9.0	9.0
Producer NPC (coeff.)	1.01	1.01	1.10	1.10	1.10	1.10
Wool						
Producer SCT (million USD)	79	13	1	1	0	0
Percentage SCT (%)	47.8	12.9	1.1	2.4	0.4	0.4
Producer NPC (coeff.)	1.01	1.01	1.01	1.02	1.00	1.00
Pigmeat						
Producer SCT (million USD)	-66	-2	0	0	0	0
Percentage SCT (%)	-0.7	0.0	0.0	0.0	0.0	0.0
Producer NPC (coeff.)	1.00	1.00	1.00	1.00	1.00	1.00
Poultry						
Producer SCT (million USD)	725	65	0	0	0	0
Percentage SCT (%)	8.8	0.4	0.0	0.0	0.0	0.0
Producer NPC (coeff.)	1.11	1.00	1.00	1.00	1.00	1.00
Eggs						
Producer SCT (million USD)	136	133	0	0	0	0
Percentage SCT (%)	4.4	3.3	0.0	0.0	0.0	0.0
Producer NPC (coeff.)	1.06	1.04	1.00	1.00	1.00	1.00
Cotton						
Producer SCT (million USD)	208	343	625	813	587	473
Percentage SCT (%)	6.2	5.4	9.5	10.6	8.6	9.1
Producer NPC (coeff.)	1.06	1.03	1.00	1.00	1.00	1.01
Other Commodities[1]						
Producer SCT (million USD)	3 749	3 848	1 842	1 219	2 394	1 915
Percentage SCT (%)	9.1	6.7	1.9	1.4	2.5	1.9
Producer NPC (coeff.)	1.11	1.07	1.01	1.01	1.02	1.01

Note: p: provisional. SCT: Single Commodity Transfers. PSE: Producer Support Estimate. NPC: Nominal Protection Coefficient.

   1. Producer SCT for Other Commodities: Total Producer SCT minus the Producer SCTs for the commodities listed above.

Source: OECD (2014), "Producer and Consumer Support Estimates", OECD *Agriculture Statistics Database, doi: http://dx.doi.org/10.1787/agr-pcse-data-en.*

StatLink ⟨ᴍᴤ⟩ *http://dx.doi.org/10.1787/888933111246*

Table A.23. **OECD: Consumer Single Commodity Transfers**

	1986-88	1995-97	2011-13	2011	2012	2013p
TOTAL						
CSE (million USD)	-159 865	-171 139	-94 833	-91 578	-105 929	-86 992
CSE (million EUR)	-144 680	-137 960	-71 268	-65 859	-82 413	-65 531
Consumer SCT (million USD)	-173 061	-190 273	-134 899	-130 257	-145 264	-129 174
Consumer SCT (million EUR)	-156 651	-153 497	-101 333	-93 676	-113 016	-97 307
Wheat						
Consumer SCT (million USD)	-12 472	-8 446	-812	-675	-1 057	-704
Consumer SCT (million EUR)	-11 289	-6 820	-613	-485	-822	-531
Consumer NPC (coeff.)	2.06	1.31	1.02	1.01	1.02	1.01
Maize						
Consumer SCT (million USD)	-1 979	-304	-25	-35	-17	-23
Consumer SCT (million EUR)	-1 796	-239	-18	-25	-13	-17
Consumer NPC (coeff.)	1.24	1.04	1.00	1.00	1.00	1.00
Barley						
Consumer SCT (million USD)	-4 112	-3 166	-753	-827	-825	-608
Consumer SCT (million EUR)	-3 723	-2 541	-565	-594	-642	-458
Consumer NPC (coeff.)	2.39	1.35	1.06	1.06	1.06	1.05
Oats						
Consumer SCT (million USD)	-190	-49	24	11	33	27
Consumer SCT (million EUR)	-177	-40	18	8	26	21
Consumer NPC (coeff.)	1.52	1.24	1.00	1.00	1.01	1.00
Sorghum						
Consumer SCT (million USD)	0	33	0	0	0	0
Consumer SCT (million EUR)	0	27	0	0	0	0
Consumer NPC (coeff.)	1.07	1.01	1.00	1.00	1.00	1.00
Rice						
Consumer SCT (million USD)	-23 427	-29 660	-20 943	-19 524	-23 256	-20 050
Consumer SCT (million EUR)	-21 229	-23 846	-15 746	-14 041	-18 093	-15 103
Consumer NPC (coeff.)	4.96	4.32	2.54	2.37	2.75	2.49
Rapeseed						
Consumer SCT (million USD)	-515	-189	-144	-151	-131	-149
Consumer SCT (million EUR)	-465	-151	-108	-109	-102	-113
Consumer NPC (coeff.)	1.35	1.06	1.01	1.01	1.01	1.01
Sunflower						
Consumer SCT (million USD)	-61	-160	-633	-631	-659	-610
Consumer SCT (million EUR)	-58	-132	-475	-454	-513	-460
Consumer NPC (coeff.)	1.07	1.07	1.13	1.12	1.14	1.14
Soyabean						
Consumer SCT (million USD)	-216	-432	-697	-738	-567	-785
Consumer SCT (million EUR)	-193	-349	-521	-531	-441	-591
Consumer NPC (coeff.)	1.02	1.02	1.02	1.02	1.01	1.02
Sugar						
Consumer SCT (million USD)	-7 285	-7 515	-3 511	-4 193	-4 116	-2 225
Consumer SCT (million EUR)	-6 632	-6 099	-2 631	-3 015	-3 202	-1 676
Consumer NPC (coeff.)	2.46	1.92	1.27	1.32	1.31	1.19
Milk						
Consumer SCT (million USD)	-38 507	-38 969	-15 947	-13 082	-19 147	-15 612
Consumer SCT (million EUR)	-34 956	-31 581	-12 021	-9 408	-14 896	-11 760
Consumer NPC (coeff.)	2.79	1.88	1.13	1.10	1.17	1.13
Beef and Veal						
Consumer SCT (million USD)	-18 231	-16 496	-17 334	-12 200	-18 762	-21 039
Consumer SCT (million EUR)	-16 575	-13 390	-13 073	-8 774	-14 597	-15 849
Consumer NPC (coeff.)	1.41	1.27	1.16	1.11	1.17	1.20
Sheepmeat						
Consumer SCT (million USD)	-3 561	-2 597	-845	-206	-827	-1 500
Consumer SCT (million EUR)	-3 205	-2 079	-641	-149	-644	-1 130
Consumer NPC (coeff.)	2.06	1.47	1.10	1.02	1.10	1.19
Wool						
Consumer SCT (million USD)	-8	0	3	3	3	3
Consumer SCT (million EUR)	-7	0	2	2	2	3
Consumer NPC (coeff.)	1.04	1.02	1.00	1.00	1.00	1.00
Pigmeat						
Consumer SCT (million USD)	-7 121	-7 981	-10 512	-12 186	-10 778	-8 572
Consumer SCT (million EUR)	-6 302	-6 380	-7 869	-8 764	-8 385	-6 457
Consumer NPC (coeff.)	1.20	1.16	1.14	1.17	1.15	1.11
Poultry						
Consumer SCT (million USD)	-4 509	-5 314	-6 526	-7 663	-6 946	-4 969
Consumer SCT (million EUR)	-4 017	-4 272	-4 886	-5 511	-5 404	-3 743
Consumer NPC (coeff.)	1.25	1.18	1.11	1.14	1.12	1.08
Eggs						
Consumer SCT (million USD)	-3 849	-2 634	-1 710	-1 858	-1 458	-1 814
Consumer SCT (million EUR)	-3 487	-2 107	-1 279	-1 336	-1 134	-1 367
Consumer NPC (coeff.)	1.35	1.17	1.06	1.07	1.05	1.06

Table A.23. **OECD: Consumer Single Commodity Transfers** (cont.)

	1986-88	1995-97	2011-13	2011	2012	2013p
Other Commodities[1]						
Consumer SCT (million USD)	-47 017	-66 393	-54 534	-56 302	-56 755	-50 545
Consumer SCT (million EUR)	-42 538	-53 497	-40 907	-40 490	-44 156	-38 075
Consumer NPC (coeff.)	1.31	1.30	1.14	1.15	1.15	1.13

Note: p: provisional. SCT: Single Commodity Transfers. CSE: Consumer Support Estimate. NPC: Nominal Protection Coefficient.

Total Consumer SCT may differ from the Total CSE by the amount of subsidies to consumers which are not specific to a single commodity.

1. Consumer SCT for Other Commodities: Total Consumer SCT minus the Consumer SCTs for the commodities listed above.

Source: OECD (2014), "Producer and Consumer Support Estimates", OECD *Agriculture Statistics Database*, doi: *http://dx.doi.org/10.1787/agr-pcse-data-en.*

StatLink ▄▄█▄ *http://dx.doi.org/10.1787/888933111265*

Table A.24. **Australia: Consumer Single Commodity Transfers**

	1986-88	1995-97	2011-13	2011	2012	2013p
TOTAL						
CSE (million AUD)	-848	-386	0	0	0	0
Consumer SCT (million AUD)	-848	-386	0	0	0	0
Wheat						
Consumer SCT (million AUD)	-16	-6	0	0	0	0
Consumer NPC (coeff.)	1.05	1.01	1.00	1.00	1.00	1.00
Barley						
Consumer SCT (million AUD)	0	0	0	0	0	0
Consumer NPC (coeff.)	1.00	1.00	1.00	1.00	1.00	1.00
Oats						
Consumer SCT (million AUD)	0	0	0	0	0	0
Consumer NPC (coeff.)	1.00	1.00	1.00	1.00	1.00	1.00
Sorghum						
Consumer SCT (million AUD)	0	0	0	0	0	0
Consumer NPC (coeff.)	1.00	1.00	1.00	1.00	1.00	1.00
Rice						
Consumer SCT (million AUD)	-4	-2	0	0	0	0
Consumer NPC (coeff.)	1.13	1.02	1.00	1.00	1.00	1.00
Rapeseed						
Consumer SCT (million AUD)	0	0	0	0	0	0
Consumer NPC (coeff.)	1.00	1.00	1.00	1.00	1.00	1.00
Sunflower						
Consumer SCT (million AUD)	0	0	0	0	0	0
Consumer NPC (coeff.)	1.00	1.00	1.00	1.00	1.00	1.00
Soyabean						
Consumer SCT (million AUD)	0	0	0	0	0	0
Consumer NPC (coeff.)	1.00	1.00	1.00	1.00	1.00	1.00
Sugar						
Consumer SCT (million AUD)	-66	-30	0	0	0	0
Consumer NPC (coeff.)	1.12	1.03	1.00	1.00	1.00	1.00
Milk						
Consumer SCT (million AUD)	-590	-246	0	0	0	0
Consumer NPC (coeff.)	2.71	1.22	1.00	1.00	1.00	1.00
Beef and Veal						
Consumer SCT (million AUD)	0	0	0	0	0	0
Consumer NPC (coeff.)	1.00	1.00	1.00	1.00	1.00	1.00
Sheepmeat						
Consumer SCT (million AUD)	-5	0	0	0	0	0
Consumer NPC (coeff.)	1.01	1.00	1.00	1.00	1.00	1.00
Wool						
Consumer SCT (million AUD)	-1	-1	0	0	0	0
Consumer NPC (coeff.)	1.01	1.01	1.00	1.00	1.00	1.00
Pigmeat						
Consumer SCT (million AUD)	-1	0	0	0	0	0
Consumer NPC (coeff.)	1.00	1.00	1.00	1.00	1.00	1.00
Poultry						
Consumer SCT (million AUD)	0	0	0	0	0	0
Consumer NPC (coeff.)	1.00	1.00	1.00	1.00	1.00	1.00
Eggs						
Consumer SCT (million AUD)	-43	-2	0	0	0	0
Consumer NPC (coeff.)	1.18	1.01	1.00	1.00	1.00	1.00
Cotton						
Consumer SCT (million AUD)	0	0	0	0	0	0
Consumer NPC (coeff.)	1.03	1.00	1.00	1.00	1.00	1.00
Other Commodities[1]						
Consumer SCT (million AUD)	-120	-98	0	0	0	0
Consumer NPC (coeff.)	1.13	1.03	1.00	1.00	1.00	1.00

Note: p: provisional. SCT: Single Commodity Transfers. CSE: Consumer Support Estimate. NPC: Nominal Protection Coefficient. Total Consumer SCT may differ from the Total CSE by the amount of subsidies to consumers which are not specific to a single commodity.

1. Consumer SCT for Other Commodities: Total Consumer SCT minus the Consumer SCTs for the commodities listed above.

Source: OECD (2014), "Producer and Consumer Support Estimates", OECD *Agriculture Statistics Database, doi: http://dx.doi.org/10.1787/agr-pcse-data-en.*

StatLink ⚞⚟ *http://dx.doi.org/10.1787/888933111284*

Table A.25. **Canada: Consumer Single Commodity Transfers**

	1986-88	1995-97	2011-13	2011	2012	2013p
TOTAL						
CSE (million CAD)	-3 758	-2 415	-5 010	-4 697	-5 477	-4 857
Consumer SCT (million CAD)	-3 758	-2 415	-5 011	-4 698	-5 478	-4 858
Wheat						
Consumer SCT (million CAD)	-259	6	0	0	0	0
Consumer NPC (coeff.)	1.54	1.00	1.00	1.00	1.00	1.00
Maize						
Consumer SCT (million CAD)	-2	-1	0	0	0	0
Consumer NPC (coeff.)	1.02	1.00	1.00	1.00	1.00	1.00
Barley						
Consumer SCT (million CAD)	11	0	0	0	0	0
Consumer NPC (coeff.)	1.83	1.00	1.00	1.00	1.00	1.00
Oats						
Consumer SCT (million CAD)	0	0	0	0	0	0
Consumer NPC (coeff.)	1.00	1.00	1.00	1.00	1.00	1.00
Rapeseed						
Consumer SCT (million CAD)	-46	0	0	0	0	1
Consumer NPC (coeff.)	1.11	1.00	1.00	1.00	1.00	1.00
Soyabean						
Consumer SCT (million CAD)	0	0	0	0	0	0
Consumer NPC (coeff.)	1.00	1.00	1.00	1.00	1.00	1.00
Milk						
Consumer SCT (million CAD)	-2 566	-1 850	-3 197	-2 966	-3 497	-3 127
Consumer NPC (coeff.)	5.81	1.94	1.85	1.76	2.02	1.78
Beef and Veal						
Consumer SCT (million CAD)	-62	0	0	0	0	0
Consumer NPC (coeff.)	1.02	1.00	1.00	1.00	1.00	1.00
Pigmeat						
Consumer SCT (million CAD)	0	0	0	0	0	0
Consumer NPC (coeff.)	1.00	1.00	1.00	1.00	1.00	1.00
Poultry						
Consumer SCT (million CAD)	-157	-47	-842	-795	-923	-807
Consumer NPC (coeff.)	1.19	1.03	1.49	1.49	1.57	1.42
Eggs						
Consumer SCT (million CAD)	-90	-139	-220	-208	-250	-202
Consumer NPC (coeff.)	1.28	1.31	1.34	1.34	1.38	1.28
Dried Beans						
Consumer SCT (million CAD)	0	0	0	0	0	0
Consumer NPC (coeff.)	1.00	1.00	1.00	1.00	1.00	1.00
Dried Peas						
Consumer SCT (million CAD)	0	0	0	0	0	0
Consumer NPC (coeff.)	1.00	1.00	1.00	1.00	1.00	1.00
Flax						
Consumer SCT (million CAD)	0	0	0	0	0	0
Consumer NPC (coeff.)	1.00	1.00	1.00	1.00	1.00	1.00
Lentils						
Consumer SCT (million CAD)	0	0	0	0	0	0
Consumer NPC (coeff.)	1.00	1.00	1.00	1.00	1.00	1.00
Potatoes						
Consumer SCT (million CAD)	0	0	0	0	0	0
Consumer NPC (coeff.)	1.00	1.00	1.00	1.00	1.00	1.00
Other Commodities[1]						
Consumer SCT (million CAD)	-588	-384	-753	-728	-808	-723
Consumer NPC (coeff.)	1.23	1.11	1.16	1.15	1.17	1.16

Note: p: provisional. SCT: Single Commodity Transfers. CSE: Consumer Support Estimate. NPC: Nominal Protection Coefficient. Total Consumer SCT may differ from the Total CSE by the amount of subsidies to consumers which are not specific to a single commodity.
1. Consumer SCT for Other Commodities: Total Consumer SCT minus the Consumer SCTs for the commodities listed above.
Source: OECD (2014), "Producer and Consumer Support Estimates", OECD *Agriculture Statistics Database, doi: http://dx.doi.org/10.1787/agr-pcse-data-en.*

StatLink ᴍᴸᴾ *http://dx.doi.org/10.1787/888933111303*

Table A.26. **Chile: Consumer Single Commodity Transfers**

	1995-97	2011-13	2011	2012	2013p
TOTAL					
CSE (million CLP)	-172 494	-14 223	-17 967	-14 834	-9 867
Consumer SCT (million CLP)	-172 494	-14 223	-17 967	-14 834	-9 867
Wheat					
Consumer SCT (million CLP)	-9 500	0	0	0	0
Consumer NPC (coeff.)	1.07	1.00	1.00	1.00	1.00
Maize					
Consumer SCT (million CLP)	-3 946	0	0	0	0
Consumer NPC (coeff.)	1.05	1.00	1.00	1.00	1.00
Sugar					
Consumer SCT (million CLP)	-39 910	-8 548	-10 763	-8 794	-6 086
Consumer NPC (coeff.)	1.39	1.03	1.03	1.03	1.02
Milk					
Consumer SCT (million CLP)	-34 353	0	0	0	0
Consumer NPC (coeff.)	1.24	1.00	1.00	1.00	1.00
Beef and Veal					
Consumer SCT (million CLP)	-23 036	0	0	0	0
Consumer NPC (coeff.)	1.10	1.00	1.00	1.00	1.00
Pigmeat					
Consumer SCT (million CLP)	0	0	0	0	0
Consumer NPC (coeff.)	1.00	1.00	1.00	1.00	1.00
Poultry					
Consumer SCT (million CLP)	0	0	0	0	0
Consumer NPC (coeff.)	1.00	1.00	1.00	1.00	1.00
Apples					
Consumer SCT (million CLP)	0	0	0	0	0
Consumer NPC (coeff.)	1.00	1.00	1.00	1.00	1.00
Grapes					
Consumer SCT (million CLP)	0	0	0	0	0
Consumer NPC (coeff.)	1.00	1.00	1.00	1.00	1.00
Tomatoes					
Consumer SCT (million CLP)	0	0	0	0	0
Consumer NPC (coeff.)	1.00	1.00	1.00	1.00	1.00
Other Commodities[1]					
Consumer SCT (million CLP)	-61 749	-5 675	-7 204	-6 040	-3 780
Consumer NPC (coeff.)	1.09	1.00	1.00	1.00	1.00

Note: p: provisional. SCT: Single Commodity Transfers. CSE: Consumer Support Estimate. NPC: Nominal Protection Coefficient. Total Consumer SCT may differ from the Total CSE by the amount of subsidies to consumers which are not specific to a single commodity.

  1. Consumer SCT for Other Commodities: Total Consumer SCT minus the Consumer SCTs for the commodities listed above.

Source: OECD (2014), "Producer and Consumer Support Estimates", OECD *Agriculture Statistics Database, doi: http://dx.doi.org/10.1787/agr-pcse-data-en.*

StatLink http://dx.doi.org/10.1787/888933111322

Table A.27. **European Union: Consumer Single Commodity Transfers**

	1986-88	1995-97	2011-13	2011	2012	2013p
TOTAL						
CSE (million EUR)	-65 589	-47 130	-15 782	-9 513	-17 536	-20 298
Consumer SCT (million EUR)	-66 496	-47 933	-16 436	-10 423	-18 027	-20 856
Wheat						
Consumer SCT (million EUR)	-4 244	-263	0	0	0	0
Consumer NPC (coeff.)	2.14	1.05	1.00	1.00	1.00	1.00
Maize						
Consumer SCT (million EUR)	-1 371	-421	0	0	0	0
Consumer NPC (coeff.)	2.20	1.28	1.00	1.00	1.00	1.00
Barley						
Consumer SCT (million EUR)	-1 121	-201	0	0	0	0
Consumer NPC (coeff.)	2.58	1.17	1.00	1.00	1.00	1.00
Oats						
Consumer SCT (million EUR)	-150	-41	0	0	0	0
Consumer NPC (coeff.)	1.58	1.33	1.00	1.00	1.00	1.00
Rice						
Consumer SCT (million EUR)	-398	-252	-40	-120	0	0
Consumer NPC (coeff.)	2.50	1.50	1.03	1.10	1.00	1.00
Rapeseed						
Consumer SCT (million EUR)	15	0	0	0	0	0
Consumer NPC (coeff.)	1.00	1.00	1.00	1.00	1.00	1.00
Sunflower						
Consumer SCT (million EUR)	12	0	0	0	0	0
Consumer NPC (coeff.)	1.00	1.00	1.00	1.00	1.00	1.00
Soyabean						
Consumer SCT (million EUR)	4	0	0	0	0	0
Consumer NPC (coeff.)	1.00	1.00	1.00	1.00	1.00	1.00
Sugar						
Consumer SCT (million EUR)	-2 779	-2 547	-16	0	0	-49
Consumer NPC (coeff.)	3.35	2.33	1.01	1.00	1.00	1.02
Milk						
Consumer SCT (million EUR)	-17 622	-16 027	73	113	-13	119
Consumer NPC (coeff.)	4.56	2.07	1.00	1.00	1.00	1.00
Beef and Veal						
Consumer SCT (million EUR)	-9 696	-7 185	-7 159	-2 582	-8 212	-10 682
Consumer NPC (coeff.)	2.07	1.66	1.36	1.11	1.39	1.58
Sheepmeat						
Consumer SCT (million EUR)	-2 993	-1 914	-498	0	-484	-1 009
Consumer NPC (coeff.)	2.70	1.71	1.11	1.00	1.10	1.23
Pigmeat						
Consumer SCT (million EUR)	-1 675	-1 727	-221	0	0	-664
Consumer NPC (coeff.)	1.13	1.08	1.01	1.00	1.00	1.02
Poultry						
Consumer SCT (million EUR)	-2 078	-2 382	-2 586	-3 274	-2 991	-1 492
Consumer NPC (coeff.)	1.46	1.51	1.22	1.30	1.25	1.11
Eggs						
Consumer SCT (million EUR)	-1 958	-552	-55	-69	-92	-5
Consumer NPC (coeff.)	1.64	1.14	1.01	1.01	1.01	1.00
Flowers						
Consumer SCT (million EUR)	-684	-778	-382	-423	-361	-363
Consumer NPC (coeff.)	1.09	1.06	1.02	1.02	1.02	1.02
Potatoes						
Consumer SCT (million EUR)	-572	-704	-1 028	-1 010	-1 022	-1 051
Consumer NPC (coeff.)	1.17	1.14	1.10	1.10	1.10	1.10
Tomatoes						
Consumer SCT (million EUR)	-963	-60	-349	-362	-304	-379
Consumer NPC (coeff.)	1.16	1.01	1.03	1.03	1.02	1.03
Wine						
Consumer SCT (million EUR)	-691	-606	-1	-2	0	0
Consumer NPC (coeff.)	1.09	1.05	1.00	1.00	1.00	1.00
Other Commodities[1]						
Consumer SCT (million EUR)	-17 531	-12 272	-4 175	-2 694	-4 548	-5 282
Consumer NPC (coeff.)	1.70	1.30	1.05	1.03	1.05	1.06

Note: p: provisional. SCT: Single Commodity Transfers. CSE: Consumer Support Estimate. NPC: Nominal Protection Coefficient. Total Consumer SCT may differ from the Total CSE by the amount of subsidies to consumers which are not specific to a single commodity. EU12 for 1986-88; EU15 for 1995-97; and EU27 from 2007.

1. Consumer SCT for Other Commodities: Total Consumer SCT minus the Consumer SCTs for the commodities listed above.

Source: OECD (2014), "Producer and Consumer Support Estimates", OECD *Agriculture Statistics Database, doi: http://dx.doi.org/10.1787/agr-pcse-data-en.*

StatLink ⏷⏷⏷ *http://dx.doi.org/10.1787/888933111341*

Table A.28. **Iceland: Consumer Single Commodity Transfers**

	1986-88	1995-97	2011-13	2011	2012	2013p
TOTAL						
CSE (million ISK)	-4 566	-4 012	-6 408	-5 613	-7 256	-6 353
Consumer SCT (million ISK)	-4 566	-4 012	-6 408	-5 613	-7 256	-6 353
Milk						
Consumer SCT (million ISK)	-1 664	-1 369	-1 861	-1 812	-2 519	-1 253
Consumer NPC (coeff.)	9.45	2.01	1.31	1.29	1.45	1.18
Beef and Veal						
Consumer SCT (million ISK)	-208	-281	0	0	0	0
Consumer NPC (coeff.)	2.40	1.58	1.00	1.00	1.00	1.00
Sheepmeat						
Consumer SCT (million ISK)	-747	-3	0	0	0	0
Consumer NPC (coeff.)	3.57	1.11	1.00	1.00	1.00	1.00
Wool						
Consumer SCT (million ISK)	98	106	366	350	325	422
Consumer NPC (coeff.)	1.20	2.05	1.11	1.10	1.23	1.00
Pigmeat						
Consumer SCT (million ISK)	-316	-456	-724	-636	-784	-752
Consumer NPC (coeff.)	3.81	2.05	1.47	1.43	1.50	1.47
Poultry						
Consumer SCT (million ISK)	-192	-466	-2 152	-1 762	-2 325	-2 369
Consumer NPC (coeff.)	5.80	6.39	3.30	3.15	3.42	3.31
Eggs						
Consumer SCT (million ISK)	-261	-383	-796	-806	-706	-875
Consumer NPC (coeff.)	5.37	4.00	2.44	2.86	2.11	2.36
Other Commodities[1]						
Consumer SCT (million ISK)	-1 277	-1 160	-1 240	-947	-1 248	-1 527
Consumer NPC (coeff.)	4.44	1.82	1.37	1.36	1.44	1.32

Note: p: provisional. SCT: Single Commodity Transfers. CSE: Consumer Support Estimate. NPC: Nominal Protection Coefficient. Total Consumer SCT may differ from the Total CSE by the amount of subsidies to consumers which are not specific to a single commodity.

1. Consumer SCT for Other Commodities: Total Consumer SCT minus the Consumer SCTs for the commodities listed above.

Source: OECD (2014), "Producer and Consumer Support Estimates", OECD Agriculture Statistics Database, doi: http://dx.doi.org/10.1787/agr-pcse-data-en.

StatLink ᵐᵉᵖ http://dx.doi.org/10.1787/888933111360

Table A.29. **Israel: Consumer Single Commodity Transfers**

	1995-97	2011-13	2011	2012	2013p
TOTAL					
CSE (million ILS)	-2 127	-2 731	-3 403	-2 627	-2 162
Consumer SCT (million ILS)	-2 127	-2 731	-3 403	-2 627	-2 162
Wheat					
Consumer SCT (million ILS)	-57	-150	-211	-57	-182
Consumer NPC (coeff.)	1.22	1.17	1.25	1.07	1.19
Milk					
Consumer SCT (million ILS)	-783	-772	-693	-1 001	-622
Consumer NPC (coeff.)	2.48	1.37	1.32	1.53	1.27
Beef and Veal					
Consumer SCT (million ILS)	-309	-1 060	-1 141	-973	-1 067
Consumer NPC (coeff.)	1.42	1.73	1.73	1.65	1.81
Sheepmeat					
Consumer SCT (million ILS)	-63	-206	-240	-206	-171
Consumer NPC (coeff.)	1.50	1.37	1.50	1.30	1.30
Poultry					
Consumer SCT (million ILS)	-338	29	-179	44	222
Consumer NPC (coeff.)	1.27	0.99	1.07	0.98	0.92
Eggs					
Consumer SCT (million ILS)	-15	79	-54	177	113
Consumer NPC (coeff.)	1.04	0.92	1.08	0.81	0.87
Apples					
Consumer SCT (million ILS)	0	-26	-67	-28	15
Consumer NPC (coeff.)	1.00	1.05	1.14	1.05	0.97
Avocado					
Consumer SCT (million ILS)	0	0	0	0	0
Consumer NPC (coeff.)	1.00	1.00	1.00	1.00	1.00
Bananas					
Consumer SCT (million ILS)	32	-92	-150	-70	-57
Consumer NPC (coeff.)	0.85	1.42	1.73	1.26	1.28
Cotton					
Consumer SCT (million ILS)	4	0	0	0	0
Consumer NPC (coeff.)	0.90	0.97	1.06	0.88	0.97
Grapefruit					
Consumer SCT (million ILS)	0	0	0	0	0
Consumer NPC (coeff.)	1.00	1.00	1.00	1.00	1.00
Grapes					
Consumer SCT (million ILS)	0	0	0	0	0
Consumer NPC (coeff.)	1.00	1.00	1.00	1.00	1.00
Orange					
Consumer SCT (million ILS)	0	0	0	0	0
Consumer NPC (coeff.)	1.00	1.00	1.00	1.00	1.00
Peppers					
Consumer SCT (million ILS)	0	0	0	0	0
Consumer NPC (coeff.)	1.00	1.00	1.00	1.00	1.00
Peanuts					
Consumer SCT (million ILS)	0	0	0	0	0
Consumer NPC (coeff.)	1.00	1.00	1.00	1.00	1.00
Potatoes					
Consumer SCT (million ILS)	0	0	0	0	0
Consumer NPC (coeff.)	1.00	1.00	1.00	1.00	1.00
Tomatoes					
Consumer SCT (million ILS)	0	0	0	0	0
Consumer NPC (coeff.)	1.00	1.00	1.00	1.00	1.00
Other Commodities[1]					
Consumer SCT (million ILS)	-598	-532	-669	-513	-415
Consumer NPC (coeff.)	1.30	1.15	1.19	1.14	1.11

Note: p: provisional. SCT: Single Commodity Transfers. CSE: Consumer Support Estimate. NPC: Nominal Protection Coefficient. Total Consumer SCT may differ from the Total CSE by the amount of subsidies to consumers which are not specific to a single commodity. The statistical data for Israel are supplied by and under the responsibility of the relevant Israeli authorities. The use of such data by the OECD is without prejudice to the status of the Golan Heights, East Jerusalem and Israeli settlements in the West Bank under the terms of international law.

1. Consumer SCT for Other Commodities: Total Consumer SCT minus the Consumer SCTs for the commodities listed above.

Source: OECD (2014), "Producer and Consumer Support Estimates", OECD *Agriculture Statistics Database, doi: http://dx.doi.org/10.1787/agr-pcse-data-en.*

StatLink 🔗 *http://dx.doi.org/10.1787/888933111379*

Table A.30. Japan: Consumer Single Commodity Transfers

	1986-88	1995-97	2011-13	2011	2012	2013p
TOTAL						
CSE (billion JPY)	-8 910	-8 080	-5 404	-5 111	-5 671	-5 430
Consumer SCT (billion JPY)	-8 910	-8 080	-5 404	-5 111	-5 671	-5 430
Wheat						
Consumer SCT (billion JPY)	-897	-780	0	0	0	0
Consumer NPC (coeff.)	6.56	5.34	1.00	1.00	1.00	1.00
Barley						
Consumer SCT (billion JPY)	-304	-269	-57	-58	-63	-49
Consumer NPC (coeff.)	6.18	4.36	1.76	1.87	1.85	1.57
Rice						
Consumer SCT (billion JPY)	-2 559	-2 230	-1 320	-1 163	-1 429	-1 368
Consumer NPC (coeff.)	5.61	4.93	3.64	3.32	4.12	3.49
Soyabean						
Consumer SCT (billion JPY)	0	0	0	0	0	0
Consumer NPC (coeff.)	1.00	1.00	1.00	1.00	1.00	1.00
Sugar						
Consumer SCT (billion JPY)	-267	-171	-168	-168	-169	-168
Consumer NPC (coeff.)	2.50	2.34	55.86	30.50	154.37	-17.28
Milk						
Consumer SCT (billion JPY)	-776	-679	-591	-518	-639	-618
Consumer NPC (coeff.)	7.06	3.27	2.48	2.09	2.71	2.65
Beef and Veal						
Consumer SCT (billion JPY)	-558	-355	-307	-300	-322	-298
Consumer NPC (coeff.)	3.65	1.46	1.39	1.39	1.39	1.39
Pigmeat						
Consumer SCT (billion JPY)	-356	-414	-604	-634	-641	-536
Consumer NPC (coeff.)	1.73	2.07	2.77	2.89	3.07	2.35
Poultry						
Consumer SCT (billion JPY)	-51	-42	-37	-37	-37	-38
Consumer NPC (coeff.)	1.13	1.12	1.12	1.12	1.12	1.12
Eggs						
Consumer SCT (billion JPY)	-71	-73	-66	-70	-63	-66
Consumer NPC (coeff.)	1.20	1.19	1.17	1.17	1.17	1.17
Apples						
Consumer SCT (billion JPY)	-35	-24	-29	-47	-19	-22
Consumer NPC (coeff.)	1.34	1.21	1.32	1.58	1.17	1.20
Chinese cabbage						
Consumer SCT (billion JPY)	-9	-50	-74	-73	-73	-78
Consumer NPC (coeff.)	1.11	2.09	3.82	4.07	3.51	3.89
Cucumbers						
Consumer SCT (billion JPY)	-34	-33	-4	-4	-4	-4
Consumer NPC (coeff.)	1.24	1.23	1.03	1.03	1.03	1.03
Grapes						
Consumer SCT (billion JPY)	-38	-64	-70	-71	-67	-71
Consumer NPC (coeff.)	1.54	2.04	2.75	2.92	2.52	2.80
Mandarins						
Consumer SCT (billion JPY)	-27	-74	-77	-76	-76	-79
Consumer NPC (coeff.)	1.20	1.55	2.01	1.93	2.04	2.04
Pears						
Consumer SCT (billion JPY)	-21	-30	-44	-36	-51	-46
Consumer NPC (coeff.)	1.34	1.43	2.26	1.80	2.67	2.32
Spinach						
Consumer SCT (billion JPY)	-47	-80	-3	-3	-3	-3
Consumer NPC (coeff.)	2.17	4.19	1.03	1.03	1.03	1.03
Strawberries						
Consumer SCT (billion JPY)	-13	-40	-34	-31	-38	-32
Consumer NPC (coeff.)	1.10	1.29	1.28	1.25	1.32	1.26
Welsh Onion						
Consumer SCT (billion JPY)	-32	-65	-102	-98	-102	-107
Consumer NPC (coeff.)	1.63	1.94	3.67	3.70	3.46	3.84
Other Commodities[1]						
Consumer SCT (billion JPY)	-2 816	-2 607	-1 817	-1 727	-1 875	-1 849
Consumer NPC (coeff.)	2.66	2.17	1.85	1.80	1.92	1.84

Note: p: provisional. SCT: Single Commodity Transfers. CSE: Consumer Support Estimate. NPC: Nominal Protection Coefficient. Total Consumer SCT may differ from the Total CSE by the amount of subsidies to consumers which are not specific to a single commodity.

1. Consumer SCT for Other Commodities: Total Consumer SCT minus the Consumer SCTs for the commodities listed above.

Source: OECD (2014), "Producer and Consumer Support Estimates", OECD *Agriculture Statistics Database, doi: http://dx.doi.org/10.1787/agr-pcse-data-en.*

StatLink ⬛🖩➧ *http://dx.doi.org/10.1787/888933111398*

Table A.31. **Korea: Consumer Single Commodity Transfers**

	1986-88	1995-97	2011-13	2011	2012	2013p
TOTAL						
CSE (billion KRW)	-9 425	-19 748	-28 012	-29 622	-27 812	-26 600
Consumer SCT (billion KRW)	-9 481	-20 002	-28 030	-29 639	-27 832	-26 619
Barley						
Consumer SCT (billion KRW)	-210	-209	-21	-27	-19	-18
Consumer NPC (coeff.)	3.42	3.50	1.14	1.18	1.14	1.10
Rice						
Consumer SCT (billion KRW)	-4 452	-6 933	-5 967	-5 276	-6 017	-6 607
Consumer NPC (coeff.)	5.59	5.89	2.34	2.09	2.38	2.54
Soyabean						
Consumer SCT (billion KRW)	-175	-264	-772	-817	-638	-859
Consumer NPC (coeff.)	1.72	1.65	1.75	1.81	1.64	1.81
Milk						
Consumer SCT (billion KRW)	-302	-604	-1 710	-1 354	-1 738	-2 037
Consumer NPC (coeff.)	3.11	2.50	2.05	1.79	2.16	2.19
Beef and Veal						
Consumer SCT (billion KRW)	-495	-2 046	-1 872	-1 812	-1 839	-1 964
Consumer NPC (coeff.)	2.23	2.89	1.46	1.45	1.45	1.47
Pigmeat						
Consumer SCT (billion KRW)	-303	-781	-2 650	-3 830	-2 302	-1 819
Consumer NPC (coeff.)	1.50	1.69	2.29	2.77	2.08	2.02
Poultry						
Consumer SCT (billion KRW)	-132	-398	-745	-891	-687	-655
Consumer NPC (coeff.)	2.09	2.33	1.75	1.98	1.67	1.58
Eggs						
Consumer SCT (billion KRW)	28	-63	-216	-181	-38	-430
Consumer NPC (coeff.)	0.92	1.12	1.20	1.15	1.03	1.43
Chinese cabbage						
Consumer SCT (billion KRW)	-74	-104	-199	-150	-208	-239
Consumer NPC (coeff.)	1.30	1.29	1.27	1.27	1.27	1.27
Garlic						
Consumer SCT (billion KRW)	-257	-542	-443	-603	-343	-382
Consumer NPC (coeff.)	3.50	2.62	2.66	3.69	1.97	2.32
Red pepper						
Consumer SCT (billion KRW)	-395	-713	-2 012	-2 478	-2 098	-1 461
Consumer NPC (coeff.)	2.75	2.55	4.31	5.04	4.08	3.80
Other Commodities[1]						
Consumer SCT (billion KRW)	-2 713	-7 344	-11 424	-12 221	-11 906	-10 146
Consumer NPC (coeff.)	2.94	2.91	1.96	2.00	1.93	1.97

Note: p: provisional. SCT: Single Commodity Transfers. CSE: Consumer Support Estimate. NPC: Nominal Protection Coefficient. Total Consumer SCT may differ from the Total CSE by the amount of subsidies to consumers which are not specific to a single commodity.
   1. Consumer SCT for Other Commodities: Total Consumer SCT minus the Consumer SCTs for the commodities listed above.
Source: OECD (2014), "Producer and Consumer Support Estimates", OECD Agriculture Statistics Database, doi: http://dx.doi.org/10.1787/agr-pcse-data-en.

StatLink http://dx.doi.org/10.1787/888933111417

Table A.32. **Mexico: Consumer Single Commodity Transfers**

	1991-93	1995-97	2011-13	2011	2012	2013p
TOTAL						
CSE (million MXN)	-19 400	-760	-24 272	-15 591	-31 053	-26 171
Consumer SCT (million MXN)	-19 403	-765	-26 354	-18 178	-32 854	-28 029
Wheat						
Consumer SCT (million MXN)	189	375	0	0	0	0
Consumer NPC (coeff.)	1.24	0.99	1.00	1.00	1.00	1.00
Maize						
Consumer SCT (million MXN)	-4 659	2 016	0	0	0	0
Consumer NPC (coeff.)	1.70	0.99	1.00	1.00	1.00	1.00
Barley						
Consumer SCT (million MXN)	-147	-26	0	0	0	0
Consumer NPC (coeff.)	1.51	1.02	1.00	1.00	1.00	1.00
Sorghum						
Consumer SCT (million MXN)	79	253	0	0	0	0
Consumer NPC (coeff.)	1.17	1.03	1.00	1.00	1.00	1.00
Rice						
Consumer SCT (million MXN)	-30	-66	-48	-68	-46	-31
Consumer NPC (coeff.)	1.06	1.06	1.01	1.02	1.01	1.01
Soyabean						
Consumer SCT (million MXN)	-229	-857	0	0	0	0
Consumer NPC (coeff.)	1.19	1.13	1.00	1.00	1.00	1.00
Sugar						
Consumer SCT (million MXN)	-1 699	-2 724	-3 413	-1 333	-8 906	0
Consumer NPC (coeff.)	1.98	1.51	1.13	1.05	1.35	1.00
Milk						
Consumer SCT (million MXN)	-1 013	1 516	268	1 180	-1 462	1 087
Consumer NPC (coeff.)	1.51	1.06	1.01	1.00	1.04	1.00
Beef and Veal						
Consumer SCT (million MXN)	-1 816	-389	0	0	0	0
Consumer NPC (coeff.)	1.32	1.03	1.00	1.00	1.00	1.00
Pigmeat						
Consumer SCT (million MXN)	-275	1 302	0	0	0	0
Consumer NPC (coeff.)	1.07	0.86	1.00	1.00	1.00	1.00
Poultry						
Consumer SCT (million MXN)	-1 955	-1 966	-10 969	-9 942	-11 546	-11 419
Consumer NPC (coeff.)	1.58	1.13	1.16	1.16	1.16	1.15
Eggs						
Consumer SCT (million MXN)	-152	0	-1 184	0	0	-3 551
Consumer NPC (coeff.)	1.05	1.00	1.02	1.00	1.00	1.07
Dried Beans						
Consumer SCT (million MXN)	-667	627	-2 098	-1 851	0	-4 445
Consumer NPC (coeff.)	1.44	0.85	1.22	1.32	1.00	1.35
Coffee						
Consumer SCT (million MXN)	55	681	0	0	0	0
Consumer NPC (coeff.)	0.90	0.64	1.00	1.00	1.00	1.00
Tomatoes						
Consumer SCT (million MXN)	-308	1 400	0	0	0	0
Consumer NPC (coeff.)	1.21	0.60	1.00	1.00	1.00	1.00
Other Commodities[1]						
Consumer SCT (million MXN)	-6 777	-2 908	-8 909	-6 164	-10 893	-9 671
Consumer NPC (coeff.)	1.36	1.05	1.04	1.03	1.04	1.04

Note: p: provisional. SCT: Single Commodity Transfers. CSE: Consumer Support Estimate. NPC: Nominal Protection Coefficient. Total Consumer SCT may differ from the Total CSE by the amount of subsidies to consumers which are not specific to a single commodity.

1. Consumer SCT for Other Commodities: Total Consumer SCT minus the Consumer SCTs for the commodities listed above.

Source: OECD (2014), "Producer and Consumer Support Estimates", OECD *Agriculture Statistics Database*, doi: *http://dx.doi.org/10.1787/agr-pcse-data-en*.

StatLink ᵐˢ▄ *http://dx.doi.org/10.1787/888933111436*

Table A.33. **New Zealand: Consumer Single Commodity Transfers**

	1986-88	1995-97	2011-13	2011	2012	2013p
TOTAL						
CSE (million NZD)	-110	-51	-135	-158	-143	-105
Consumer SCT (million NZD)	-110	-51	-135	-158	-143	-105
Wheat						
Consumer SCT (million NZD)	0	0	0	0	0	0
Consumer NPC (coeff.)	1.00	1.00	1.00	1.00	1.00	1.00
Maize						
Consumer SCT (million NZD)	0	0	0	0	0	0
Consumer NPC (coeff.)	1.00	1.00	1.00	1.00	1.00	1.00
Barley						
Consumer SCT (million NZD)	0	0	0	0	0	0
Consumer NPC (coeff.)	1.00	1.00	1.00	1.00	1.00	1.00
Oats						
Consumer SCT (million NZD)	0	0	0	0	0	0
Consumer NPC (coeff.)	1.00	1.00	1.00	1.00	1.00	1.00
Milk						
Consumer SCT (million NZD)	-21	0	0	0	0	0
Consumer NPC (coeff.)	1.09	1.00	1.00	1.00	1.00	1.00
Beef and Veal						
Consumer SCT (million NZD)	0	0	0	0	0	0
Consumer NPC (coeff.)	1.00	1.00	1.00	1.00	1.00	1.00
Sheepmeat						
Consumer SCT (million NZD)	0	0	0	0	0	0
Consumer NPC (coeff.)	1.00	1.00	1.00	1.00	1.00	1.00
Wool						
Consumer SCT (million NZD)	0	0	0	0	0	0
Consumer NPC (coeff.)	1.00	1.00	1.00	1.00	1.00	1.00
Pigmeat						
Consumer SCT (million NZD)	-2	0	0	0	0	0
Consumer NPC (coeff.)	1.02	1.00	1.00	1.00	1.00	1.00
Poultry						
Consumer SCT (million NZD)	-16	-16	-99	-102	-111	-83
Consumer NPC (coeff.)	1.25	1.10	1.31	1.37	1.34	1.22
Eggs						
Consumer SCT (million NZD)	-40	-22	-7	-21	0	0
Consumer NPC (coeff.)	1.97	1.43	1.06	1.19	1.00	1.00
Other Commodities[1]						
Consumer SCT (million NZD)	-31	-14	-29	-35	-32	-21
Consumer NPC (coeff.)	1.07	1.02	1.04	1.04	1.04	1.03

Note: p: provisional. SCT: Single Commodity Transfers. CSE: Consumer Support Estimate. NPC: Nominal Protection Coefficient. Total Consumer SCT may differ from the Total CSE by the amount of subsidies to consumers which are not specific to a single commodity.
1. Consumer SCT for Other Commodities: Total Consumer SCT minus the Consumer SCTs for the commodities listed above.

Source: OECD (2014), "Producer and Consumer Support Estimates", OECD *Agriculture Statistics Database, doi: http://dx.doi.org/10.1787/agr-pcse-data-en.*

StatLink ᝦᖉ *http://dx.doi.org/10.1787/888933111455*

Table A.34. **Norway: Consumer Single Commodity Transfers**

	1986-88	1995-97	2011-13	2011	2012	2013p
TOTAL						
CSE (million NOK)	-9 141	-8 343	-9 597	-9 738	-10 484	-8 569
Consumer SCT (million NOK)	-9 141	-8 343	-9 597	-9 738	-10 484	-8 569
Wheat						
Consumer SCT (million NOK)	-121	-332	-183	-232	-147	-171
Consumer NPC (coeff.)	2.05	2.21	1.43	1.51	1.42	1.36
Barley						
Consumer SCT (million NOK)	-521	-313	-106	-183	45	-179
Consumer NPC (coeff.)	5.30	2.12	1.35	1.41	1.32	1.33
Oats						
Consumer SCT (million NOK)	-88	61	137	60	191	161
Consumer NPC (coeff.)	2.90	2.18	1.18	1.19	1.28	1.07
Milk						
Consumer SCT (million NOK)	-700	-2 654	-2 369	-2 120	-3 116	-1 871
Consumer NPC (coeff.)	3.37	2.36	1.58	1.51	1.88	1.36
Beef and Veal						
Consumer SCT (million NOK)	-1 665	-1 436	-1 920	-1 934	-2 039	-1 788
Consumer NPC (coeff.)	3.40	2.35	1.84	1.96	1.93	1.64
Sheepmeat						
Consumer SCT (million NOK)	-356	-171	-73	39	-129	-131
Consumer NPC (coeff.)	2.53	1.44	1.08	0.96	1.14	1.13
Wool						
Consumer SCT (million NOK)	-55	0	0	0	0	0
Consumer NPC (coeff.)	2.01	1.00	1.00	1.00	1.00	1.00
Pigmeat						
Consumer SCT (million NOK)	-1 487	-969	-1 573	-1 682	-1 667	-1 371
Consumer NPC (coeff.)	2.99	1.80	1.93	2.05	2.00	1.73
Poultry						
Consumer SCT (million NOK)	-256	-321	-945	-901	-1 051	-882
Consumer NPC (coeff.)	3.96	3.14	2.21	2.36	2.43	1.84
Eggs						
Consumer SCT (million NOK)	-590	-299	-432	-557	-435	-305
Consumer NPC (coeff.)	4.48	2.45	1.92	2.55	1.77	1.45
Other Commodities[1]						
Consumer SCT (million NOK)	-3 302	-1 909	-2 132	-2 227	-2 136	-2 032
Consumer NPC (coeff.)	3.24	2.13	1.48	1.67	1.30	1.47

Note: p: provisional. SCT: Single Commodity Transfers. CSE: Consumer Support Estimate. NPC: Nominal Protection Coefficient. Total Consumer SCT may differ from the Total CSE by the amount of subsidies to consumers which are not specific to a single commodity.
1. Consumer SCT for Other Commodities: Total Consumer SCT minus the Consumer SCTs for the commodities listed above.
Source: OECD (2014), "Producer and Consumer Support Estimates", OECD *Agriculture Statistics Database, doi: http://dx.doi.org/10.1787/agr-pcse-data-en.*

StatLink ᴍˢᴸ *http://dx.doi.org/10.1787/888933111474*

Table A.35. **Switzerland: Consumer Single Commodity Transfers**

	1986-88	1995-97	2011-13	2011	2012	2013p
TOTAL						
CSE (million CHF)	-7 535	-4 994	-2 133	-2 260	-2 345	-1 792
Consumer SCT (million CHF)	-7 749	-5 115	-2 136	-2 263	-2 348	-1 796
Wheat						
Consumer SCT (million CHF)	-538	-399	-87	-75	-104	-82
Consumer NPC (coeff.)	4.02	3.10	1.24	1.21	1.30	1.21
Maize						
Consumer SCT (million CHF)	-139	-32	-12	-10	-16	-11
Consumer NPC (coeff.)	3.46	2.13	1.22	1.18	1.31	1.17
Barley						
Consumer SCT (million CHF)	-207	-44	-11	-9	-13	-10
Consumer NPC (coeff.)	4.80	2.50	1.22	1.18	1.29	1.19
Rapeseed						
Consumer SCT (million CHF)	-313	-252	-132	-134	-123	-139
Consumer NPC (coeff.)	6.45	4.32	1.60	1.58	1.53	1.69
Sugar						
Consumer SCT (million CHF)	-143	-146	-17	-9	-10	-33
Consumer NPC (coeff.)	4.51	3.51	1.12	1.06	1.06	1.24
Milk						
Consumer SCT (million CHF)	-1 900	-1 102	-175	-189	-336	0
Consumer NPC (coeff.)	9.85	3.27	1.12	1.12	1.24	1.00
Beef and Veal						
Consumer SCT (million CHF)	-1 382	-712	-442	-502	-448	-375
Consumer NPC (coeff.)	4.21	2.40	1.53	1.63	1.54	1.42
Sheepmeat						
Consumer SCT (million CHF)	-106	-102	-20	-11	-21	-27
Consumer NPC (coeff.)	5.08	3.70	1.31	1.16	1.32	1.45
Pigmeat						
Consumer SCT (million CHF)	-908	-651	-373	-417	-386	-317
Consumer NPC (coeff.)	2.45	2.17	1.73	1.83	1.75	1.60
Poultry						
Consumer SCT (million CHF)	-301	-298	-237	-236	-239	-234
Consumer NPC (coeff.)	6.08	6.10	4.38	4.55	4.45	4.15
Eggs						
Consumer SCT (million CHF)	-399	-299	-235	-261	-224	-220
Consumer NPC (coeff.)	6.87	5.28	3.32	4.10	2.97	2.88
Other Commodities[1]						
Consumer SCT (million CHF)	-1 414	-1 079	-395	-409	-427	-349
Consumer NPC (coeff.)	4.34	2.99	1.25	1.27	1.30	1.18

Note: p: provisional. SCT: Single Commodity Transfers. CSE: Consumer Support Estimate. NPC: Nominal Protection Coefficient. Total Consumer SCT may differ from the Total CSE by the amount of subsidies to consumers which are not specific to a single commodity.

1. Consumer SCT for Other Commodities: Total Consumer SCT minus the Consumer SCTs for the commodities listed above.

Source: OECD (2014), "Producer and Consumer Support Estimates", OECD *Agriculture Statistics Database*, doi: *http://dx.doi.org/10.1787/agr-pcse-data-en*.

StatLink ᵐᵗᵍᴸ *http://dx.doi.org/10.1787/888933111493*

Table A.36. **Turkey: Consumer Single Commodity Transfers**

	1986-88	1995-97	2011-13	2011	2012	2013p
TOTAL						
CSE (million TRY)	-3	-492	-15 642	-18 239	-13 810	-14 877
Consumer SCT (million TRY)	-3	-492	-15 642	-18 239	-13 810	-14 877
Wheat						
Consumer SCT (million TRY)	0	-54	-1 155	-819	-1 624	-1 022
Consumer NPC (coeff.)	1.36	1.14	1.13	1.09	1.19	1.11
Maize						
Consumer SCT (million TRY)	0	-4	-20	-39	0	-20
Consumer NPC (coeff.)	1.16	1.23	1.03	1.05	1.00	1.03
Barley						
Consumer SCT (million TRY)	0	-1	-53	-45	-31	-83
Consumer NPC (coeff.)	1.36	1.16	1.12	1.08	1.10	1.17
Sunflower						
Consumer SCT (million TRY)	0	-20	-1 133	-1 055	-1 181	-1 162
Consumer NPC (coeff.)	1.16	1.43	1.63	1.60	1.61	1.67
Sugar						
Consumer SCT (million TRY)	0	-41	-114	0	-181	-161
Consumer NPC (coeff.)	1.11	1.67	1.06	1.00	1.10	1.09
Milk						
Consumer SCT (million TRY)	-1	-104	-2 494	-2 208	-1 705	-3 570
Consumer NPC (coeff.)	2.46	2.11	1.31	1.29	1.19	1.45
Beef and Veal						
Consumer SCT (million TRY)	0	-53	-3 068	-3 542	-3 331	-2 330
Consumer NPC (coeff.)	1.19	1.54	1.54	1.66	1.60	1.36
Sheepmeat						
Consumer SCT (million TRY)	0	-4	-113	-72	-135	-131
Consumer NPC (coeff.)	1.17	1.09	1.08	1.04	1.09	1.09
Poultry						
Consumer SCT (million TRY)	0	-18	-91	-107	-41	-127
Consumer NPC (coeff.)	0.93	1.39	1.02	1.03	1.01	1.03
Eggs						
Consumer SCT (million TRY)	0	-21	-50	-150	0	0
Consumer NPC (coeff.)	1.21	1.59	1.03	1.10	1.00	1.00
Apples						
Consumer SCT (million TRY)	0	-3	-1 536	-1 707	-1 415	-1 487
Consumer NPC (coeff.)	1.04	1.07	1.96	2.14	1.83	1.90
Cotton						
Consumer SCT (million TRY)	0	0	0	0	0	0
Consumer NPC (coeff.)	1.00	1.00	1.00	1.00	1.00	1.00
Grapes						
Consumer SCT (million TRY)	0	-6	0	0	0	0
Consumer NPC (coeff.)	1.05	1.05	1.00	1.00	1.00	1.00
Potatoes						
Consumer SCT (million TRY)	0	-16	-886	-1 113	-735	-810
Consumer NPC (coeff.)	1.23	1.39	2.52	2.69	2.51	2.35
Tobacco						
Consumer SCT (million TRY)	0	-17	0	0	0	0
Consumer NPC (coeff.)	1.14	1.54	1.00	1.00	1.00	1.00
Tomatoes						
Consumer SCT (million TRY)	0	-10	0	0	0	0
Consumer NPC (coeff.)	1.41	1.06	1.00	1.00	1.00	1.00
Other Commodities[1]						
Consumer SCT (million TRY)	-1	-121	-4 929	-7 383	-3 431	-3 974
Consumer NPC (coeff.)	1.26	1.29	1.13	1.21	1.09	1.09

Note: p: provisional. SCT: Single Commodity Transfers. CSE: Consumer Support Estimate. NPC: Nominal Protection Coefficient. Total Consumer SCT may differ from the Total CSE by the amount of subsidies to consumers which are not specific to a single commodity.
1. Consumer SCT for Other Commodities: Total Consumer SCT minus the Consumer SCTs for the commodities listed above.

Source: OECD (2014), "Producer and Consumer Support Estimates", OECD Agriculture Statistics Database, doi: http://dx.doi.org/10.1787/agr-pcse-data-en.

StatLink ⫘⫘ http://dx.doi.org/10.1787/888933111512

Table A.37. **United States: Consumer Single Commodity Transfers**

	1986-88	1995-97	2011-13	2011	2012	2013p
TOTAL						
CSE (million USD)	-3 794	4 452	34 381	33 927	31 837	37 379
Consumer SCT (million USD)	-13 856	-13 284	-4 638	-3 270	-6 720	-3 923
Wheat						
Consumer SCT (million USD)	-353	-26	0	0	0	0
Consumer NPC (coeff.)	1.20	1.01	1.00	1.00	1.00	1.00
Maize						
Consumer SCT (million USD)	0	0	0	0	0	0
Consumer NPC (coeff.)	1.00	1.00	1.00	1.00	1.00	1.00
Barley						
Consumer SCT (million USD)	-100	-4	0	0	0	0
Consumer NPC (coeff.)	1.73	1.01	1.00	1.00	1.00	1.00
Sorghum						
Consumer SCT (million USD)	0	0	0	0	0	0
Consumer NPC (coeff.)	1.00	1.00	1.00	1.00	1.00	1.00
Rice						
Consumer SCT (million USD)	-5	-1	0	0	0	0
Consumer NPC (coeff.)	1.01	1.00	1.00	1.00	1.00	1.00
Soyabean						
Consumer SCT (million USD)	0	0	0	0	0	0
Consumer NPC (coeff.)	1.00	1.00	1.00	1.00	1.00	1.00
Sugar						
Consumer SCT (million USD)	-1 997	-1 624	-1 150	-1 951	-1 187	-313
Consumer NPC (coeff.)	3.18	2.00	1.36	1.66	1.33	1.08
Milk						
Consumer SCT (million USD)	-6 164	-7 576	-2 201	-494	-3 857	-2 252
Consumer NPC (coeff.)	1.56	1.57	1.07	1.01	1.12	1.06
Beef and Veal						
Consumer SCT (million USD)	-378	0	-109	0	0	-328
Consumer NPC (coeff.)	1.02	1.00	1.00	1.00	1.00	1.01
Sheepmeat						
Consumer SCT (million USD)	-6	-4	-74	-91	-66	-66
Consumer NPC (coeff.)	1.01	1.01	1.10	1.10	1.10	1.10
Wool						
Consumer SCT (million USD)	-2	-1	0	0	0	0
Consumer NPC (coeff.)	1.01	1.01	1.00	1.00	1.00	1.00
Pigmeat						
Consumer SCT (million USD)	0	0	0	0	0	0
Consumer NPC (coeff.)	1.00	1.00	1.00	1.00	1.00	1.00
Poultry						
Consumer SCT (million USD)	-727	-56	0	0	0	0
Consumer NPC (coeff.)	1.11	1.00	1.00	1.00	1.00	1.00
Eggs						
Consumer SCT (million USD)	-140	-111	0	0	0	0
Consumer NPC (coeff.)	1.06	1.04	1.00	1.00	1.00	1.00
Cotton						
Consumer SCT (million USD)	0	-16	62	77	60	48
Consumer NPC (coeff.)	1.00	1.03	1.00	1.00	1.00	1.00
Other Commodities[1]						
Consumer SCT (million USD)	-3 983	-3 865	-1 165	-812	-1 671	-1 012
Consumer NPC (coeff.)	1.12	1.08	1.01	1.01	1.02	1.01

Note: p: provisional. SCT: Single Commodity Transfers. CSE: Consumer Support Estimate. NPC: Nominal Protection Coefficient. Total Consumer SCT may differ from the Total CSE by the amount of subsidies to consumers which are not specific to a single commodity.

1. Consumer SCT for Other Commodities: Total Consumer SCT minus the Consumer SCTs for the commodities listed above.

Source: OECD (2014), "Producer and Consumer Support Estimates", OECD *Agriculture Statistics Database, doi: http://dx.doi.org/10.1787/agr-pcse-data-en.*

StatLink ᵃᵐˢᵖ *http://dx.doi.org/10.1787/888933111531*

Table A.38. **Australia: Payments made on the basis of area, animal numbers, receipts or income**

Million AUD

	1986-88	1995-97	2011-13	2011	2012	2013p
Payments based on current A/An/R/I, production required	**0**	**19**	**202**	**413**	**98**	**96**
of which:						
Payments based on area	0	0	1	2	2	0
Payments based on animal numbers	0	0	0	0	0	0
Payments based on farm receipts	0	0	0	0	0	0
Payments based on farm income	0	19	201	411	96	96
Memo items: as percentage of PSE (%)	**0.0**	**1.1**	**15.5**	**26.8**	**10.1**	**9.6**
Payments based on non-current A/An/R/I, production required	**0**	**0**	**0**	**0**	**0**	**0**
of which:						
Payments based on area	0	0	0	0	0	0
Payments based on animal numbers	0	0	0	0	0	0
Payments based on farm receipts	0	0	0	0	0	0
Payments based on farm income	0	0	0	0	0	0
Memo items: as percentage of PSE (%)	**0.0**	**0.0**	**0.0**	**0.0**	**0.0**	**0.0**
Payments based on non-current A/An/R/I, production not required	**250**	**227**	**407**	**559**	**330**	**333**
of which:						
Payments based on area	0	34	72	162	27	27
Payments based on animal numbers	0	0	0	0	0	0
Payments based on farm receipts	0	0	0	0	0	0
Payments based on farm income	250	193	335	396	303	307
Memo items: as percentage of PSE (%)	**12.6**	**13.8**	**34.6**	**36.2**	**34.0**	**33.5**

Note: p: provisional. A/An/R/I: Area planted/Animal numbers/Receipts/Income. PSE: Producer Support Estimate.
Source: OECD (2014), "Producer and Consumer Support Estimates", OECD *Agriculture Statistics Database*, doi: *http://dx.doi.org/10.1787/agr-pcse-data-en.*

StatLink ⬛📊 *http://dx.doi.org/10.1787/888933111550*

Table A.39. **Canada: Payments made on the basis of area, animal numbers, receipts or income**

Million CAD

	1986-88	1995-97	2011-13	2011	2012	2013p
Payments based on current A/An/R/I, production required	**1 787**	**840**	**1 945**	**2 225**	**2 188**	**1 422**
of which:						
Payments based on area	1 075	223	770	867	877	566
Payments based on animal numbers	81	159	277	321	269	241
Payments based on farm receipts	632	396	402	447	480	279
Payments based on farm income	0	63	496	589	563	336
Memo items: as percentage of PSE (%)	**21.6**	**17.2**	**27.0**	**29.9**	**28.1**	**22.9**
Payments based on non-current A/An/R/I, production required	**0**	**0**	**1**	**2**	**0**	**0**
of which:						
Payments based on area	0	0	1	2	0	0
Payments based on animal numbers	0	0	0	0	0	0
Payments based on farm receipts	0	0	0	0	0	0
Payments based on farm income	0	0	0	0	0	0
Memo items: as percentage of PSE (%)	**0.0**	**0.0**	**0.0**	**0.0**	**0.0**	**0.0**
Payments based on non-current A/An/R/I, production not required	**0**	**790**	**137**	**365**	**46**	**1**
of which:						
Payments based on area	0	755	136	360	47	2
Payments based on animal numbers	0	0	2	7	0	0
Payments based on farm receipts	0	35	0	0	0	0
Payments based on farm income	0	0	-1	-2	-2	-1
Memo items: as percentage of PSE (%)	**0.0**	**15.1**	**1.8**	**4.9**	**0.6**	**0.0**

Note: p: provisional. A/An/R/I: Area planted/Animal numbers/Receipts/Income. PSE: Producer Support Estimate.
Source: OECD (2014), "Producer and Consumer Support Estimates", OECD *Agriculture Statistics Database*, doi: *http://dx.doi.org/10.1787/agr-pcse-data-en.*

StatLink ⬛📊 *http://dx.doi.org/10.1787/888933111569*

Table A.40. **Chile: Payments made on the basis of area, animal numbers, receipts or income**

Million CLP

	1995-97	2011-13	2011	2012	2013p
Payments based on current A/An/R/I, production required	**4 158**	**1 781**	**301**	**419**	**4 623**
of which:					
Payments based on area	4 158	1 781	301	419	4 623
Payments based on animal numbers	0	0	0	0	0
Payments based on farm receipts	0	0	0	0	0
Payments based on farm income	0	0	0	0	0
Memo items: as percentage of PSE (%)	**2.5**	**0.9**	**0.2**	**0.2**	**2.3**
Payments based on non-current A/An/R/I, production required	**0**	**0**	**0**	**0**	**0**
of which:					
Payments based on area	0	0	0	0	0
Payments based on animal numbers	0	0	0	0	0
Payments based on farm receipts	0	0	0	0	0
Payments based on farm income	0	0	0	0	0
Memo items: as percentage of PSE (%)	**0.0**	**0.0**	**0.0**	**0.0**	**0.0**
Payments based on non-current A/An/R/I, production not required	**0**	**0**	**0**	**0**	**0**
of which:					
Payments based on area	0	0	0	0	0
Payments based on animal numbers	0	0	0	0	0
Payments based on farm receipts	0	0	0	0	0
Payments based on farm income	0	0	0	0	0
Memo items: as percentage of PSE (%)	**0.0**	**0.0**	**0.0**	**0.0**	**0.0**

Note: p: provisional. A/An/R/I: Area planted/Animal numbers/Receipts/Income. PSE: Producer Support Estimate.
Source: OECD (2014), "Producer and Consumer Support Estimates", OECD *Agriculture Statistics Database, doi: http://dx.doi.org/10.1787/agr-pcse-data-en.*

StatLink ⟶ http://dx.doi.org/10.1787/888933111588

Table A.41. **European Union: Payments made on the basis of area, animal numbers, receipts or income**

Million EUR

	1986-88	1995-97	2011-13	2011	2012	2013p
Payments based on current A/An/R/I, production required	**3 195**	**29 775**	**14 473**	**14 560**	**14 433**	**14 426**
of which:						
Payments based on area	515	20 609	10 251	10 369	9 998	10 386
Payments based on animal numbers	2 548	9 101	3 213	3 317	3 206	3 115
Payments based on farm receipts	91	47	613	468	779	593
Payments based on farm income	41	18	396	406	450	332
Memo items: as percentage of PSE (%)	**3.6**	**31.6**	**17.3**	**18.7**	**16.7**	**16.5**
Payments based on non-current A/An/R/I, production required	**0**	**0**	**91**	**107**	**80**	**87**
of which:						
Payments based on area	0	0	91	107	80	87
Payments based on animal numbers	0	0	0	0	0	0
Payments based on farm receipts	0	0	0	0	0	0
Payments based on farm income	0	0	0	0	0	0
Memo items: as percentage of PSE (%)	**0.0**	**0.0**	**0.1**	**0.1**	**0.1**	**0.1**
Payments based on non-current A/An/R/I, production not required	**0**	**24**	**37 952**	**37 555**	**38 066**	**38 234**
of which:						
Payments based on area	0	24	14 954	14 003	15 131	15 727
Payments based on animal numbers	0	0	0	0	0	0
Payments based on farm receipts	0	0	22 998	23 552	22 935	22 507
Payments based on farm income	0	0	0	0	0	0
Memo items: as percentage of PSE (%)	**0.0**	**0.0**	**45.3**	**48.2**	**44.1**	**43.7**

Note: p: provisional. A/An/R/I: Area planted/Animal numbers/Receipts/Income. PSE: Producer Support Estimate.
EU12 for 1986-88; EU15 for 1995-97; and EU27 from 2007.
Source: OECD (2014), "Producer and Consumer Support Estimates", OECD *Agriculture Statistics Database, doi: http://dx.doi.org/10.1787/agr-pcse-data-en.*

StatLink ⟶ http://dx.doi.org/10.1787/888933111607

Table A.42. **Iceland: Payments made on the basis of area, animal numbers, receipts or income**

Million ISK

	1986-88	1995-97	2011-13	2011	2012	2013p
Payments based on current A/An/R/I, production required	-49	-181	220	143	282	236
of which:						
Payments based on area	0	0	3	5	6	0
Payments based on animal numbers	0	0	606	581	610	628
Payments based on farm receipts	0	0	45	43	49	44
Payments based on farm income	-49	-181	-434	-485	-382	-436
Memo items: as percentage of PSE (%)	-0.6	-2.0	1.2	0.9	1.5	1.3
Payments based on non-current A/An/R/I, production required	0	1 011	3 598	3 449	3 621	3 724
of which:						
Payments based on area	0	0	0	0	0	0
Payments based on animal numbers	0	1 011	3 598	3 449	3 621	3 724
Payments based on farm receipts	0	0	0	0	0	0
Payments based on farm income	0	0	0	0	0	0
Memo items: as percentage of PSE (%)	0.0	11.4	20.5	21.2	19.5	20.8
Payments based on non-current A/An/R/I, production not required	48	14	0	0	0	0
of which:						
Payments based on area	0	0	0	0	0	0
Payments based on animal numbers	48	14	0	0	0	0
Payments based on farm receipts	0	0	0	0	0	0
Payments based on farm income	0	0	0	0	0	0
Memo items: as percentage of PSE (%)	0.6	0.2	0.0	0.0	0.0	0.0

Note: p: provisional. A/An/R/I: Area planted/Animal numbers/Receipts/Income. PSE: Producer Support Estimate.
Source: OECD (2014), "Producer and Consumer Support Estimates", OECD *Agriculture Statistics Database*, doi: *http://dx.doi.org/10.1787/agr-pcse-data-en*.

StatLink ⫘ *http://dx.doi.org/10.1787/888933111626*

Table A.43. **Israel: Payments made on the basis of area, animal numbers, receipts or income**

Million ILS

	1995-97	2011-13	2011	2012	2013p
Payments based on current A/An/R/I, production required	102	202	163	219	222
of which:					
Payments based on area	5	27	27	31	22
Payments based on animal numbers	0	0	0	0	0
Payments based on farm receipts	0	0	0	0	0
Payments based on farm income	97	175	136	188	201
Memo items: as percentage of PSE (%)	4.1	6.9	4.4	7.1	9.1
Payments based on non-current A/An/R/I, production required	0	0	0	0	0
of which:					
Payments based on area	0	0	0	0	0
Payments based on animal numbers	0	0	0	0	0
Payments based on farm receipts	0	0	0	0	0
Payments based on farm income	0	0	0	0	0
Memo items: as percentage of PSE (%)	0.0	0.0	0.0	0.0	0.0
Payments based on non-current A/An/R/I, production not required	56	34	35	35	34
of which:					
Payments based on area	0	0	0	0	0
Payments based on animal numbers	0	0	0	0	0
Payments based on farm receipts	0	0	0	0	0
Payments based on farm income	56	34	35	35	34
Memo items: as percentage of PSE (%)	2.4	1.2	0.9	1.1	1.4

Note: p: provisional. A/An/R/I: Area planted/Animal numbers/Receipts/Income. PSE: Producer Support Estimate.
 The statistical data for Israel are supplied by and under the responsibility of the relevant Israeli authorities. The use of such data by the OECD is without prejudice to the status of the Golan Heights, East Jerusalem and Israeli settlements in the West Bank under the terms of international law.
Source: OECD (2014), "Producer and Consumer Support Estimates", OECD *Agriculture Statistics Database*, doi: *http://dx.doi.org/10.1787/agr-pcse-data-en*.

StatLink ⫘ *http://dx.doi.org/10.1787/888933111645*

Table A.44. Japan: Payments made on the basis of area, animal numbers, receipts or income

Billion JPY

	1986-88	1995-97	2011-13	2011	2012	2013p
Payments based on current A/An/R/I, production required	**0**	**0**	**323**	**419**	**231**	**320**
of which:						
Payments based on area	0	0	247	335	159	248
Payments based on animal numbers	0	0	0	0	0	0
Payments based on farm receipts	0	0	0	0	0	0
Payments based on farm income	0	0	76	84	72	72
Memo items: as percentage of PSE (%)	**0.0**	**0.0**	**6.4**	**8.7**	**4.4**	**6.1**
Payments based on non-current A/An/R/I, production required	**0**	**0**	**0**	**0**	**0**	**0**
of which:						
Payments based on area	0	0	0	0	0	0
Payments based on animal numbers	0	0	0	0	0	0
Payments based on farm receipts	0	0	0	0	0	0
Payments based on farm income	0	0	0	0	0	0
Memo items: as percentage of PSE (%)	**0.0**	**0.0**	**0.0**	**0.0**	**0.0**	**0.0**
Payments based on non-current A/An/R/I, production not required	**228**	**119**	**374**	**366**	**366**	**390**
of which:						
Payments based on area	228	119	374	366	366	390
Payments based on animal numbers	0	0	0	0	0	0
Payments based on farm receipts	0	0	0	0	0	0
Payments based on farm income	0	0	0	0	0	0
Memo items: as percentage of PSE (%)	**3.1**	**1.9**	**7.3**	**7.6**	**7.0**	**7.4**

Note: p: provisional. A/An/R/I: Area planted/Animal numbers/Receipts/Income. PSE: Producer Support Estimate.
Source: OECD (2014), "Producer and Consumer Support Estimates", OECD Agriculture Statistics Database, doi: http://dx.doi.org/10.1787/agr-pcse-data-en.

StatLink ⟐⟐ http://dx.doi.org/10.1787/888933111664

Table A.45. Korea: Payments made on the basis of area, animal numbers, receipts or income

Billion KRW

	1986-88	1995-97	2011-13	2011	2012	2013p
Payments based on current A/An/R/I, production required	**24**	**206**	**549**	**1 080**	**254**	**312**
of which:						
Payments based on area	0	0	311	847	44	41
Payments based on animal numbers	0	11	0	0	0	0
Payments based on farm receipts	11	14	0	0	0	0
Payments based on farm income	13	182	238	233	210	271
Memo items: as percentage of PSE (%)	**0.3**	**1.1**	**2.3**	**4.6**	**1.1**	**1.3**
Payments based on non-current A/An/R/I, production required	**0**	**0**	**0**	**0**	**0**	**0**
of which:						
Payments based on area	0	0	0	0	0	0
Payments based on animal numbers	0	0	0	0	0	0
Payments based on farm receipts	0	0	0	0	0	0
Payments based on farm income	0	0	0	0	0	0
Memo items: as percentage of PSE (%)	**0.0**	**0.0**	**0.0**	**0.0**	**0.0**	**0.0**
Payments based on non-current A/An/R/I, production not required	**0**	**0**	**677**	**653**	**652**	**726**
of which:						
Payments based on area	0	0	677	653	652	726
Payments based on animal numbers	0	0	0	0	0	0
Payments based on farm receipts	0	0	0	0	0	0
Payments based on farm income	0	0	0	0	0	0
Memo items: as percentage of PSE (%)	**0.0**	**0.0**	**2.9**	**2.8**	**2.8**	**3.0**

Note: p: provisional. A/An/R/I: Area planted/Animal numbers/Receipts/Income. PSE: Producer Support Estimate.
Source: OECD (2014), "Producer and Consumer Support Estimates", OECD Agriculture Statistics Database, doi: http://dx.doi.org/10.1787/agr-pcse-data-en.

StatLink ⟐⟐ http://dx.doi.org/10.1787/888933111683

Table A.46. **Mexico: Payments made on the basis of area, animal numbers, receipts or income**

Million MXN

	1991-93	1995-97	2011-13	2011	2012	2013p
Payments based on current A/An/R/I, production required	**10**	**234**	**6 586**	**4 903**	**4 698**	**10 159**
of which:						
Payments based on area	10	134	3 875	2 922	2 616	6 086
Payments based on animal numbers	0	0	2 712	1 980	2 082	4 073
Payments based on farm receipts	0	0	0	0	0	0
Payments based on farm income	0	100	0	0	0	0
Memo items: as percentage of PSE (%)	**0.0**	**0.5**	**7.0**	**5.7**	**5.1**	**10.2**
Payments based on non-current A/An/R/I, production required	**0**	**0**	**3 832**	**3 956**	**4 041**	**3 497**
of which:						
Payments based on area	0	0	0	0	0	0
Payments based on animal numbers	0	0	3 832	3 956	4 041	3 497
Payments based on farm receipts	0	0	0	0	0	0
Payments based on farm income	0	0	0	0	0	0
Memo items: as percentage of PSE (%)	**0.0**	**0.0**	**4.2**	**4.6**	**4.4**	**3.5**
Payments based on non-current A/An/R/I, production not required	**0**	**6 701**	**13 774**	**13 878**	**14 956**	**12 488**
of which:						
Payments based on area	0	6 701	13 774	13 878	14 956	12 488
Payments based on animal numbers	0	0	0	0	0	0
Payments based on farm receipts	0	0	0	0	0	0
Payments based on farm income	0	0	0	0	0	0
Memo items: as percentage of PSE (%)	**0.0**	**-1.4**	**14.9**	**16.0**	**16.3**	**12.5**

Note: p: provisional. A/An/R/I: Area planted/Animal numbers/Receipts/Income. PSE: Producer Support Estimate.
Source: OECD (2014), "Producer and Consumer Support Estimates", OECD *Agriculture Statistics Database*, doi: http://dx.doi.org/10.1787/agr-pcse-data-en.

StatLink http://dx.doi.org/10.1787/888933111702

Table A.47. **New Zealand: Payments made on the basis of area, animal numbers, receipts or income**

Million NZD

	1986-88	1995-97	2011-13	2011	2012	2013p
Payments based on current A/An/R/I, production required	**42**	**1**	**1**	**1**	**0**	**1**
of which:						
Payments based on area	0	0	0	0	0	0
Payments based on animal numbers	0	0	0	0	0	0
Payments based on farm receipts	0	0	0	0	0	0
Payments based on farm income	42	1	1	1	0	1
Memo items: as percentage of PSE (%)	**11.4**	**0.7**	**0.3**	**0.4**	**0.1**	**0.4**
Payments based on non-current A/An/R/I, production required	**315**	**0**	**0**	**0**	**0**	**0**
of which:						
Payments based on area	0	0	0	0	0	0
Payments based on animal numbers	315	0	0	0	0	0
Payments based on farm receipts	0	0	0	0	0	0
Payments based on farm income	0	0	0	0	0	0
Memo items: as percentage of PSE (%)	**20.8**	**0.0**	**0.0**	**0.0**	**0.0**	**0.0**
Payments based on non-current A/An/R/I, production not required	**0**	**0**	**0**	**0**	**0**	**0**
of which:						
Payments based on area	0	0	0	0	0	0
Payments based on animal numbers	0	0	0	0	0	0
Payments based on farm receipts	0	0	0	0	0	0
Payments based on farm income	0	0	0	0	0	0
Memo items: as percentage of PSE (%)	**0.0**	**0.0**	**0.0**	**0.0**	**0.0**	**0.0**

Note: p: provisional. A/An/R/I: Area planted/Animal numbers/Receipts/Income. PSE: Producer Support Estimate.
Source: OECD (2014), "Producer and Consumer Support Estimates", OECD *Agriculture Statistics Database*, doi: http://dx.doi.org/10.1787/agr-pcse-data-en.

StatLink http://dx.doi.org/10.1787/888933111721

Table A.48. **Norway: Payments made on the basis of area, animal numbers, receipts or income**

Million NOK

	1986-88	1995-97	2011-13	2011	2012	2013p
Payments based on current A/An/R/I, production required	**3 577**	**6 254**	**7 314**	**7 167**	**7 167**	**7 609**
of which:						
Payments based on area	974	3 335	2 289	2 308	2 308	2 251
Payments based on animal numbers	2 603	2 920	4 162	4 070	4 070	4 347
Payments based on farm receipts	0	0	0	0	0	0
Payments based on farm income	0	0	863	789	789	1 012
Memo items: as percentage of PSE (%)	**18.6**	**32.5**	**33.1**	**33.1**	**30.7**	**35.3**
Payments based on non-current A/An/R/I, production required	**0**	**0**	**2 950**	**2 791**	**2 791**	**3 268**
of which:						
Payments based on area	0	0	1 708	1 608	1 608	1 908
Payments based on animal numbers	0	0	0	0	0	0
Payments based on farm receipts	0	0	1 242	1 183	1 183	1 359
Payments based on farm income	0	0	0	0	0	0
Memo items: as percentage of PSE (%)	**0.0**	**0.0**	**13.3**	**12.9**	**11.9**	**15.2**
Payments based on non-current A/An/R/I, production not required	**0**	**0**	**0**	**0**	**0**	**0**
of which:						
Payments based on area	0	0	0	0	0	0
Payments based on animal numbers	0	0	0	0	0	0
Payments based on farm receipts	0	0	0	0	0	0
Payments based on farm income	0	0	0	0	0	0
Memo items: as percentage of PSE (%)	**0.0**	**0.0**	**0.0**	**0.0**	**0.0**	**0.0**

Note: p: provisional. A/An/R/I: Area planted/Animal numbers/Receipts/Income. PSE: Producer Support Estimate.
Source: OECD (2014), "Producer and Consumer Support Estimates", OECD Agriculture Statistics Database, doi: http://dx.doi.org/10.1787/agr-pcse-data-en.

StatLink ᐧᐧᒲᒲ http://dx.doi.org/10.1787/888933111740

Table A.49. **Switzerland: Payments made on the basis of area, animal numbers, receipts or income**

Million CHF

	1986-88	1995-97	2011-13	2011	2012	2013p
Payments based on current A/An/R/I, production required	**612**	**1 203**	**1 310**	**1 309**	**1 310**	**1 311**
of which:						
Payments based on area	259	804	223	219	224	225
Payments based on animal numbers	338	399	1 087	1 090	1 086	1 086
Payments based on farm receipts	0	0	0	0	0	0
Payments based on farm income	15	0	0	0	0	0
Memo items: as percentage of PSE (%)	**7.2**	**16.3**	**24.6**	**24.0**	**23.5**	**26.3**
Payments based on non-current A/An/R/I, production required	**28**	**569**	**102**	**102**	**102**	**102**
of which:						
Payments based on area	0	0	0	0	0	0
Payments based on animal numbers	28	60	102	102	102	102
Payments based on farm receipts	0	0	0	0	0	0
Payments based on farm income	0	509	0	0	0	0
Memo items: as percentage of PSE (%)	**0.3**	**7.7**	**1.9**	**1.9**	**1.8**	**2.0**
Payments based on non-current A/An/R/I, production not required	**0**	**0**	**1 203**	**1 218**	**1 195**	**1 195**
of which:						
Payments based on area	0	0	1 203	1 218	1 195	1 195
Payments based on animal numbers	0	0	0	0	0	0
Payments based on farm receipts	0	0	0	0	0	0
Payments based on farm income	0	0	0	0	0	0
Memo items: as percentage of PSE (%)	**0.0**	**0.0**	**22.6**	**22.4**	**21.5**	**24.0**

Note: p: provisional. A/An/R/I: Area planted/Animal numbers/Receipts/Income. PSE: Producer Support Estimate.
Source: OECD (2014), "Producer and Consumer Support Estimates", OECD Agriculture Statistics Database, doi: http://dx.doi.org/10.1787/agr-pcse-data-en.

StatLink ᐧᐧᒲᒲ http://dx.doi.org/10.1787/888933111759

Table A.50. **Turkey: Payments made on the basis of area, animal numbers, receipts or income**

Million TRY

	1986-88	1995-97	2011-13	2011	2012	2013p
Payments based on current A/An/R/I, production required	**0**	**4**	**2 901**	**2 646**	**2 952**	**3 105**
of which:						
Payments based on area	0	4	1 711	1 539	1 740	1 856
Payments based on animal numbers	0	0	922	858	949	959
Payments based on farm receipts	0	0	268	249	263	290
Payments based on farm income	0	0	0	0	0	0
Memo items: as percentage of PSE (%)	**0.0**	**0.7**	**10.2**	**9.6**	**10.8**	**10.4**
Payments based on non-current A/An/R/I, production required	**0**	**0**	**0**	**0**	**0**	**0**
of which:						
Payments based on area	0	0	0	0	0	0
Payments based on animal numbers	0	0	0	0	0	0
Payments based on farm receipts	0	0	0	0	0	0
Payments based on farm income	0	0	0	0	0	0
Memo items: as percentage of PSE (%)	**0.0**	**0.0**	**0.0**	**0.0**	**0.0**	**0.0**
Payments based on non-current A/An/R/I, production not required	**0**	**0**	**1**	**1**	**1**	**1**
of which:						
Payments based on area	0	0	1	1	1	1
Payments based on animal numbers	0	0	0	0	0	0
Payments based on farm receipts	0	0	0	0	0	0
Payments based on farm income	0	0	0	0	0	0
Memo items: as percentage of PSE (%)	**0.0**	**0.0**	**0.0**	**0.0**	**0.0**	**0.0**

Note: p: provisional. A/An/R/I: Area planted/Animal numbers/Receipts/Income. PSE: Producer Support Estimate.
Source: OECD (2014), "Producer and Consumer Support Estimates", OECD *Agriculture Statistics Database, doi: http://dx.doi.org/10.1787/agr-pcse-data-en*.

StatLink ᵐᵃᵖᵐ http://dx.doi.org/10.1787/888933111778

Table A.51. **United States: Payments made on the basis of area, animal numbers, receipts or income**

Million USD

	1986-88	1995-97	2011-13	2011	2012	2013p
Payments based on current A/An/R/I, production required	**12 231**	**1 825**	**9 135**	**10 323**	**8 512**	**8 570**
of which:						
Payments based on area	11 053	1 104	8 026	9 410	7 309	7 358
Payments based on animal numbers	267	0	0	0	0	0
Payments based on farm receipts	0	0	10	10	9	10
Payments based on farm income	912	721	1 100	902	1 194	1 203
Memo items: as percentage of PSE (%)	**33.5**	**7.7**	**28.8**	**33.3**	**25.4**	**27.6**
Payments based on non-current A/An/R/I, production required	**0**	**0**	**0**	**0**	**0**	**0**
of which:						
Payments based on area	0	0	0	0	0	0
Payments based on animal numbers	0	0	0	0	0	0
Payments based on farm receipts	0	0	0	0	0	0
Payments based on farm income	0	0	0	0	0	0
Memo items: as percentage of PSE (%)	**0.0**	**0.0**	**0.0**	**0.0**	**0.0**	**0.0**
Payments based on non-current A/An/R/I, production not required	**338**	**3 824**	**5 665**	**5 799**	**5 776**	**5 420**
of which:						
Payments based on area	338	3 824	4 710	4 846	4 822	4 460
Payments based on animal numbers	0	0	0	0	0	0
Payments based on farm receipts	0	0	955	953	953	960
Payments based on farm income	0	0	0	0	0	0
Memo items: as percentage of PSE (%)	**0.9**	**12.9**	**17.8**	**18.7**	**17.2**	**17.5**

Note: p: provisional. A/An/R/I: Area planted/Animal numbers/Receipts/Income. PSE: Producer Support Estimate.
Source: OECD (2014), "Producer and Consumer Support Estimates", OECD *Agriculture Statistics Database, doi: http://dx.doi.org/10.1787/agr-pcse-data-en*.

StatLink ᵐᵃᵖᵐ http://dx.doi.org/10.1787/888933111797

Table A.52. **Contribution to change in Producer Support Estimate by country, 2012 to 2013**

	Producer Support Estimate (PSE)		Contribution of		Contribution of MPS elements	
			MPS	BP	Quantity	Price gap
	Million USD, 2013	% change[1]	% change in nominal PSE if all other variables are held constant			
Australia	961	2.5	0.0	2.6	0.0	0.0
Canada	6 028	-20.3	-8.3	-12.0	-0.4	-7.9
Chile	413	5.5	-0.5	6.0	0.2	-0.7
European Union[2]	109 972	1.5	2.6	-1.2	-0.8	3.4
Iceland	146	-3.9	-5.6	1.6	0.2	-5.8
Israel[3]	677	-20.9	-20.1	-0.8	-0.5	-19.6
Japan	53 947	0.6	-3.3	3.9	-0.2	-3.1
Korea	22 134	5.1	4.3	0.8	3.9	0.4
Mexico	7 814	8.5	-0.5	9.0	1.3	-1.8
New Zealand	111	-24.1	-24.4	0.3	-1.3	-23.1
Norway	3 663	-7.9	-12.5	4.6	0.9	-13.4
Switzerland	5 376	-10.5	-10.6	0.1	-0.3	-10.3
Turkey	15 687	9.0	8.1	0.8	-1.4	9.5
United States	31 022	-7.5	-6.9	-0.6	0.0	-6.9
OECD[4]	258 642	-0.1	-0.6	0.5	-0.1	-0.5

1. Percent changes of nominal values expressed in national currency.
2. European Union 27.
3. The statistical data for Israel are supplied by and under the responsibility of the relevant Israeli authorities. The use of such data by the OECD is without prejudice to the status of the Golan Heights, East Jerusalem and Israeli settlements in the West Bank under the terms of international law.
4. An average of per cent changes in individual country PSEs in national currencies, weighted by the shares of the country PSEs in the OECD PSE in the previous year; not equivalent to the variation in OECD PSE in any common currency.

Source: OECD (2014), "Producer and Consumer Support Estimates", OECD *Agriculture Statistics Database*.

StatLink ᴍˢᴸ *http://dx.doi.org/10.1787/888933111816*

Table A.53. **Contribution of budgetary payments to change in Producer Support Estimate by country, 2012 to 2013**

	Producer Support Estimate (PSE)	Contribution of BP	Contribution of budgetary payments (BP) based on:						
			Output	Input use	Current A/An/R/I, production required	Non-current A/An/R/I, production required	Non-current A/An/R/I, production not required	Non-commodity criteria	Miscellaneous
	% change[1]	% change in nominal PSE if all other variables are held constant							
Australia	2.5	2.6	0.0	2.6	-0.2	0.0	0.4	-0.2	0.0
Canada	-20.3	-12.0	0.0	-1.1	-9.8	0.0	-0.6	0.0	-0.5
Chile	5.5	6.0	0.0	3.8	2.2	0.0	0.0	0.0	0.0
European Union[2]	1.5	-1.2	0.1	-1.2	0.0	0.0	0.2	0.0	-0.2
Iceland	-3.9	1.6	0.8	0.5	-0.2	0.6	0.0	0.0	0.0
Israel[3]	-20.9	-0.8	-0.1	-0.8	0.1	0.0	0.0	0.0	0.0
Japan	0.6	3.9	1.5	0.3	1.7	0.0	0.5	0.0	0.0
Korea	5.1	0.8	0.0	0.2	0.3	0.0	0.3	0.0	0.0
Mexico	8.5	9.0	-1.2	7.5	5.9	-0.6	-2.7	0.0	0.0
New Zealand	-24.1	0.3	0.0	0.0	0.2	0.0	0.0	0.0	0.0
Norway	-7.9	4.6	0.5	0.1	1.9	2.0	0.0	0.0	0.0
Switzerland	-10.5	0.1	0.0	0.1	0.0	0.0	0.0	0.0	0.0
Turkey	9.0	0.8	-0.4	0.7	0.6	0.0	0.0	0.0	0.0
United States	-7.5	-0.6	-0.6	0.8	0.2	0.0	-1.1	0.1	0.0
OECD[4]	-0.1	0.5	0.3	-0.1	0.4	0.0	0.0	0.0	-0.1

1. Percent changes of nominal values expressed in national currency.
2. European Union 27.
3. The statistical data for Israel are supplied by and under the responsibility of the relevant Israeli authorities. The use of such data by the OECD is without prejudice to the status of the Golan Heights, East Jerusalem and Israeli settlements in the West Bank under the terms of international law.
4. An average of per cent changes in individual country PSEs in national currencies, weighted by the shares of the country PSEs in the OECD PSE in the previous year; not equivalent to the variation in OECD PSE in any common currency.

Source: OECD (2014), "Producer and Consumer Support Estimates", OECD *Agriculture Statistics Database.*

StatLink 🔗 *http://dx.doi.org/10.1787/888933111835*

Table A.54. **Contribution to change in border price by country, 2012 to 2013**

	Producer price	Border price	Contribution to % change in border price[1] of:	
			Exchange rate	Border price (USD)
	%change[2]	%change[2]	if all other variables are held constant	
Australia	18.8	18.8	7.7	11.2
Canada	2.6	15.3	3.3	12.0
Chile	-8.6	-8.3	1.7	-10.0
European Union[3]	2.2	-2.4	-3.1	0.7
Iceland	3.7	14.8	-2.6	17.3
Israel[4]	0.0	9.3	-6.3	15.6
Japan	-0.3	12.2	21.4	-9.2
Korea	-2.9	-5.2	-2.7	-2.5
Mexico	-8.8	-3.9	-2.9	-1.0
New Zealand	1.8	11.5	-1.3	12.7
Norway	2.2	28.5	1.2	27.3
Switzerland	-1.8	9.2	-1.2	10.4
Turkey	3.5	6.3	6.3	0.0
United States	6.9	13.9	0.0	13.9
OECD[5]	0.4	6.4	8.8	-2.4

1. Border price at farm gate, i.e. price net of marketing margins between border and farm gate.
2. An average of per cent changes in Producer price/Border prices for individual commodities in national currencies, weighted by the shares of individual commodity MPS in total MPS in the previous year.
3. European Union 27.
4. The statistical data for Israel are supplied by and under the responsibility of the relevant Israeli authorities. The use of such data by the OECD is without prejudice to the status of the Golan Heights, East Jerusalem and Israeli settlements in the West Bank under under the terms of international law.
5. An average of per cent changes in Producer price/Border price for individual countries, weighted by the value of countries' MPS in OECD total MPS in the previous year.

Source: OECD (2014), "Producer and Consumer Support Estimates", OECD *Agriculture Statistics Database*.

StatLink ⟐⟐⟐ http://dx.doi.org/10.1787/888933111854

ORGANISATION FOR ECONOMIC CO-OPERATION AND DEVELOPMENT

The OECD is a unique forum where governments work together to address the economic, social and environmental challenges of globalisation. The OECD is also at the forefront of efforts to understand and to help governments respond to new developments and concerns, such as corporate governance, the information economy and the challenges of an ageing population. The Organisation provides a setting where governments can compare policy experiences, seek answers to common problems, identify good practice and work to co-ordinate domestic and international policies.

The OECD member countries are: Australia, Austria, Belgium, Canada, Chile, the Czech Republic, Denmark, Estonia, Finland, France, Germany, Greece, Hungary, Iceland, Ireland, Israel, Italy, Japan, Korea, Luxembourg, Mexico, the Netherlands, New Zealand, Norway, Poland, Portugal, the Slovak Republic, Slovenia, Spain, Sweden, Switzerland, Turkey, the United Kingdom and the United States. The European Union takes part in the work of the OECD.

OECD Publishing disseminates widely the results of the Organisation's statistics gathering and research on economic, social and environmental issues, as well as the conventions, guidelines and standards agreed by its members.

OECD PUBLISHING, 2, rue André-Pascal, 75775 PARIS CEDEX 16
(51 2014 05 1 P) ISBN 978-92-64-21090-5 – 2014

9 789264 210905